The Sciences and the Humanities

THE SCIENCES AND
THE HUMANITIES

Conflict and Reconciliation

by W. T. Jones

UNIVERSITY OF CALIFORNIA PRESS
BERKELEY AND LOS ANGELES *1965*

University of California Press
Berkeley and Los Angeles, California

Cambridge University Press
London, England

© 1965 by The Regents of the University of California
Library of Congress Catalog Card Number: 65-24179

Printed in the United States of America

For M M J

PREFACE

THIS BOOK has been in gestation as long, comparatively speaking, as an elephant. During all this time I have had much advice and criticism, for which I have now the pleasure of recording my thanks.

Fifteen years ago, when I was writing *A History of Western Philosophy,* it became clear to me that the whole modern period—not merely in philosophy, but in every aspect of the culture—has been marked by an increasing tension between the new scientific view of man and the traditional humanistic view; and I concluded that the reconciliation of these conflicting views had become a matter of urgency, not merely for professional philosophers but for men and women everywhere. At the outset, however, I formulated the difficulty as the problem of finding a place for values in the world of fact. I did not make much progress until it occurred to me that this definition was culture-bound—was, indeed, a reflection of the predominance in our society of scientific ways of thinking. It makes as much sense to talk about the need of finding a place for facts in the world of values; indeed, in some cultures this would be the natural way of formulating my problem.

Shortly after making this discovery, I had the good fortune to receive a Guggenheim Fellowship; the generosity of the Foundation enabled me to produce a complete draft in a far shorter time than would otherwise have been possible. And in 1961 I had an opportunity to try out parts of four chapters of this draft (i, ii, v, vii), when I was invited to give the Knoles Lectures at the University of the Pacific. I am most grateful to the University, and to Professor William D. Nietmann in particular, for their cordial hospitality, for the provision of a splendid array of critics, and for permission to use material from *Facts and Values,* the published version of my lectures. In 1963–64 I tested still more chapters in a series of lectures I gave as Phi Beta Kappa Visiting Scholar at a number of universities and colleges. I am grateful to all those, most of whom I can identify only as members of the audience, whose questions and challenges have helped me improve the book. They have made me see more clearly both what I had to say (which was not always, at least at the outset, what I wanted to say) and also how to say it (which was often not how I had originally said it).

I have also presented parts of the manuscript at meetings of the Claremont Philosophical Discussion Group. For vigorous discussions at these meetings and for reading the manuscript, in whole or in part, in one or the other of several drafts, I thank many friends and colleagues— among them Morton Beckner, James Doyle, Stephen Erickson, Robert Fogelin, Josiah Gould, Douglas Greenlee, John Hospers, Oliver Johnson, Gordon Kaufman, Stephen Pepper, Philip Rhinelander, Frederick Sontag, W. T. Stace, Tracy Westen, and John Wilkinson. In particular, I am much indebted to Theodore Greene and Edwin Fussell for the enormously detailed comments that each of them sent me—the former on the earliest version, the latter on the last but one. Geoffrey Ashton of the University of California Press has saved me from a number of egregious slips and has greatly helped me in other ways.

In addition, I am grateful to the Research Committee of Claremont Graduate School and University Center for grants over a number of years; to Mrs. Dorothy Overaker and Mrs. Frances Gentile, who have done most of the typing; and to my wife, who has helped me read proof.

Finally, I must thank the following publishers and authors for permission to quote from copyrighted works:

Appleton-Century-Crofts for Ernest R. Hilgard's *Theories of Learning.*
Basil Blackwell, Ltd., for John Wisdom's *Philosophy and Psychoanalysis.*
The Beacon Press for John Dewey's *Reconstruction in Philosophy.*

J. M. Dent & Sons, Ltd., and the Trustees of the Joseph Conrad Estate for Joseph Conrad's *Heart of Darkness*.

Faber & Faber, Ltd., and Harcourt, Brace & World, Inc., for T. S. Eliot's *The Waste Land, The Cocktail Party, Murder in the Cathedral,* "Gerontion," and "Burbank with a Badaeker: Bleistein with a Cigar."

Harper & Row, Inc., for Edward Weismiller's "College Town."

Harper & Row, Inc., and Curtis Brown, Ltd., for Joyce Cary's *The Horse's Mouth*.

Alfred A. Knopf, Inc., and Martin Secker & Warburg, Ltd., for Thomas Mann's *The Magic Mountain*.

Alfred A. Knopf, Inc., for Albert Camus' *The Stranger*.

Vladimir Nabokov and Weidenfeld & Nicolson, Ltd., for Mr. Nabokov's *Bend Sinister*.

New American Library of World Literature, Inc., for John Ciardi's translation of *The Inferno*.

Philosophical Library, Inc., for Herbert Feigl's "Logical Empiricism."

Random House, Inc., and Chatto & Windus, Ltd., for William Faulkner's "The Bear" (Copyright 1942 by The Curtis Publishing Co., Copyright 1942 by William Faulkner; reprinted from *Go Down, Moses* by William Faulkner, by permission of Random House, Inc.) and "Old Man" (Copyright 1939 by Random House, Inc.; reprinted from *The Faulkner Reader,* by permission).

May Sarton for her "The Writing of a Poem"; Miss Sarton and W. W. Norton & Co., Inc., for her "On Being Given Time."

W. T. J.

CONTENTS

INTRODUCTION: *Jumping High and to the Right*

IN A WELL-KNOWN experiment in learning theory, rats jump from a stand toward a pair of cards. There is a white card that is fixed in place; if the rats jump toward it, they fall to the ground. But if the rats jump toward the other, a black card, the card falls and the rats can eat food that the experimenter has placed behind the card. The rats easily learn which card is which. If the cards are shifted around, they learn always to jump to the black card wherever it happens to be. But in the next stage of the experiment the unambiguously white and unambiguously black cards are replaced by cards that successively approach a neutral gray. At some point the grays become so similar that the rats cannot distinguish between them: they can no longer tell which card is which. In this ambiguous situation they refuse to jump. If they are driven off the stand by an air blast, their behavior becomes rigid and stereotyped. A typical pattern consists in jumping high and to the right.

I believe that rat behavior in this ambiguous, indiscriminable situation is symptomatic of the tensions and anxieties that the conditions of contemporary life are producing in men. Just as a rat's behavior becomes irrational, compulsive, and neurotic when his perceptual field is no longer meaningful to him, so many men, confronted with a fragmented world that no longer makes sense to them, try to withdraw from it; if they cannot, their responses become irrational, stereotyped, and essentially neurotic. There is—alas!—a human equivalent of "jumping high and to the right."

Some of the uninterpretable situations we encounter are concerned with foreign policy. How are we to deal with the Russians? How solve the problem of Communist China? How prevent the nuclear destruction of the whole human race? Like the rats' dilemma, these are policy problems. Like the rats, we have to act; like them, we lack the clues that would enable us to choose a line of action that will get us what we want. Just as the rats were unable to devise a policy by which they could satisfy their hunger, because they could not discriminate between the gray that yields food and the gray that yields acute discomfort, so we men are unable to devise a policy to preserve peace and security because we cannot discriminate between all the interests and forces involved. We don't know whether to go to a summit conference or to stay away; we don't know whether to make concessions on disarmament or to insist on inspection. We don't know whether to put resources into nuclear or into conventional armaments for fighting limited wars. On the other hand, many of the uninterpretable situations we encounter are merely private and personal. But the inability to see any exit from some domestic dilemma—a marriage going on the rocks or a financial crisis—is no less painful and frustrating to the persons involved than are the large-scale dilemmas of public policy.

This book does not make detailed recommendations on foreign policy or on marriage and the family. Nonetheless its major purpose is practical. Philosophy can illumine the general nature of problems and so help people learn how to face the numerous specific problems, large and small, which they daily fumble—or evade. One of the primary reasons why so many of us fail to deal adequately with uninterpretable situations, whether public or private, is the attitude we adopt, or rather the attitude we fall into, when confronted with them. A rational, rather than a neurotic, attitude toward dilemmas is the first condition for the formulation of successful policy.

For instance, in the rats' case it was rational to remain on the stand and sit it out, when they could not discriminate between the two gray cards. When forced to act, when driven off the stand by the air blast, it would have been rational to jump for one or the other of the cards— either one—on the assumption there is a 50–50 chance that either one is correct. It was *not* rational to try to escape from the dilemma by jumping high and to the right, thereby missing any chance to hit the correct card.

What prevents people from acting rationally in ambiguous situations? Doubtless many factors enter in, but the metaphysical beliefs men carry around with them are surely important. Many people, of course, do not know and probably will never know what their metaphysical beliefs are; they may even deny that they have any. Nevertheless, there is a seepage effect by which the consciously held opinions of an intelligent minority, who do interest themselves in abstract questions, gradually pass into and become the unconscious beliefs of the majority. It is to this minority that this book is addressed, in the conviction that their beliefs are critical for our society as a whole. I believe that a widely held but mistaken view of the nature of reality is at the heart of the difficulties and anxieties that the contemporary culture experiences. In this book I undertake to expose this mistaken metaphysics. I shall show how it has created fundamental conflicts that haunt men's minds, thereby infecting and exacerbating the various specific problems that men have to try to solve.

In this respect I write in an old tradition. Plato thought that there is a fundamental connection between the metaphysical beliefs people hold and the ways in which they deal with the concrete moral, social, and political problems of their time. This is why in his dialogues he sought to bring the unconscious metaphysics of the average intelligent Athenian up to the level of consciousness where it could be examined and criticized. Thus, though Plato was often preoccupied with questions that seem at first sight remote from practical problems, the underlying impetus of his philosophy was pragmatic. To make life more viable, more humane, he believed that a major philosophical reconstruction was needed.

Plato, of course, held that the trouble infecting his society was relativism, which he sought to replace with an absolutist metaphysics. Today, there are still people who agree with Plato. Relativism, these people say, is precisely the trouble; it only increases anxiety. What is needed to allay anxiety and to make us more effective decision-makers, is an assurance that there are ultimate answers, that God is in His heaven taking care of the world. This seems to me a wholly unrealistic stance. The root of the trouble today is not too much, but too little, relativism. The root of the trouble is a decadent absolutism which nobody any longer really believes.

Indeed, the development of modern science has made it very difficult to find a rational basis for any of the standard metaphysical frameworks by which, in the past, men have found the security and confidence they yearn for. Hence there has been an increasing tendency to avoid metaphysical problems instead of trying to solve them. Thus some surrender themselves to political or religious absolutism: in effect, they turn the basic problems of contemporary culture over to Big Brother to do the worrying and to make the decisions. Others escape the ordeal of decision on basic issues by retiring to their gardens and devoting themselves to their jobs, their professions, or their families—to the accumulation of fact, to the polishing of technique, or to the acquisition of status and its symbols.

Though some of these escapes are less harmful than others, none is more than a partial solution; each of them ignores one or another aspect of the complex culture that has made us the kind of men we are. The cost of escape is high: always at our back we hear the voices that we are vainly trying to silence—those other voices to which we must be willing to respond if we are to be whole men. Accordingly, a more courageous, and also more rational, attitude would be to face up to, instead of trying to evade, the fundamental problems of our culture.

I believe, and in this book I try to show, that philosophy can perform an immensely important social function. Let us admit that the old metaphysical frameworks are gone; therefore it is pointless to regret them, and still more pointless to try to revive them. Men must learn to accept relativity, change, complexity, hazard, ambiguity; they must learn not merely to put up with such a world, but to enjoy it. To enjoy this world, to live in it without falling into facile cynicism or existential despair, without succumbing to authoritarian certainty, without retreating into a barren scientism, requires intellectual and moral maturity. Philosophy cannot give us this maturity, but it can help each of us win it for himself.

I THE CRISIS OF CONTEMPORARY CULTURE

THE RATS' PROBLEM described in the Introduction was a policy problem because they had to devise a line of action that would get them what they wanted—food. But it was also a cognitive problem, since their perceptual field, which had formerly been well-ordered into unambiguous blacks and whites, no longer made any sense—it had collapsed into a chaos of indistinguishable grays.

As a matter of fact, all policy problems—whether those of rats or of men—are at the same time cognitive problems, since the need to choose between alternative lines of action arises only because some conceptual structure by means of which we have formerly interpreted our experience has broken down. This is easy to see when, as with the rats, the conceptual structure that has been guiding policy is a very simple one. In the jumping-stand experiment the experimenter might say that he had taught the rats by repeated trials to associate black with feeding. This is a perfectly acceptable way of describing what has happened, but I can bring out a point of importance by putting it somewhat differently. To say that some particular rat has learned to associate black with feeding is equivalent to saying that a certain stable structure has been introduced into his experience, as a result of which what he sees from the jumping stand is well-ordered. That is, black has come to have cognitive meaning

for the rat—it means food, in the way that, for us, "food" means food.
At the same time he can get what he wants; thus black also has action
meaning—it means "Jump here!" in the way that for us "Jump!" is an
instruction to jump.

As long as the rat's environment remains more or less constant he
has no problems: his experiential field is meaningful and he can feed
whenever he feels hungry. But in the changed situation, where the cards
become indistinguishable, the old structural relation between black and
feeding is no longer relevant—no longer of use in interpreting the perceptual field. Accordingly, the rat experiences two closely related frustrations: there is the frustration of his hunger drive; there is also a cognitive frustration. That is, there is the frustration of being in a disordered
situation that does not make sense, in addition to the frustration of not
being able to feed without risking an unpleasant fall.

Of course, men are not so easily frustrated as rats. In the first place, the
conceptual structures that we men use to interpret experience are much
more powerful (black-means-food is a very elementary structure by human
standards); in the second place, usually we have in our repertoire various
reserve structures that come into operation in problematic situations. Thus,
if we are walking along a path at night we may suddenly notice something
just ahead of us: what is it—a snake or a shadow? There may be a slight
shock; momentarily, we may be pulled up short. But, almost automatically, procedures for dealing with this undiscriminated object come
into operation: we turn on our flashlight, or retreat down the path and
go home by a different route. Fortunately for us, most of our problematic
situations are of this kind. Usually there is a finite set of standard categories to one or the other of which we are "sure" the ambiguous object
belongs—either it is a snake or a stick or a shadow. Also we have readily
available standard procedures for resolving the ambiguity and determining to which of the various possible categories the object "really" belongs.
If we are puzzled about what material a suit is made of, a great number
of techniques are available—some simple, rule-of-thumb procedures, like
feeling it or getting it into a better light; some much more sophisticated.
Indeed, from this point of view, the methods of science—for example,
subjecting the material to chemical analysis—are simply more precise
methods for interpreting ambiguous experiences and so resolving hesi-
tations and doubts about how to act. Most discrimination problems are of
this kind—unlike the poor rats, we are confident that there *is* a solution,

and our only difficulty lies in finding the correct conceptual structure from among a more or less extensive available set. Most of the time, that is to say, we are dealing not with uninterpretable situations but with not-yet-interpreted situations.

One of the functions of culture is to prevent truly uninterpretable situations from occurring. Generally, high cultures are distinguished from primitive ones by the presence of whole hierarchies of conceptual structures of the kind described, that is, hierarchies of procedures for resolving ambiguities and preventing serious breakdowns. Thus the legal system is a set of standard procedures for dealing with discrimination problems of a very special but important kind: Is this man a murderer, or not? Is this act a violation of the income-tax law, or not? Trial by jury is a routine for dealing with ambiguities regarding guilt or innocence; and if this procedure fails to resolve our doubt, there are reserve routines, in the form of the appellate courts, for finer discriminations that hopefully settle the issue.

Unfortunately, despite all the built-in safeguards of culture, major breakdowns occasionally occur. In these cases it is not just a question of finding which one of several possible categories is correct, since none of the available conceptual schemes serves to interpret the situation. At these times a crisis occurs in the life of the individual or the society, comparable, at the human level, to the crisis the rats encountered on the jumping stand.

We are in such a situation today in foreign affairs, where changes in the environment—close-coupled economic systems, massive accumulations of power, nuclear fission—have made all of the old procedures of negotiation between sovereign nation-states completely obsolete. What is required, presumably, for the solution of these problems is some radical restructuring of the field—a reorganization whose outlines are not yet in sight.

But it is easier to take for detailed examination a historical example, where the solution is happily behind us rather than still ahead of us. Toward the end of 1609 Galileo "betook" himself, as he says, "to observation of the heavenly bodies." On the night of January 7, 1610, he chanced to turn his telescope in the direction of Jupiter. What he saw is shown below: three small stars, too small to be seen by the naked eye

●   ● ○   ●

and so never observed before, near the planet.[1] Of course, there was nothing strange in this: in whatever direction he turned his telescope he saw stars that no man had seen, but he "wondered a little" because these three stars happened to be "exactly in a straight line parallel to the ecliptic." Since this could be chance, he did not wonder enough to feel in the presence of a problem. Nevertheless, on the next night he looked at Jupiter again. "Led by some strange fatality," he turned his telescope again on those three small stars. What he now saw was this:

$$O \quad \bullet \quad \bullet \quad \bullet$$

But this was totally impossible, because, as everyone knew and had known for centuries, the only movable objects in the sky were the seven planets. Beyond these seven "wanderers," all the other stars were eternally fixed—imbedded in a crystalline sphere which turned in a diurnal motion and formed a kind of backdrop, a great distance behind the wandering planets. Since there were but seven planets, the newly discovered stars could only be fixed stars. Being fixed, they could not move relatively to one another. Nevertheless, during the night they *had* moved relatively to each other. Something was radically wrong.

So much so that, when Galileo invited a colleague at the University of Padua to look at the three new stars, this professor refused: Either Galileo was deluded and there were no moving stars to be seen in the telescope or, if there were, it was very dangerous to look at them. Before we ridicule this line of reasoning, we ought to ask ourselves how we would respond if someone were to tell us that he had just walked through the solid wall of his house. Since in the world we know, this is impossible (but no more impossible than moving stars were in the world of Galileo's day), we would conclude that our informant was either a fool or a knave: we would explain away (not explain) the impossible, by exactly the sort of formula that Galileo's colleague used.

This is, indeed, a "reasonable" procedure—reasonable in the same way that it was reasonable for the rats to sit on the jumping stand as long as possible. It is much more likely that a particular observation is mistaken than that a long-established world view is false. It takes an intellect of great audacity even to contemplate the possibility that the world view is wrong and the perception right; and it takes an intellect of the highest

---

[1] Galileo described and illustrated these discoveries in *The Sidereal Messenger,* published in 1610.

order of imaginative power to conceive an alternative world view—that is, to propose an explanation of the perception, instead of merely explaining it away.

Thus, while we and the professor at Padua escape from the inexplicable by explaining it away, and while we would be profoundly disturbed if we did not have some such refuge, Galileo, for his part, so far from being frightened and withdrawing, was immensely stimulated. He waited "with longing" for darkness to fall, so that he could observe again. The night was cloudy, but the following night, the 10th, was fair. What he saw was this:

● ● ○

And on the 11th, this:

● ● ○

Now, as it happened, Galileo was acquainted with the notion, put forward seventy years earlier by Copernicus as a speculative hypothesis, that the planets might be revolving about the sun, instead of the earth. It occurred to him that if those three odd stars were circling Jupiter, as Copernicus had suggested that Jupiter itself might be circling the sun, the inexplicable would be explained. For if those stars were circling Jupiter, instead of being imbedded in the sphere of the fixed stars, then their motion was understandable. For instance, whenever one of them passed directly behind Jupiter, it would be invisible from the earth, and an observer would see just what Galileo saw on the 10th and the 11th. On the former night the outermost of the three was masked; on the latter, the innermost.

This solution involved a radically new conceptual scheme and with it a massive reconstruction of the perceptual field. What Galileo had seen on January 7, 1610, when he looked up into the night sky, were fixed stars imbedded in a translucent sphere which turned about the sun. What he saw on the 10th when he looked up into the same night sky were three satellites orbiting around Jupiter.

But of course these changes in the perceptual field were only a small part of the revolution which this new conceptual structure entailed. For instance, since it now turned out that there were ten, instead of seven, moving stars, it became necessary to abandon the long-established belief that the number of planets had been fixed by divine fiat as a constant reminder of the moral life—of the seven virtues we ought to cultivate and the seven vices we ought to shun. This is but a single example of the way in which the conceptual reorganization caused all sorts of familiar things to look—and in fact, to be—very different.

Neither Galileo himself nor any of his supporters or opponents could have foreseen the far-reaching consequences of the scientific revolution that was then being launched. The repercussions of this revolution—a revolution which had begun much earlier, but which we may take to be symbolized by Galileo's dramatic discovery of the moons of Jupiter—are the theme of this first chapter. Not the technological and economic consequences, though these have been momentous, but the even more important though less obvious intellectual and moral consequences. In this area the most serious consequence has been the seeming contradiction between what we may call the *scientific* (or descriptive) and the *humanistic* (ethical, esthetic, religious) views of man. If man is a part of nature and if nature, as science seems to say, is a cloud of hurrying molecules, can the moral life be real? Where is there a place for value in the world of fact that science discloses?

This is the conflict between the two cultures about which C. P. Snow has written—scientism and humanism. He thinks of it, however, merely in social terms—as a chasm between scientists and humanists which makes it almost impossible for them to communicate or to cooperate effectively. It is more to the point to think of it as a conflict within culture (and within the individual personality that has internalized the culture) rather than as a conflict *between* separate cultures. There is certainly a regrettable chasm between men who have been educated as humanists and men who have been educated as scientists. But more serious and more fundamental is the interior split, or chasm, in most individuals. For it is very difficult today to see life steadily or see it whole. No humanist today is untouched by scientific conceptions and scientific attitudes; every day he uses and relies on a vast accumulation of experience which is virtually uninterpretable by the traditional humanistic conceptual structures. Too often he deals with this embarrassment by adopting an uneasy and misguided air of superiority or by retreating into a sentimental and romantic cultivation of feeling, as opposed to fact. Every scientist, on the other hand, is also a husband, a father, or a friend. In these relationships he is bound to see himself in ways difficult if not impossible to interpret by means of those conceptual structures which he regularly uses, as a scientist, in his study of the interactions of other husbands, fathers, and friends. Concentration on what can be coped with by scientific method, persistent suppression of this embarrassing humanistic side of human nature, is likely to show up, at best as a banal and trivial version of human values, at worst as a bland indifference to them.

Here, then, in the conflict between the scientific and the humanistic views of life there is an uninterpretable (or, at least, an as-yet-uninterpreted) situation of central importance. Even men and women who may be wholly unconscious of this conflict in the terms in which I have formulated it are nevertheless affected by it in their outlook on life, and in their neurotic, or near-neurotic, responses to contemporary social and political problems. To solve this problem of the seeming conflict between the scientific and the humanistic conceptions of life would therefore do much to alleviate the tensions of modern life.

But how, exactly, does the conflict arise? An example of the radical difference between the humanistic and the scientific interpretations of experience is the contrast between the account St. Paul gave, and the account a psychologist would give, of what happened on the road to Damascus. St. Paul's explanation is quite simple: he had seen the Risen Lord. There was a natural sequence of events: deciding to go to Damascus, mounting his horse, proceeding along the road . . . , and this natural sequence was disrupted by a transcendent, supernatural occurrence. According to St. Paul, the transcendent cause produced a complete reversal of the original causal sequence: instead of persecuting the followers of Jesus, he now gave them aid and comfort. Indeed, a radically different set of natural events (e.g., preaching the gospel) ensued, which were the direct outcome of the supernatural cause. And, of course, for St. Paul, seeing the Risen Lord was an absolutely unique occurrence, and of critical significance. This is how St. Paul interpreted the event. He explained it in terms of the great good it produced: both on the personal level, his own salvation, and on the larger level, the propagation of the truth to the Gentiles.

A modern psychologist would not question the occurrence or its effect on St. Paul's life. Indeed, he would probably say that St. Paul has given a remarkably good account of a rather well-known type of personality change. But whereas for St. Paul the event is unique, the psychologist's whole procedure presupposes that the event is a member of a set of similar events (a set of events including radical changes in personality). What he looks for is some rule that relates events of this type to another precisely defined set of events. A physiologically oriented psychologist might work on the hypothesis that the class of events to which St. Paul's experience belongs is the class of epileptical seizures, and he might therefore look for other evidence (seeing bright lights, hearing voices, loss of consciousness, etc.) that St. Paul was an epileptic. A psychologist with a psychoanalytical orientation would probably interpret the event as having its origin, not in some physiological condition but rather in some childhood experience, for instance, early weaning or severe toilet training. But, though the detailed explanation might be different in these two cases, the structure of explanation is identical, and radically different from the structure of explanation St. Paul himself used.[2] For St. Paul, the experience is unique and it has a transcendental cause—the divine will intervening directly in St. Paul's life. For the psychologist, the event is not unique but is a member of a rather large class of events, related systematically, that is, according to some rule, to another large set of events.

According to St. Paul's view (this was also the view of Greek philosophers, Christian theologians, and generally of almost everybody down to the seventeenth century), *nature is like man,* in the sense that the whole universe is conceived to be a system of purposes oriented toward a hierarchy of values; according to the scientific interpretation, *man is like nature,* in the sense that the whole universe, including human behavior, is conceived to be a nexus of reciprocally related occurrences, neutral in character and in principle predictable. According to the old view, man is a morally significant agent acting in a morally significant universe. But if man is a moral being making morally significant choices, how can we admit that his behavior is reducible to the interactions of morally insignificant particles? And if man is a part of nature, how can we escape this reduction? The resolution of this dilemma is the central problem of modern culture.

It will be seen that the conflict between these two interpretations is essentially a discrimination problem. If we use the scientific scheme of explanation, what happens to the uniqueness of St. Paul's experience and its transcendental significance? We can make no more sense of them than

---

[2] It would be beside the point to reply that psychologists have not succeeded in formulating rules that state the relevant functional relationships precisely. This is irrelevant because I am not trying to work out a scientific explanation of St. Paul's experience; I am simply showing how a scientific view of the experience differs from St. Paul's view of it.

Galileo could make of the moving pinpoints of light, as long as he used the Ptolemaic conceptual structure. On the other hand, who is prepared to abandon this scientific scheme of explanation? While acknowledging that we probably will never know enough about St. Paul's life to diagnose in detail the natural causes of his experience, how can we fail to admit that it is only our ignorance that makes diagnosis impossible, thus rejecting the claim to uniqueness and to any special, transcendental causality?

Nor is it merely a question of explanations that appeal to a transcendental, or divine, causality. Even a purely secular humanism seems to be equally at odds with the presuppositions of science. An example is the constellation of beliefs underlying American constitutional democracy: (1) that there are absolutely valid moral axioms (e.g., "inalienable rights"); (2) that the truth of these axioms is immediately certain to anyone who directs his attention to them ("We hold these truths to be self-evident"); and (3) that those who attend to these truths, and so recognize their obligatory character, are capable of acting in accordance with them (i.e., the human will is just as rational as is the human intellect).

These principles were not merely enunciated by the Founding Fathers; they were very widely held during much of the eighteenth century. In that century, geometry was everywhere regarded as the model science; it was supposed that in every field of inquiry there exists a set of self-evidently true principles (like the axioms of Euclidean geometry) from which the detailed propositions constituting the body of that science can be deduced with infallible certainty. Further, it was held that this is not only true in the sciences of nature (as it was confidently believed Newton had established) but also in the sciences of conduct—in ethics and politics. Thus Kant, who had begun his career as a physicist, held that "reason is always the same," that is, that it will lead all men everywhere to the same conclusion not only regarding what is true but also regarding what conduct is right.

This whole nexus of beliefs and assumptions explains many of our deepest convictions—for instance, the importance we attach to the rights of free speech and free assembly. Since the theory presupposes in every citizen a pure practical reason that will choose wisely if the appropriate sources of knowledge are readily accessible, the only real problem is that of making information available. Hence the doctrine, so fundamental to American policy, of a free public education for all.

Every one of these beliefs is seriously challenged by current scientific conceptions. Take perhaps the central belief in the whole configuration—the belief that geometry is the model science and that the certainty and universality that characterize this discipline are attainable in other fields, for example, in ethics and politics. Today it is widely held that geometry, far from being a paradigm, is a very special case indeed. The propositions of geometry (and of arithmetic), it is now held, are universal and necessary only because they are not *about* anything. Or, less paradoxically, they are not about anything in the real world, but only about the meanings of terms. The proposition "$2 + 2 = 4$" follows from the definitions of "2," "+," "=," and "4." The proposition "The interior angles of a triangle equal 180°" follows in the same way from definitions stated in Euclidean geometry. To deduce a theorem is merely to work out the implications of the various definitions.

If this interpretation is correct, mathematics is certain only because it is tautological. It has the sort of certainty and universality that "Bald-headed men have no hair" has—and the same sort of limitation. Since "bald-headed" means "having no hair," this proposition is absolutely certain; it is equivalent to saying, "Men with no hair have no hair"—a proposition that would be true even if there were no bald-headed men in the world. Similarly, the absolute truth of the propositions of Euclidean geometry depend on the special definitions of "line," "plane," "straight," and so forth which are introduced in this science; they throw no light in themselves on the properties of space, and we have to discover by empirical means whether space is Euclidean, or whether some parts of it may be, and other parts may not be, Euclidean—as we have to discover by empirical means whether there are some men who have no hair.

I shall now state this generally: it used to be assumed that the propositions of science could be both (a) certain, and (b) empirically relevant, because it was believed that geometry was an absolutely true description of physical space. Since this belief has now been widely abandoned, we have to choose between a science that is (a) universal but tautological, and (b) empirically relevant but only probable. Applying this to the Founding Fathers' moral axioms and inalienable rights, we have to conclude that such propositions as "Free speech is a natural right of all men" are either (a) tautological, or (b) possibly false.

But quite apart from the collapse of the geometric model of absolute certainty, moral axioms are in trouble from still another source. Much evidence has been accumulated that ethical and political beliefs are relative to social class, economic status, and, even, to professional group. It would seem, then, that the Founding Fathers, so far from formulating universally and eternally true moral axioms, merely gave expression to the prejudices of their own small social class in an English-speaking culture. It is true that in the welter of diverse customs and codes uniformities can be found—"universals" some anthropologists call them. But these universals are not at all the ethical absolutes of the Founding Fathers. They are empirical generalizations describing the sorts of things men value, not assertions of the objective validity of the values so affirmed. Such propositions assert not an "ought," but an "is"—even if this happens, in some cases, to be an is-about-an-ought.

We have indeed been driven to recognize that there is a basic distinction between saying (a) "All men ought to respect the rights of others," and (b) "In all societies we encounter the belief that all men ought to respect the rights of others." The latter proposition, even if true (which seems unlikely), would not establish the former. For the former is an ethical assertion; the latter is a factual one. We know the kind of evidence that would tend to verify or disverify the latter; it consists in empirical observations—observations of exactly the same kind as those required to test *any* empirical generalization—say, a generalization about billiard balls or molecules. The only difference is that the relevant evidence would be observations of what people do and say, rather than observations of the behavior of billiard balls or molecules. But what sort of evidence would be relevant to the former (ethical) assertion? Observation can establish only that somebody thinks something is valuable (a fact), while, as we have already pointed out, the attempt to deduce ethical assertions from moral axioms turns out to be a tautological game.

But further: the universals (or better, the uniformities) formulated in the current, empirical approach to values are, characteristically, relations between the values that people experience or affirm, and either (a) certain biological drives (sex, hunger, etc.) or (b) the facts of social interaction. For instance, the high value some people attach to the "Protestant ethic" has been related to the rise of capitalism as an economic system; the extremely strong and widespread taboo against incest has been related to the basic change, millennia ago, from a herd-like pattern of life to a proto-human pattern of life (family).

These are typical empirical generalizations—"is" statements, not "ought" statements. Such universals (or uniformities), far from establishing favored ethical absolutes, tend rather to undermine the very conception of there being any ethical absolutes at all. For, if Max Weber and Tawney are correct, it would seem to make no sense to say that the Protestant ethic is absolutely better than the Catholic ethic—or than the Hopi ethic, or the Eskimo ethic. We can say only that it is better for people who live in a capitalistically organized society, because capitalism and Protestantism turn out to be functionally interrelated.[3] Similarly for the incest taboo. We could no longer say that incest is wrong (value-assertion); at most we could say only that the incest taboo helped to make possible the transition from ape to man (fact-assertion).

Finally: what about the last cardinal presupposition of the Founding Fathers? They believed, in the words of Bishop Joseph Butler, that it is possible to "sit down in a cool hour," reach a rational decision, and then act on it. A good deal of evidence has accumulated in the recent past which suggests that cool hours are hard to come by, that the pure practical reason is a figment of the philosophical imagination—in fact, a notable instance of wish-fulfillment. Most students of human behavior today would hold that the notion of a decision completely purged of interest and bias is illusory. The old model of a will that dispassionately surveys the scene, that adds up the credits and debits, and that chooses only after all the evidence has been collected and weighed, has been replaced by a very different model—the model of a will whose choices occur in a context of personal, social, and cultural determinants, none of which can possibly be described as wholly "rational" and many of which are pre-rational or even irrational. *After* choice has been made in this way, we then invent reasons which seem to justify our doing what we have already decided to do on other grounds. Thus Freud has changed "rationalism" to "rationalization"—reasons are *ex post facto* rather than the actual determining grounds of behavior.

It would seem, then, that there is indeed a prima facie conflict between the presuppositions of the Founding Fathers (which are still the official beliefs of Americans today) and the hypotheses, conclusions, and general outlook of the sciences. This presents us with a dilemma: on the one hand,

---

[3] I am not asserting that these generalizations are true, or for that matter, false. I am merely citing them as examples of the effect that this way of thinking about values has on ethical absolutes.

we are loath to abandon the central affirmations on which our culture has depended; on the other hand, we find it possible to write off with a shrug what seem to be the wholly incompatible conclusions of anthropology, sociology, and psychology about human nature.

What Hawthorne once wrote of Melville—"He can neither believe, nor be comfortable in his unbelief"—is true of us today. But not all of us are "too honest and courageous not to try to do one or the other." [4] On the contrary, we experience tension and strain as we try desperately to hold wildly contradictory beliefs about (for instance) the nature of decision and about the status of values in a world of fact. This conflict, of which I have now given one or two examples, has made modern life profoundly anxious, because, in addition to the personal dilemmas that have always plagued men, we now confront a metaphysical dilemma: we cannot form a comprehensive and consistent conception of human nature, or of our place in the cosmos.

While, as I have already suggested, we can see these tensions and anxieties in the life of the masses—for instance, in the powerful attractions of totalitarianism—the most striking manifestations of strain and anxiety occur in the art of our times. Here the fundamental malaise of our culture is directly revealed, instead of being expressed obliquely in political behavior.

I do not want to exaggerate. Certainly despair and frustration are not limited to twentieth-century artists. The poet has always known as well as, or better than, most men that things often go wrong: he is in disgrace with fortune and men's eyes; his best-laid schemes have gone agley; his loved ones have died or deserted him. Yet, in the old days, though reconciliation might be difficult and though he might on occasion fail to achieve it, the poet held reconciliation to be in principle possible, for he believed in the existence of a cosmic justice that sooner or later restored the balance. The universe, he was persuaded, was in the most fundamental sense moral and so responsive to man's demands for justice. It is precisely this conviction that has disappeared, and its disappearance has altered the whole tonality of modern art.

Thus, though *The Divine Comedy* opens with Dante lost in a dark wood, there was a hill "at the far end of that valley of evil"; looking up, he could see the sun shining on the top,

---

[4] Quoted in Jay Leyda, *The Melville Log* (New York: Harcourt, Brace, 1951), p. 529.

> and the shining strengthened me against the fright
>   whose agony had wracked the lake of my heart
>   through all the terrors of that piteous night.[5]

The way to the top might be long and difficult, but he had the absolute assurance that there *was* a top. How different all this appeared to Tennyson! Instead of the full illumination of the sun, there was only darkness and uncertainty:

> I falter where I firmly trod,
>   And falling with my weight of cares
>   Upon the great world's altar-stairs
> That slope thro' darkness up to God,
>
> I stretch faint hands of faith, and grope,
>   And gather dust and chaff, and call
>   To what I feel is Lord of all,
> And faintly trust the larger hope.

If Tennyson at least hoped against hope that something was there, Hardy abandoned this hope. He believed that science discloses the universe to be a vast mechanism whose parts blindly run. Because they blindly run, there can be no restoration of the balance, no rectification of wrongs; hence no justice and no hope. And he wrote that he would have preferred a world of cosmic *in*justice to one in which the concept of justice is wholly irrelevant:

> If but some vengeful god would call to me
> From up the sky, and laugh: "Thou suffering thing,
> Know that thy sorrow is my ecstasy,
> That thy love's loss is my hate's profiting!"
>
> Then would I bear it, clench myself, and die,
> Steeled by the sense of ire unmerited;
> Half-eased in that a Powerfuller than I
> Had willed and meted me the tears I shed.
>
> But not so. How arrives it joy lies slain,
> And why unblooms the best hope ever sown?
> —Crass Casualty obstructs the sun and rain,

---

[5] *The Inferno,* translated by John Ciardi (New York: New American Library, 1954), Canto 1, lines 13, 19–21.

> And dicing Time for gladness casts a moan . . .
> These purblind Doomsters had as readily strown
> Blisses about my pilgrimage as pain.[6]

Thus the source of the poet's despair has changed. Once it was merely personal catastrophe or disappointment; today it is a deep sense of cosmic meaninglessness. This is perhaps the central discovery of contemporary art. The pains we suffer, the misfortunes we encounter, the defeats we experience, including that most final of all defeats—death—are literally meaningless, since the universe is neither beneficent nor hostile, but merely indifferent to us.

This is the theme, for instance, of Hans Castorp's alpine adventure in *The Magic Mountain:*

He had just begun to mount again when the expected happened, and the storm burst, the storm that had threatened so long. Or may one say "threatened" of the action of blind, nonsentient forces, which have no purpose to destroy us—that would be comforting by comparison—but are merely horribly indifferent to our fate should we become involved with them? [7]

It is also the theme of Joyce Cary's novel *The Horse's Mouth*. Everything goes wrong for Gulley Jimson: his marriage, his friendships, even his painting. Canvases of his that he feels are worthless are praised by connoisseurs; those he prizes are ignored or condemned. He does not live to complete the one picture that, above all, he wants to finish; but even had he lived, it was doomed to destruction by a philistine Borough Council, to make way for a parking lot.

Like Thomas Hardy, Gulley knows that there is no vengeful God up in heaven responsible for his misfortunes; what happens just happens. "The trouble with Robert"—he remarks about his brother-in-law, who also encounters one disaster after another—"is he won't face facts, things if you like. He wants them to come and lick his feet. But they can't—they can't lick. They can only fall about like a lot of loose rocks in a runaway train." [8]

Or there is Meursault, in Camus' *The Stranger,* an absurd man living

---

[6] "Hap," in *Collected Poems of Thomas Hardy* (New York: Macmillan, 1925), p. 7.
[7] Thomas Mann, *The Magic Mountain,* translated by H. T. Lowe-Porter (London: Secker & Warburg, 1928), p. 482.
[8] Joyce Cary, *The Horse's Mouth* (London: Michael Joseph, 1944), p. 235.

in an absurd world. He kills an Arab—for no reason at all. The murder is unpremeditated and purposeless: "And just then it crossed my mind that one might fire, or not fire—and it would come absolutely to the same thing." [9] He is convicted and sentenced to death—but the trial, too, is absurd. What turns the court against him is not the evidence that he shot the Arab, but completely irrelevant testimony to the effect that he had smoked at his mother's funeral and failed to display distress over her coffin.

As he sits in prison awaiting execution for murder, Meursault considers, but without any hope, the chances of a prison break—a symbol, I think, of modern man's struggle to reconcile himself to life and death in an absurd, amoral universe.

The only thing that interests me now is the problem of circumventing the machine, learning if the inevitable admits a loophole. . . . I am always wondering if there have been cases of condemned prisoners' escaping from the implacable machinery. . . . But . . . I was caught in the rattrap irrevocably.

The condemned prisoner is Everyman. Meursault remarks that "nothing [is] more important than an execution; . . . it's the only thing that can genuinely interest a man." This is a reference to the inevitability of death for us all. It is just this blank inevitability that revolts Meursault: "What was wanted, to my mind, was to give the criminal a chance, if only a dog's chance; say, one chance in a thousand." Yet he knows that the cosmic system, like the Algiers police system, is inescapable and ultimately unjust. Where everyone suffers the same penalty—death—there is no "proportion" between crime and punishment:

Try as I might, I couldn't stomach this brutal certitude. For really, when one came to think of it, there was a disproportion between the judgment on which it was based and the unalterable sequence of events starting from the moment when that judgment was delivered. . . .

In the old days of religious faith, though death was equally certain, there had been a grandeur and a seriousness about it; it had been a kind of summing-up, a definitive distribution of justice. But now the guillotine has been removed from its pedestal and stands on the ground.

The machine is on the same level as the man, and he walks toward it as he

---

[9] *The Stranger,* translated by Stuart Gilbert (New York: Knopf, 1946). This and the following quotations are from pp. 72, 136, 138, 139, 140, and 137.

steps forward to meet somebody he knows. In a sense, that, too, was disappointing. The business of climbing a scaffold, leaving the world below, so to speak, gave something for a man's imagination to get hold of. But, as it was, the machine dominated everything; they killed you discreetly, with a hint of shame and much efficiency.

Neither Meursault nor Gulley Jimson feels there is any point to his life—neither to what he does nor to what happens to him. Similarly, in Hemingway's *The Old Man and the Sea* there is no point (no meaning in terms of the fulfillment of any rational purpose) in continuing to fight for the fish long after it has been devoured by the shark. It is as purposeless as the artillery fire of the gunboat in *Heart of Darkness:*

In the empty immensity of earth, sky, and water, there she was, incomprehensible, firing into a continent. Pop, would go one of the six-inch guns; a small flame would dart and vanish, a little white smoke would disappear, a tiny projectile would give a feeble screech—and nothing happened. Nothing could happen. There was a touch of insanity in the proceeding, a sense of lugubrious drollery in the sight. . . .[10]

Over and over, then, we have images and symbols of cosmic meaninglessness. In *The Bear* it is the wilderness into which Isaac McCaslin plunges to hunt down Old Ben: "the tall and endless wall of dense November woods under the dissolving afternoon and the year's death, sombre, impenetrable," so huge that the hunters are "dwarfed by that perspective into an almost ridiculous diminishment." [11] In *Old Man* it is the rampaging Mississippi in flood:

. . . . he was being toyed with by a current of water going nowhere, beneath a day which would wane toward no evening. . . . The skiff ran in pitch streaming darkness upon a roiling expanse which . . . apparently had no boundaries. . . . Wild and invisible, it tossed and heaved about and beneath the boat, ridged with dirty phosphorescent foam and filled with a debris of destruction—objects nameless and enormous and invisible, which struck and slashed at the skiff and whirled on.[12]

And what is true of the lives of obscure individuals, is equally true of the policies of empires, or the sweep of history as a whole:

---

[10] Joseph Conrad, *Heart of Darkness* (New York: New American Library, 1950), p. 69.

[11] William Faulkner, "The Bear," *in* Malcolm Cowley, ed., *The Portable Faulkner* (New York: Viking, 1954), p. 230.

[12] William Faulkner, "Old Man," in *The Portable Faulkner,* pp. 568, 578.

History has many cunning passages, contrived corridors
And issues, deceives with whispering ambitions,
Guides us by vanities. . . .
Neither fear nor courage saves us. Unnatural vices
Are fathered by our heroism. Virtues
Are forced upon us by our impudent crimes.[13]

The central, appalling discovery is the brute factuality of things, the indifference of the universe to men and their purposes.

If this, then, is what life is, how should men respond to this knowledge? How should we face a world without cosmic justice? Some contemporary poets and artists react simply with an exclamation of despair —as in Edvard Munch's lithograph of a screaming, frenzied figure in a quivering landscape, in the margin of which Munch wrote, "I felt a great cry in the whole universe." Or as in George Grosz's terrible drawings of hollow men looking blankly at us from behind the barbed wires of prison camps. Or as in Kurtz's cry, in *Heart of Darkness,* as he lay dying and reviewing his life—"The horror! The horror!" But if some artists thus merely reflect in their works, as in a mirror, the loneliness and the incoherence of the modern world, others have worked their way to some sort of position which they are willing to recommend to the rest of us. Joyce Cary has told us that Gulley Jimson's solution was laughter, because that is the only possible alternative to tears. For Eliot it is a return to the faith of our fathers. For Aldous Huxley it is a more oriental type of mysticism. For Proust it is submergence in one's private memories.

For Hemingway and Faulkner it is living by, being true to, one's own code, even though one knows that codes are only subjective affairs, without any ontological standing in the cosmos. Thus, in *The Sun Also Rises* Brett's code includes sleeping as often as she likes with as many men as she likes, but it does not include seducing a nineteen-year-old boy; she is ashamed (she hates "to feel like a bitch") when she goes off with Romero, the young bullfighter. Here stoical pride is the central value—pride in one's capacity to do something arduous and difficult; pride, above all, in being able to force oneself to take unnecessary and dangerous risks, pride in being able to face death knowing that it is the end, yet facing it unafraid. "Be scared," old Sam tells young Isaac McCaslin. "You can't help that. But don't be afraid."

[13] T. S. Eliot, "Gerontion," in *Complete Poems and Plays* (New York: Harcourt, Brace, 1960), p. 22.

The recommendations, then, are various, but they reduce in the end to two types: robust proposals and counsels of despair. As counsels of despair I count solutions, like those of the protagonists of Eliot's plays, that involve turning away from this world—the only arena in which solutions are needed, the only arena in which they are relevant, significant, or meaningful. Eliot's heroes and heroines act from completely nontemporal, nonempirical considerations. Their actions are sheer madness, if judged by any sort of prudential or utilitarian calculation. As one of them says:

> I know
> What yet remains to show you of my history
> Will seem to most of you at best futility,
> Senseless self-slaughter of a lunatic,
> Arrogant passion of a fanatic.[14]

They are justified, if at all, only by an act of faith:

> The kind of faith that issues from despair.
> The destination cannot be described;
> You will know very little until you get there;
> You will journey blind. But the way leads towards possession
> Of what you have sought for in the wrong place.[15]

To many men today a solution of this kind will seem an act of desperation rather than of reason, because it ignores, instead of seeking to find a reconciliation with, the scientific outlook on life.

But the robust proposals, in their own way, are also counsels of despair —or better, counsels *in* despair—not positive solutions. For, while they do not recommend capitulation, they hold out no hope for victory—they simply insist that a brave man goes down fighting. Thus the robust solutions also involve a turning-away from life. Whether this turn consists in a retreat into oneself (as in the existential solutions) or in a retreat into the past (as with Proust) is relatively unimportant, for in both cases there is withdrawal from the living context of the contemporary culture and its problems. Thus all of these proposals, even those of the robust type, can be fairly described as refuges—as escapes—rather than constructive solutions, since it cannot be constructive to turn one's back on science and its achievements. The old man in Hemingway's tale, the

---

[14] *Murder in the Cathedral,* in *Complete Poems and Plays* (New York: Harcourt, Brace, 1960), pp. 196–197.
[15] *The Cocktail Party,* in *Complete Poems and Plays,* pp. 364–365.

convict in Faulkner's, Thomas à Becket in *Murder in the Cathedral,* Celia in *The Cocktail Party,* and Meursault in *The Stranger* are not facing and solving their problems. They are evading them, and then justifying these evasions in more or less complicated and sophisticated ways. They are jumping high and to the right in the sense that, like the rats, they are responding in radically inappropriate ways to the problems that confront them—ways that are almost guaranteed not to solve their problems but to exaggerate them.

Historically, of course, it has been the business of philosophy to find answers to the questions that harass Meursault, Jimson, Kurtz, and the others. And in the old days, before the implications of the scientific conception of man were fully understood, there was a stable and pervasive metaphysics which performed precisely this function. Since it provided satisfactory answers to the great cosmic questions as these questions were then framed, the dilemmas men had to resolve were, however difficult, merely personal; the dilemmas were not a part of the very fabric of the culture. But, as the conflict between the scientific and the humanistic conceptions of life has gradually forced its way into men's consciousness, the situation has radically changed.

The need for a metaphysical reconstruction has been generally recognized, but none of those put forward has met with wide acceptance. Rationalists (among whom we may include both the Catholic and the secular Thomists) are committed to a conceptual framework that is so out of keeping with the fundamentally empirical temper of modern society that it can hardly satisfy those who take science and its methods seriously. Solutions of this type are indeed no more satisfactory than the position of the irrationalists and mystics, who would explicitly require us to reject the whole scientific view of life. Finally, there are those who adopt the opposite form of root-and-branch—who would require us to accept the scientific position wholly, either emphasizing the cognitive superiority of science (e.g., the Logical Positivists) or its technological achievements and the possibility for social control and "progress" (e.g., the Pragmatists). These solutions are all alike unsatisfactory because all of them involve, in effect, abandoning either the humanistic or the scientific view of life.

It is because the poets are aware of this philosophical failure that their recommendations amount to no more than those counsels of despair; it is because the general public, at its own level and in its own way, also senses this failure that our culture everywhere exhibits the anxiety and malaise I have described. But worse than the failure of philosophy to develop a satisfactory answer is the abandonment by many philosophers of the attempt to find an answer. The present tendency of many philosophers to direct their energy and their skill toward small-scale problems is indeed the philosophic form of escapism. The philosopher's own special refuge from the central issues of our culture is to busy himself with the clearing-up of semantic muddles and with similar problems that have determinate solutions. This may be helpful in reviving the philosopher's self-confidence, but below the surface an intellectual and moral chaos remains, and is revealed in the aggressive intolerance and dogmatism with which rival schools attack one another.

Thus everywhere in modern society, and at various levels of explicitness and self-consciousness, from modern philosophy to modern art, we see the results of the failure to achieve a unified world view. Men need some sort of general conceptual scheme in terms of which to organize their experience. Without some unifying scheme, experience breaks down into fragments. Of course, as long as a man can confine his attention to one or the other of these fragments and reconcile himself to the partiality and incompleteness of his view by a studied disvaluing of all that he is ignorant of, he may make do. But insofar as our minds reach out from their own island to try to understand its relation to others and to the vast sea of human experience, we are continually frustrated by the "inexplicables" and contradictions we encounter.

II THOUGHT AND ITS OBJECTS: *Thinking*

IN THE PREVIOUS chapter I argued that the basic problem of modern culture is to find a place for value in the world of fact. Science seems to deal with facts, and only with facts. If, as almost everyone believes, science is our best means for ascertaining what is objectively real, it follows that reality must consist in facts. Among these facts, naturally, are facts about values, including, for instance, the fact that St. Paul highly valued his experience on the road to Damascus. But the value itself, from the point of view of science, is merely a subjective state, merely the emotion St. Paul felt, and without the cosmological significance St. Paul himself attached to it.

In a word, where two versions of what has happened conflict (for instance, as to whether there was, or was not, a transcendental cause of the events on the road to Damascus), we tend to believe that the scientific version is more reliable, and accordingly reject the Pauline version as mythical or illusory. If St. Paul's statement has to be construed as a rival description of what happened, then we do indeed face a dilemma. But this conclusion rests on the assumption that we are dealing with two versions, or descriptions, of what happened.

I hold, however, that though St. Paul's statement looks like a description, it actually isn't one. I hold that these are two quite different sorts of sentences (the scientific sort and St. Paul's sort) and that it is only because of a linguistic confusion that we suppose them to be functioning in the same way. Therefore I propose to resolve the seeming contradiction by clearing up the confusion and showing that these sentences have very different functions. If we define language in terms of function (as I would do), we can say that these sentences occur in different languages, each of which is useful for certain purposes but neither of which is ultimately or absolutely "true."

What I have just said about the mistake being a linguistic confusion may sound like the sort of thing positivists and linguistic analysts sometimes say—that there is no contradiction because the humanistic languages are only subjective. I agree with these philosophers that a correct linguistic analysis will show that the conflict between facts and values is what they call a pseudo-problem. But the confusion is linguistic in a deeper—or, since "deeper" is itself a value term, in a different—way. This difference, I hope, will gradually emerge; here I shall say only that it will enable us to explain, and not merely explain away, the humanistic claim that values, too, are "objective." Reducing the humanistic view of man to "emotive" meanings certainly resolves the contradiction formally, but at too high a price: it will not relieve men's anxieties to be told that the scientific view does not conflict with their humanistic beliefs only because these are "mere" poetry and myth. Hence I am not content merely to maintain, with the positivists, that scientific language and religious language perform different functions; I shall argue that these functions supplement each other and that, in consequence, it is a serious oversimplification to draw a sharp distinction between facts and values.

Before discussing particular languages and their particular functions, however, we must reconsider the relationship between minds and their objects. So far I have said that the whole conflict whose unfortunate effects we are considering results from the belief that separate and independently real minds confront a separate and independently real world of objects. Underlying this belief is a dualistic metaphysics. Reality, it is held, consists of two sorts of things: (1) physical things, events in time and space; and (2) minds, which are not physical and not events, but which are somehow connected with certain physical things—our bodies —and indirectly via our bodies, with other physical things. Minds come to know, by processes called perception and cognition, the physical world and (to some extent) themselves. Minds can cause changes in the physical world (by acts of will), and the physical world can cause changes in minds: perception is one such change in minds caused by physical things. For instance, when an airplane comes into my field of vision, a physical thing, the plane, is causing a change in my mind: I perceive the plane, which is "out there" in the external world, as a result of light waves impinging on my retina, changes in the rods and cones, an electric impulse passing along my optic nerve, etc., etc.

If this theory sounds completely obvious, even "self-evident," this is because it underlies (as a more or less tacit assumption) much current scientific theory (for instance, theories of the physiology of sense perception) and also a great deal of philosophical theory.

Yet, however deeply entrenched this dualistic metaphysics is in our present ways of thinking, however self-evident and commonsensical it may now seem, it was not always so. In classical times, for instance, and in the Middle Ages the relation between minds and their objects was very differently conceived. Indeed, the metaphysical scheme we are considering was worked out only at the beginning of the seventeenth century and was already under severe criticism by the end of the century. Yet, so persuasive was it, that rather than abandon it, philosophers chose to try to escape its difficulties by all sorts of extraordinary and paradoxical devices, such as Leibniz's theory that minds and physical things are not what they appear to be but monads, or "centers of force." And many philosophers who may seem to dissent radically from the scheme in a sense accept it, since the alternatives they propose all start from it as a basis. Thus, one characteristic strategy of dissent has been to reduce one of the two independent reals to the other. One school (the materialists) made minds the mere epiphenomenal effects, or by-products, of matter, while the other (the idealists) argued that independently existing minds somehow spin the material world out of themselves. But philosophers only became idealists (or materialists, as the case may be) because, while they were unhappy with dualism, they were unwilling, or unable, to think the whole question through afresh. Idealism and materialism are merely ad hoc hypotheses which modify, without abandoning, the fundamental dualistic stance of independence and separation.

We ought to abandon this metaphysics altogether, rather than continue to tinker with it. I do not say that it is mistaken, for I do not believe that "true" or "false" are appropriate terms by which to characterize a theory (whether metaphysical or otherwise). I do believe, however, that it is dysfunctional and uneconomical. Everything that it accounts for can be accounted for as well, or better, on an alternative view and without involving us in the conflict between the scientific and humanistic conceptions of life which I have called the fundamental crisis of our times. Instead of solving the problems it was intended to solve, this dualistic metaphysics has actually complicated them and so has hopelessly failed to serve the social and cultural functions that metaphysics ought to fulfill.

First, I shall show that if this dualistic metaphysics is accepted, the conflict between the humanistic and scientific world views is really insoluble. If the world is just whatever it is, quite apart from our minds and the judgments these minds make about that world, then obviously either St. Paul's judgment about the events that took place on the road to Damascus is correct or Freud's is correct. They can no more both be correct than can my judgment that the U.S. population is now 180 million and someone else's judgment that it is now 200 million both be correct. Of course, both judgments may be incorrect, but the point here is simply that at least one of them must be mistaken. Applying this reasoning to the judgments of Freud and St. Paul, at least one of *these* must be mistaken. And this has extremely unhappy consequences. For to abandon either view is to deny something which we very much want to hold to be true. This dilemma—this forced choice—is the clear consequence of the dualistic metaphysics we have been describing.

But all this depends on a dualistic metaphysics and on the epistemological theories that it entails. Can we develop a theory that escapes these difficulties? The main outlines of such a theory were in fact worked out at the end of the eighteenth century by Immanuel Kant. The impetus for this Kantian reconstruction was a series of difficulties which Hume had discovered in the dualistic formula. Hume had pointed out that if the mind is simply one object among others and if it becomes aware of these other objects through the impressions they make on our senses, we are confined to making particular judgments. We can, for instance, judge that *this* body gravitates (for we can perceive it gravitating); we can judge that this other body gravitates, and so on. But we shall never be in a position to judge, "All bodies gravitate," for such a judgment goes far beyond anything we can possibly experience. Since we can never experience more than a tiny fraction of all the bodies in the universe, we can never be sure that the judgment "All bodies gravitate" in fact corresponds to the behavior of all bodies everywhere. The trouble with accepting this Humean argument is that it limits science to being a kind of historical summary of segments of the past, while the whole aim of the sciences has been to formulate laws, that is, to make universal judgments, such as the Newtonian "law of universal gravitation."

In a word, Kant saw that if Hume was correct, the whole scientific enterprise was "a vain and chimerical illusion." And since he was unwilling to accept this radical limitation of the sciences, he rejected the basic premise of the argument, viz. the assumption that truth consists in the mind being in agreement with an independent and external reality. Thus he abandoned the dualistic metaphysics I have been describing, and he did so because this metaphysics led to a conclusion about the sciences which he regarded as intolerable.

The root of the trouble, Kant held, lay in thinking of knowledge as a relation between two separate and distinct kinds of things. Pre-Kantian metaphysics, we may say, had conceived of the mind as it came to know, rather like a ship coming alongside a dock. This makes cognition too much an external relation: Both ship and dock exist independently of each other and will go on existing after the ship leaves the shore. Rather, according to Kant, cognition is an organizing, or structuring, relation; and both mind and its objects, so far from existing as distinct things prior to this relation, only emerge in the course of this structuring process.

Kant thought he could prove (1) that there are twelve, and only twelve, structuring relationships (which he called "categories"), and (2) that these twelve categories yield, as end products of the organizing process, just those characteristics attributed to the world by Newtonian physics. Hence Kant held that his new conception of cognition as an organizing relationship had solved the problem of validating science. Kant believed he had established an objective, absolute world after all, though not one independent of minds. On the contrary, it was absolute and objective *only* because it was organized by minds, only because all minds everywhere employed, and necessarily employed, the same twelve standard structures, or processes, to produce a uniform standard product —Newtonian nature.

Few, if any, philosophers today believe that Kant was correct in holding that his twelve categories completely validate Newtonian physics, and the question is academic anyhow since nobody nowadays supposes, as Kant did, that Newton had said the last word about nature and its processes. Further, Kant did not completely free himself, any more than did the idealists and materialists, from metaphysical dualism. Independent self and independent object crept back into his theory in the form of noumenal things-in-themselves and noumenal selves-in-themselves—real, even though admittedly unknowable.

Finally, and most serious of all, Kant believed that he was describing the nature of reality. Kant's critics believe that this is what he ought to have tried to do; they simply believe him to be mistaken. Most philosophers (not just Kant and his critics) conceive of philosophical inquiry in this way—as an attempt to ascertain the nature of reality. The world is thereby presented with the spectacle of rival philosophers heatedly asserting that quite different and irreconcilable things are real—for instance, with the spectacle of Kant maintaining that things-in-themselves exist and other philosophers maintaining that the very notion of a thing-in-itself is absurd.

For my part, I believe that while philosophy is to some extent concerned with finding out what is real, it is also, and chiefly, an attempt to find an appropriate language for describing what everybody already agrees to be real. Thus, though I shall not go into this here, at least a part of the dispute between Kant and his critics is not over what reality is, but over what is the most suitable language for describing it. Many seemingly inconclusive philosophical debates can be quickly resolved once this is realized.

The difference between these two conceptions of the nature of the philosophical enterprise will occupy us again and again in this book. Thus the account that I am going to put forward, in this and the following chapters, as an alternative to dualism, is not a rival *metaphysical* theory. It is an alternative description of what we all experience—a description that I recommend (but only for philosophical, not for everyday, purposes, of course) since it is less misleading than other descriptions.

To put this differently: I am not offering an answer to the question, "What is reality? What is out there apart from us?" Instead, I am answering the question, "When we ask, 'What is reality? What is out there apart from us?' what do we mean?" I hold that while philosophers have believed themselves to be offering us rival, and incompatible, metaphysical hypotheses about the true nature of an ultimate reality, they are arguing only about how best to describe what they all agree it is.

If the distinction I am drawing is not clear, an analogy may help: A child is about to tell his mother that he has broken her best Spode teapot; the president of a corporation is about to announce to his board of directors that profits are declining sharply; a diplomat is trying to find a formula that the foreign ministers of other countries will accept. Each of these people is going to tell—honestly and truthfully—what has occurred: that the teapot is broken, that the losses have been incurred, that the present policies of the Cuban government are hostile to the Interamerican system. But each still has to find the "right" words to announce it, for one way of describing the situation will enrage mother or the board of directors, and another way will moderate annoyance; one way of putting the U.S. case against Cuba will antagonize the other American states, while another way will antagonize Congress.[1] The "right" way of describing Cuban policy is the way that will be acceptable to all the parties concerned, and this means taking into account complex national prejudices and Congressional biases. Of course, it is quite possible to say that the various prejudices and biases are a part of the total situation that the diplomats confront; that the child's past record in respect to breakage and damage is a part of the total situation he confronts. This is a useful way of looking at the matter. Nevertheless, when we undertake to give an adequate account of the total situation (in this sense of "total"), we do not directly describe the whole of the situation; we *describe* part of it (say, the attitude of the Cuban government) and *take account of the rest* of it (say, Congressional prejudices) by the *way* in which we describe that part.

Even our analogy has now become rather complicated; but the point is basically simple—a diplomat (or a child, or a corporation president) who realizes that he has to take account of prejudices and biases, and who recognizes that this is often a difficult and tricky matter, is more likely to give an adequate account of what has happened than is one who assumes that he has only to report what has happened, period. I believe that this is applicable to philosophy. Philosophy is rather like diplomacy in this respect. But Kant (and many other philosophers, too) assumed that the philosophical enterprise is more like science, that it consists simply in correctly describing—say—the relation between minds and their objects. Actually, philosophers always do, more or less unconsciously, take account of attitudes and values, of prejudices and biases. But because they do not realize this is what they are doing, their descriptions are all

---

[1] See below, p. 116.

more or less inadequate and unacceptable. Thus, even if the view I am going to propose is in many respects Kantian, it is going to differ from Kant's radically in respect to the stance adopted toward it, just as the stance of two diplomats toward the same draft treaty will differ depending on whether they are conscious or unconscious of the various national prejudices and biases that are affecting the draft.

Though there are thus many ways in which the view I am putting forward differs from Kantianism, there is nevertheless one important respect in which it is Kantian. I believe that Kant was correct in conceiving subject and object, mind and things, as functionally related, rather than as absolutely and metaphysically distinct things. Though, as I have pointed out, he slipped back into dualism at the noumenal level, he was on the right track in conceiving what he called the empirical self and the empirical world as interrelated elements within experience. Hence, like Kant, I want to start with experience as a basic concept. But what is experience?

Instead of dealing directly with this question, let us raise a different one. Why do I choose the term "experience" to designate whatever it is that I want to start with? My reason is this. Most available terms are seriously infected by that seventeenth-century distinction between subjective and objective, which I want to avoid but into which we are all too likely to slip merely as a result of a seemingly innocuous choice of terms. Most terms, that is to say, either have a strong objective connotation (terms like "object" or "thing," for instance) or else a strong subjective connotation (terms like "feeling" or "awareness," for instance). If I were to begin with "thing" or "object" as a basic concept, I would already be committed to an objectivist bias; on the other hand, if I were to begin with "feeling" or "awareness" I would be equally committed to a subjectivist bias.

"Experience" is a good term precisely because it has both subjective and objective connotations. If, for instance, in a letter of recommendation, I write, "My experience of Mr. Smith has always been happy," the recipient of the letter may regard this as somewhat guarded: perhaps I am hinting that other people's experience of Smith may be quite different. On the other hand, in some contexts, "experience" has an objective, not a subjective, connotation. If I write that "Smith is a man of much experience," the recipient will take me to mean that he has had extensive contacts with the "real" world. Thus "experience" is ambiguous, because, depending on the context, it may refer either to *what* is encountered (the object experienced) or to the encounter (the experiencing). This ambiguity makes it a useful term for us, since it does not commit us in advance to an exclusively objective or to an exclusively subjective stance.

Having now explained why I choose the term "experience" to designate what I want to talk about, I return to the prior question, What is experience? What is it that I am designating by the term "experience"? The answer is that experience is just the flow of . . . experience—the chair I am sitting in, the table across the room, the wall behind the table, the window in the wall, the lawn beyond the window. We can talk in objective terms about the chair that I experience; we can, and do, also talk about my experience of the chair. Sometimes we prefer one way of talking, sometimes the other. But the fact that we have these two ways of talking about experience should not mislead us into supposing that there are two different things: (a) the chair, which is not in experience at all, and (b) the chair's subjective counterpart, which is in experience. There are not two different things; there are two ways of talking about the segment of experience that I call the chair. If we look at experience from one point of view it is natural for us to use an "objects-for-minds" type of language; if we look at it from another point of view, we use a "mind's-awareness-of-objects" type of language. The difference is a difference in perspective.

So, when I talk about the subjective "aspect" of experience in this chapter, I am not talking about an illusion like a ghost or a mirage; I am talking about my experience of the chair I am sitting on, or of the table across the room. Of course, we do experience hallucinations; the defeated predictions and frustrations that occur in experience are the starting point, psychologically speaking, for the distinction we come to draw between what is out there (real) and what is merely my experience (illusion, hallucination, dream). This is a distinction we come to make, but we make it *within* experience, not *between* experience and something else which isn't experience at all. It is a distinction that the very young baby hasn't begun to make; one that even the most wary and sophisticated adult doesn't make *all* of the time. For though, on occasion, we certainly note the difference between subjective and objective, much of the time we don't ask ourselves whether what we are experiencing is merely our experience or whether it is really out there, as we experience it to be. Much of the time we just experience (encounter) whatever we happen to be experiencing. Thus experience is that in which we make distinctions, including the distinction between what is "real" and what is "illusory" and also the distinction between what is "there" and what is "my awareness of what is there." The starting point of the whole analysis that is to follow is experience: experience as it occurs.

Starting, then, from experience, we must account for the emergence both of a self that does (or has) the experiencing and of the objective world that is the object of the self's experience. When I say "account for the emergence" I don't mean that I propose to give a psychological account of the genesis of this distinction in somebody's biography. Rather, I propose to describe self and object in a way that will account for the reality of them both. We want to hold that both self and world are real— and that each is as real as, and real in the same sense as, the other. We do not want to collapse self into the epiphenomenon of a prior existing world, nor to collapse world into a mere product of a prior existing self. We want to assert the existence *both* of self and of world, but without falling back into dualism, which once looked like a way out but which has proved to be largely responsible for the crisis of contemporary culture.

So far, I have introduced only the concept of "experience." Surely it will be allowed that this term designates something real and meaningful —namely, something we experience. I shall now introduce two more terms—"foreground" and "background"—and I shall indicate what, in experience, each of them designates. Suppose I look over there and see a cat. Because I am a creature of memory, there is much that I don't actually see now but that I recall, infer, deduce, or suspect about the cat. I think it likely, for instance, that the cat belongs to Mr. Smith, that it is the one he was looking for yesterday, that it has the mange, that it has a mean disposition. I see the cat now; that is certain. But I don't see Mr. Smith, still less do I see his ownership of the cat, nor do I now see its mangy skin or its mean disposition. These are things I believe (rightly or wrongly) about the cat that I now see. Surely this sort of distinction is familiar? Surely we make it constantly? Surely it is *in* experience? Very well; I shall call "foreground" anything that I now directly experience, as I directly experience the cat now; I shall call "background" anything that I know, believe, suspect, or hope about what I directly experience now.

Now, using this foreground-, background-language, we can say the following:

(1) Everything that is background at this time might be foreground at another time. For instance, on seeing Mr. Smith today (foreground) I might recall that he was looking for a cat yesterday (background). Indeed, something can be background for a present foreground only because it has been foreground on another occasion. Thus, when I see the cat now (foreground) and think that it probably has a mean disposition (background), this can be only because on some other occasion I saw the cat bite and scratch (foreground on that earlier occasion).

(2) What is foreground for one person at one time may be background for another person at the same time: I walk into a strange room and see a white blob on the floor beside the sofa. That is my foreground. I think it possible that it is the cat's tail, though it may be a crumpled piece of paper (background). Smith, whose room it is, walks in and sees his cat (foreground), since that's the animal's accustomed place.

(3) Different people may have different backgrounds with respect to the same foreground: You and I both visit Westminster Abbey and see a chair there. Because I have studied English history (background) I believe that it is the throne. You have no reason to believe this, because you have not. Or again: we both see the book on the table over there and recognize it as a book. But you have read it, while I know nothing of its content.

(4) What is background for one person at one time may become part of the foreground for that same person at another time: When I visit Westminster Abbey for the first time I may see a chair (foreground) and infer that it is the throne (background), because I have read in a guide-book that the kings and queens of England are crowned in the Abbey. Subsequently, however, after frequent visits I may see the throne, where once I saw only a chair. Or again, I may pass a man in the street and infer that he is a physician, because of the kind of bag he is carrying. Subsequently, after I have come to know him well, after he has pulled me through a severe illness, I see, not man-who-may-be-a-doctor, but, quite simply, my doctor.

(5) What is now part of my foreground may become background for me: Traveling across a desert, I see an oasis a little way ahead (foreground). I inform my companion, who inquires, "Are you sure?" I reconsider and reply, "Well, I see something shimmering; it *may* be water." "Oasis," which was foreground, has now become background.

(6) The amount, richness, complexity, and variety of background will

obviously vary enormously from one individual to another and from one occasion to another. Nevertheless, there is no experience that is absolutely bare foreground. There will always be *some* background around any foreground, even if the background is no more than the thought, "What? That again?" Or the thought, "Never seen that before."

(7) Though there is, within any given experience, a distinguishable line between foreground and background, the line of demarcation shifts back and forth: what, at one time, is a tentative inference may, through habituation and repetition, become incorporated in the foreground.

Now we have three basic concepts: experience, foreground, background. I shall have to introduce a few more as we go along, but these will do for the present. In this chapter I shall give an account of the subjective aspects of experience—thinking, believing, perceiving, etc.—in terms of these concepts. Then, in the next chapter, still using these concepts, I shall give an account of the objective side of experience and show how, in terms of foregrounds and backgrounds, it is possible to account for the objectivity, the hardness, the over-thereness of some of the contents of experience.

To begin, then, with an account of the subjective side of experience, What is thought? According to one eminent contemporary philosopher, "Thought is that activity of mind which aims directly at truth." To put this somewhat differently, thought is an activity that aims at ceasing— as soon as it can. We men think much less frequently than we flatter ourselves that we do. In fact, because thinking is difficult and painful, we think only when we have to and only as long as we have to. The reason we can get by for so much of the time without thinking is that in any stable sort of environment we build up routines which are viable responses to the various standard situations in which we find ourselves. For instance, when we get up in the morning elaborate routines take us through toothbrushing, shaving, and dressing. Even in such a simple business as tying one's shoes, various complex routines are cued off one after the other by sensations in our finger tips, all without having to take thought at all. Indeed, if we try to think about what we are doing or to make decisions, the routines are likely to break down, and we are lost. And all of these first-order routines, as we may call them, are backed up and reinforced by second- and third-order routines which came into play smoothly and automatically: if a shoelace breaks as I am tying it, I look in the drawer for an extra pair; or repair it by tying the ends together;

or call my wife. As we have seen, the so-called high cultures are societies that prevent emergencies from occurring (and so the need for taking thought) by developing elaborate hierarchies of reserve routines.

Nor is it merely in respect of overt behavior that we develop routines. There are also elaborate mental routines as well, such as those used for programming a computer, for solving quadratic equations or crossword puzzles, or, indeed, for conducting a conversation. Much of what passes in society for thinking consists in routine responses to verbal stimuli:

A. "How do you do?"
B. "Quite nicely, thank you. And you?"
A. "What wretched weather we've been having lately!"
B. "Yes, I can't recall a worse winter since the blizzard of—was it?—1940."
A. "No, surely it was '39."
B. "Yes, of course, 1939, I remember. . . ."

And so on and so forth. In none of this conversational give-and-take is there any thought at all. Thought may have entered at some point into the *formation* of some of the routines we use, but a great many of them are sheerly the result of trial-and-error learning, accidental associations, or habits—like the learning by which the rats acquired the routine for feeding and for avoiding a fall.

Only when a routine breaks down does thinking occur; and it lasts only long enough either to ascertain the appropriate existing second-order routine, or (if none is available) to develop a new routine. Thus, in the midst of a conversation like the above, where the exchanges are more or less automatic responses to auditory cues, we may be suddenly struck by a remark, or perhaps even by something a little odd about a tone of voice, which we cannot "place." We are puzzled about how to take it: Is the speaker serious? Or ironic? Does he mean more than he seems to? Is he hinting at something below the surface level of his remark? Such a check is an occasion for thought. Thinking is the effort to place, to understand, the puzzling remark. It is the kind of activity that intervenes when finer (more precise) discriminations are required.

It follows that the old, sharp distinction which some people draw between "purely practical" and "purely intellectual" problems is a gross oversimplification. *All* problems have a cognitive, or intellectual, element: This is the problem of adequately discriminating among the cues, that is, understanding what they "mean"; but all problems arise in a practical context (we don't know what to do next) and all solutions issue in actions (we do whatever we have discovered is appropriate). The cognitive aspect of a problem consists in discovering what acts are appropriate, and this is a problem because the perceptual cues are ambiguous: any one of several different responses or routines *might* be appropriate. Until we develop adequate procedures for discriminating among the cues we can't tell which response is appropriate.

Accordingly, the distinction between practical and intellectual problems is a difference in degree, not a difference in kind. In some problems (e.g., in the rats') the behavioral blockage is striking and the release of behavior after the achievement of a solution is also obvious. We are likely to think of such cases as "purely" practical because we overlook the cause of the breakdown—the cognitive, or perceptual, failure—the inability to discriminate between the two similar grays. On the other hand, solving a crossword puzzle may seem to be a "purely" cognitive, or intellectual, problem; we overlook the fact that the problem arises because we don't know what word to write down next (the clue is ambiguous and does not enable us to determine among several possible words which is the "right" one). But there *is* a behavioral consequence when the problem is eventually solved: we write down the correct word.

Thus an intellectual problem is simply one in which the discriminative stage is primary and the behavioral consequences are relatively secondary: There is usually no difficulty about writing down the word once we have found the correct one. Our problem would be primarily practical, instead of primarily cognitive, if, for instance, we knew the correct word but didn't know how, or where, to write it down (e.g., if we had misplaced our pencil or lost our place on the puzzle). Another way of putting this is to say that sometimes practical urgency (e.g., hunger and fear in the rats' case) dominates both the problem and its solution. At such times the test of successful discrimination is, Does it relieve the practical tension? Sometimes, however, the frustration is primarily of a different kind: the perceptual field doesn't make sense—as in an anagram,

NECCIES

—and we want, more or less intensely, to have it make sense. In these cases, discrimination is itself the end, rather than a means for releasing the appropriate behavioral response. That there is, in addition to such drives as fear and hunger, a drive that we may call curiosity—the drive to make sense of a situation—seems clear. This drive is probably never *wholly* absent: even rats experience curiosity, according to Tolman's interpretation of their behavior (see below, p. 110). On the other hand, it is probably never *exclusively* present: curiosity may be the primary drive in the case of the man solving the crossword puzzle, but other drives are probably also present—for instance, the desire to emulate, or excel, other crossword-puzzle fans. The part played by curiosity in any particular problem-situation depends to a large extent on the context; the situation in which we find ourselves determines what other drives are active and their intensity. For instance, a woman sitting quietly at home, looking through an album of old snapshots may be struck by a dark patch on one photograph which she has never noticed before. What can that be, there in the background? She may be sufficiently tantalized to spend some time figuring it out. Curiosity, here, is surely the primary drive. But suppose the woman is an intelligence officer in London in the spring of 1944; suppose the photograph is a reconnaissance picture of the German Air Force research center at Peenemünde, and suppose there have been underground reports of intense activity at this base connected with a radical new weapon. Now the dark patch on the photograph is much more than an object of "idle" curiosity; in this situation curiosity is reinforced by drives rooted in patriotism, in desires for personal security, and also, perhaps, in pride in professional achievement.

Accordingly, if we want to understand the nature of thought—which is our task in this chapter—we must concentrate on the discrimination-stage (or "factor," or "element") in problem-solving, whether the problem be primarily practical or primarily cognitive.

Thus, as a man walks along a path he sees a tree, another tree, a bird nestling in the bushes, the path itself, and so on. What is happening? As a first approximation, let us say that he is constantly discriminating cues and smoothly interpreting them. Discrimination problems are being solved so easily that the walker is unaware that a process is occurring. He would become aware of the process only when, for one reason or another, an ambiguous cue occurred which caused him to hesitate, to ask himself, "What is it?" Nevertheless, though he is unaware of it, a process of interpreting cues is going on. This is evidenced by the fact (among other facts) that the policy dominating his acts at this point determines in large measure what he experiences (i.e., what cues he picks up and interprets). There is a difference between what a man experiences if his primary interest is bird-watching and what he experiences if his primary interest is to get home rapidly and safely: with the latter policy all sorts of things on the path "in full sight" will be ignored which, given the former policy, would be minutely observed.

Accordingly, we can talk about experience at any given time as being a product—the product of a more or less smooth, more or less rapid, process of interpretation, in which an initial cue is structured and organized by means of funded information. In other words, the initial stage in this process is what we have called the foreground; the final stage is what we have called experience; and the medium of interpretation is the background.

This can be written as a functional relationship, as follows:

$$E = f(F, B)$$

where E is what is actually experienced, F is the initial foreground from which the process starts, and B is background—the mass of more or less organized memories, generalizations, desires, attitudes, and values which the perceiver has learned in the course of prior experience and which he brings with him to this experience.[2] Since in this chapter we are discussing the subjective aspect (or phase) of experience, we take as foreground what is actually the initial stage in the process (not necessarily what is really out there on the path); and we take as background the actual memories, fears, hopes, and aspirations of the perceiver (not necessarily what is out there).

E, it will be seen, will vary with any changes in F or in B. For instance, suppose two men are walking down the path. One of them, who happens to be rather timid, has just been reading about snakes and snake bites (B_1); the other, who is not timid, has not (B_2). Suppose, further, that for both of them the initial stage in the interpretative process is the same—F consists of a long narrow dark something in the path. The man with background B_1 will very likely interpret F as a snake ($E =$

---

[2] Since this formula has a mathematical look, and since such notation is sometimes introduced illegitimately—that is, to suggest a precision that is not in fact attainable—I must enter a caveat here. I don't mean to suggest that we can ever formulate a precise, quantitative relation between these dependent and the independent variables. I maintain only that there is a relation of dependence—changes occurring on the right-hand side are reflected in corresponding changes on the left-hand side. The symbolism I am using is introduced simply as a shorthand way of indicating this.

snake), while the man who interprets F by means of B_2 will likely see a shadow or a stick ($E =$ shadow, stick). On the other hand, if F were different (e.g., roundish and light-colored), even the man with the B_1 background might very well see a stone, not a snake.

I shall say that the man "saw" a snake, when a snake was what he actually experienced, even though he may have been mistaken. Some people may prefer to confine the usage of "see" to cases where what one actually experiences is confirmed by subsequent experience. So, in these circumstances, instead of saying that the man "saw" a snake, these people may prefer saying, "The man thought he saw a snake," or "He saw a stick which he mistook for a snake," or "He took a stick for a snake," or something of this sort. It is certainly permissible to equate "what one sees" with "what is actually there," but since there is already an acceptable expression for the confirmed cases (what is "really" there) and since it is convenient to have a way of talking about what one actually experiences, I propose to use "see" to mean what a person actually experiences, regardless of whether this experience is subsequently confirmed.

But how can we tell what a person sees, in this sense of "sees"? There are two simple, but adequate, operational tests. (1) We shall ask him what he sees; unless we suspect him of lying, we can accept his reply as a reliable report of what he sees now. (2) In doubtful cases we can watch how he behaves and make an inference from this. Thus, if a man says, "I see a ghost," we shall say that he sees a ghost (a ghost is what he experiences), even though what *we* see, and what we believe is there, is a moonbeam falling on a curtain. If a man walking on a path hesitates, draws back and looks around hurriedly for a stick, we shall say he saw a snake; and we shall continue to say this even though, when it turns out to have been only a shadow, he heatedly insists that he "knew it was a shadow all the time." Again, if we ask a man what he sees and he says "my cat," we shall say that he sees his cat, even though all of the cat except the tip of its tail is out of sight under the sofa.

We can now define some typical types of perceptual experience. First, we must distinguish between what I will call complete and incomplete perceptions. A complete perception is one in which the interpretative process by which B structures F is smooth and is carried through to completion; there is no hesitation, no mistaken identification, no readjustment. That is, the resultant E is adequate for the purposes of the perceiver, whatever these happen to be. A perception is incomplete, on the other hand, if, for any reason, the interpretative process breaks down, with the result that E is inadequate.

Some examples may be helpful. Suppose the interpreter's present policy is simply to avoid being bitten by snakes: his interpretation of the foreground (i.e., his perception) is complete, that is, adequate, if it enables him to discriminate between snakes and non-snakes, thereby permitting him to take the steps necessary to avoid snakes. Suppose, however, that the operative drive is primarily cognitive. He is not particularly afraid of snakes; he is just curious about what that thing in the path ahead of him is. Here, again, he may be content merely to *identify* the object as a snake. This will be true, if, like most laymen, his background structure contains relatively few generalizations regarding snakes, and if these generalizations are vague and imprecise (e.g., snakes are cold-blooded; snakes lay eggs; some snakes are dangerous; some snakes are helpful, etc.). But suppose the person in the path is an ophiologist. If so, his background structure contains a complex set of interconnected generalizations regarding snakes, their mode of life, their relationship with other reptiles, and so forth. In such circumstances curiosity-drive ("What is it?") is likely to be much more demanding. That is, satisfaction of the drive requires a much more extensive interpretative process. Because he will want to "place" the thing he sees on the path much more precisely than the layman, the ophiologist will not be content with an interpretation that stops merely at identifying the object as "snake." He will want to know whether it is a rattler. If so, what species? and so on. His perception is complete if he manages to satisfy these more specific needs.

Suppose, however, that our ophiologist is out for a walk with a bird-watcher, with whom he is in love. Under these circumstances, his perception may be complete even though it goes no farther than the layman's "That's a snake," since the lady and her interests have pre-empted his thoughts.

It is clear from these examples that a discrimination process can be complete at some time t_1 and incomplete at some other time t_2. A discrimination process that is adequate for one policy (avoiding any snakes that may be on the path) may be quite inadequate for another (collecting specimens for a zoological museum). And a discrimination process that is complete today, when the ophiologist is out walking with the lady bird-watcher, may be incomplete tomorrow when he is alone and has nothing to think about but his job. Also, a process that is complete today in the sense that it exhausts all the detail available in the ophiologist's background structure may be incomplete in a few years' time, when expert knowledge of ophiology has expanded.

It is also clear from these examples that there are several different types of incomplete perception, which must themselves be carefully discriminated. (1) A discrimination process may be incomplete in the sense that it is unsatisfactory for present policy purposes. In this sense, the rats' discrimination process was incomplete, because they couldn't distinguish between two shades of gray; similarly, the walker's discrimination process is incomplete if he can't decide whether it is a snake or a stick that he sees on the path and if he needs to know in order to decide whether to continue the walk or to turn back. (2) A discrimination process may be incomplete in the sense that, though it is adequate for present policy purposes, it is not carried through to the full depth of detail in the interpreter's available background structure. (An ophiologist may cease to discriminate as soon as he recognizes that the object is a snake, though he knows enough about snakes to be able, if he wanted to, to discriminate in more detail.) (3) A discrimination process may be incomplete in the sense that, though I have carried through completely as far as my own background structure goes (and so is complete in this sense), my background structure lacks detail that other people's (e.g., expert ophiologists') background structures possess.

There is still another sense in which a discrimination process may be said to be incomplete: (4) A discrimination process is incomplete, some people may want to say, if the experience that is the end result of the process fails to correspond with the facts, whatever they are. But what *are* the facts? The answer to this question obviously takes us beyond the subjective aspect of experience on which we are concentrating in this chapter, so we shall postpone consideration of this type of incompletion until chapter iii, where we shall be discussing factuality, objectivity, and "out-thereness."

Now, in the first sense of incompletion, few interpretations are incomplete. This is simply to say that, for the most part, we experience pretty much what we need to experience for our traffic with nature. From the great mass of cues bombarding us, each of us culls out those that are relevant to his current needs and organizes them just enough to satisfy these needs. If we were not able to do this in the great majority of cases, our lives would be frustrated indeed—poor, nasty, brutish, and, above all, short. But, in the second and third senses of incompletion, very few interpretations are complete, party because few of us have the relevant, detailed background structures, and partly because our purposes are limited and specialized. Even if our purpose is primarily cognitive ("What *can* that queer thing be?"), most of us are easily satisfied—for instance, with an interpretation that goes no farther than "snake," or, at the most, "rattlesnake." Thus there is a kind of *deflationary* effect in which the discrimination process stops far short of what it could be.

There is a corresponding *inflationary* effect in interpretation in which we "read into" the thing *more* than the standard interpretation. For instance, suppose the stick in the path happens to be a booby trap that I put there deliberately to frighten the timid walker. What I see, when I see this stick, is certainly different from what he sees, even when he sees a stick, not a snake. For he sees merely *a* stick, while I see *my* stick, my special device for frightening him. This inflationary effect always exists with respect to things that are our private property or about which we have special knowledge or special attitudes (my face certainly looks different to me from the way it looks to you, and so on). Deflation occurs either because our background structure lacks some available information (we don't know much about snakes), or because we fail to use some part of the background structure which we possess (we don't use the part of our background structure concerned with species of rattlers, etc.). On the other hand, inflation occurs when our background structure contains information (knowledge that the stick is a "device") that only we possess.

Variations in background structure from one person to another are much larger than most of us realize. To demonstrate this, it will be convenient to distinguish, and to consider in turn, three types of elements in background structures—memories, generalizations, and values. I shall show that all three of these may, and do, vary from one perceiver to another. (1) *Memories:* we have already given examples of this kind of variation—for instance, my memories of prior encounters with my face which you lack because it is not your face; my memory that I used this stick as a booby trap, and so on. (2) *Generalizations:* obviously interpretations (what we see) will vary depending on the presence or absence of certain generalizations in our background structure. For instance, if I believe in ghosts (if my background structure contains the generalization "Ghosts exist") and you do not believe in them, I am likely to see a ghost where you see moonlight on drapery at a window. Again, if a Zulu (or an Ainu, or a Papuan, or a Bantu) and I both look in the same direction and you ask us what we see, I may say "chair" and he may say "moo-moo." Can you assume that we are both having the same experience, and that you have now learned that the Zulu word for chair is "moo-moo"? Not at all. Zulus may sit on their haunches or on the floor, and this Zulu's background structure may very well not contain the generalization, "Things like this, with legs, backs and arms, are chairs." What *he* sees may well be not "chair," but what we would call "wood-for-burning." This may be what "moo-moo" means. But the Zulu may not form generalizations at all; or, if he does, they may not be thing-type generalizations of the kind we form (see, for instance, pp. 97–99). In this event, though "moo-moo" means roughly "firewood," it doesn't mean *thing*-for-burning, as firewood means to us thing-for-burning. In other words, it may not be merely that the Zulu experiences one thing (firewood) where we experience another (chair); it may be that he doesn't experience a *thing* at all.

Here, in this chapter, we are discussing the subject side, or aspect, of experience. Accordingly, when we say that the Zulu sees firewood, where we see a chair, we are defining "sees" in terms of what is actually experienced, not in terms of what is really there (p. 42). In chapter iii, I shall give an account—still in terms of foregrounds and backgrounds— of the difference between what the Zulu believes is there (firewood) and what is really there (chair).

But it is not necessary to take such an extreme example in order to observe the effect on what we see of the presence or absence of generalizations in the background structure. Suppose a garage repairman, a professor of physics, and a philosopher are all looking in the same direction. Bearing in mind that here "see" means "what is actually experienced," do they all see the same thing? Obviously not. The philosopher may know how to drive a car, but, being mechanically almost illiterate, he sees mostly a confusion of wires, tubes, and complex metal objects, among which he may (vaguely) identify carburetor, oil filter, and spark plugs. The garage-man sees a more coherent set of objects than does the philosopher. Not only can he name them; he knows how they are interrelated, how they function, and how to repair them. The professor of physics sees still more: for he sees the motor-car engine as exemplifying a formal theory of thermodynamics.

We tend to overlook such radical differences in actual seeing for a number of reasons: In the first place, for many purposes what matters is often not what people actually see but what happens to be there. Second, despite differences in actual seeing, all perceivers may use the same term, "engine," to describe what they see. This fact, incidentally, explains why the verbal reports of perceivers sometimes have to be corrected by observations of behavior (see p. 42). In this case, despite identical verbal responses, the three perceivers behave very differently in the presence of what they all call the engine, and these differences in behavior reflect the fact that the initial cue (F) is being interpreted by means of a variety of more or less well organized and detailed B's. Finally, a fairly deflated interpretation, which they may all actually share (even the philosopher), is adequate for many practical purposes: they can all drive the car.

So much, for the moment, as regards variations in memories and in generalizations. As regards (3) *Values,* the last component in background structure, many psychological experiments show the effect on perception of "need," "attitude," and "set."

One of the most interesting of these experiments concerns the effect of values on perceptions of size. Bruner and Goodman[3] asked each of a number of children to estimate the size of coins—pennies, nickels, dimes, quarters, and half dollars. Except for the dime, the greater the monetary value of the coin, the greater was the tendency to overestimate its size; and the poor children in the group tended to overestimate the coins' sizes more than the well-to-do children did. Moreover, the sizes of coins were overestimated to a greater extent than were the sizes of neutral gray discs with the same diameters.

In another experiment, Postman and Bruner[4] showed that children overestimated the height of 3-inch toys, as compared with neutral blocks of the same size. Further, when the experimenter failed to keep his promise to give the dolls to the children, overestimation of size increased: the unavailability of the desired object increased its value to the children; accordingly, an increase in perceived size resulted.

Other experiments show that people who are hungry are more likely to perceive food than are people who have recently eaten, when both

[3] J. S. Bruner and C. C. Goodman, "Value and Need as Organizing Factors in Perception," *J. Abnor. & Soc. Psych.,* XLII (1947), 33–44.

[4] L. Postman and J. S. Bruner, "Multiplicity of Set as a Determinant of Perceptual Behavior," *J. of Exp. Psych.,* XXXIX (1949), 369–377.

groups are shown a series of slightly ambiguous pictures.[5] Still others show that the insertion of such a word as "warm," with its favorable implications (in contrast to "cold," with unfavorable implications), in otherwise identical descriptions of a person will color the impression that person makes and influence behavior toward him.[6]

It is not surprising, perhaps, that hunger shapes the perceptual field of a hungry man in the direction of objects that will satisfy (reduce) this drive. The effect of such needs is fairly obvious; moreover they are transient and they affect the perceptual field only very selectively. However, there are more permanent and deeply rooted attitudes which color, not merely this or that particular perceptual field, but an individual's whole way of perceiving. An example is the effect on perception of an "authoritarian" personality. In one experiment children were shown a picture of a dog (i.e., a picture that "everybody" would identify as a dog). They were then shown a series of additional pictures in which changes were gradually introduced until a picture was reached which everybody would identify as a cat. Children who had scored high on a test of prejudice and racial intolerance characteristically remained committed to the initial identification "dog," despite the changes introduced, while children who scored low on this test were more ready to give up the initial identification when confronted with the changing pictures.[7] Here, in the case of the children with the more rigid personality, a value (intense dislike of ambiguity; strong drive for order) characterizes the individual's background structure *as a whole*. But whether it be the background structure as a whole that is affected or only some particular segment of it, a value component is present in all perception, and this component affects the content of the perceptual field, that is, what we "see." This is true even when we are "on our guard" against racial prejudice, even when we are trying to be objective, to measure carefully, and to reach unbiased conclusions. In such cases, the background structure is characterized by a different value—the value we attribute to "scientific" accuracy and to objectivity.

---

[5] R. Levine, I. Chein, and G. Murphy, "The Relation of the Intensity of a Need to the Amount of Perceptual Distortion," *J. Psych.*, XIII (1942), 283–293.

[6] S. E. Asch, "Forming Impressions of Personality," *J. Abnor. & Soc. Psych.*, XLI (1946), 258–290; H. H. Kelley, "The Warm-Cold Variable in First Impressions of Persons," *J. Pers.*, XVIII (1949), 431–439.

[7] E. Frenkel-Brunswik, "Intolerance of Ambiguity as an Emotional and Perceptual Personality Variable," *J. Pers.*, XVIII (1949), 108–143.

Though values thus always affect our perceiving in various ways, we usually fail to notice the differences they and other elements in the background structure create. The reason is that we tend to assume that there are always perceptual identities corresponding to verbal identities (we assume that we *see* the same things because we use the same words); and also because, for the most part, in our traffic with nature and with each other we get by nicely with very deflated, rough-and-ready versions of the standard interpretation, which "work" at the low level of efficiency and accuracy most of us usually demand.

So much, for the present, as regards smooth interpretations, that is, where, however deflated or inflated the interpretation may be, it is nevertheless adequate for the perceiver's own cognitive or policy purposes. More interesting are those interpretations that are either initially inadequate or subsequently break down. The interpretation is *initially inadequate* if, for instance, I can't see well enough to tell whether the thing on the path is a snake or a stick, and I need to know for policy purposes which it is. It *subsequently breaks down* if, for instance, I see a stick and step confidently ahead, only to be pulled up short by finding it slither away. Whether we pull in our horns before we commit ourselves to a policy or only afterward, there is a failure of discrimination. Because there is a failure of discrimination, a problem arises; and thinking occurs in response to this problem—that is, in an attempt to discriminate the cues adequately enough for current needs.

When the interpretation is smooth I will say that we have an instance of *perceiving,* if the situation is primarily cognition, and an instance of *acting* (behaving, or doing), if the situation is primarily practical. Where, on the other hand, the interpretation breaks down, we have an instance of *thinking,* if the problem is primarily cognitive, and an instance of *deciding* if the problem is primarily practical. Thus:

primarily cognitive	*primarily practical*	
perceiving	doing	*smooth interpretation*
thinking	deciding	*breakdown in interpretation*

In most cases, hesitation is only brief. For usually a finite number of standard alternatives is available—either "categories" if the problem is primarily cognitive, or "policies" if the problem is primarily practical. And we have merely to determine (think about) which of these possible solutions is the correct one. Moreover, we usually have readily available standard procedures for achieving adequate discrimination.

Often it is merely a matter of getting the object into better light (if it is the thing on the path); of looking at the whole of it (if it is the animal under the sofa, which may be a dog or a cat); of getting a little closer to it and touching it (if it is a question whether the suit our friend is wearing is wool or cotton); and so on.

In simple discrimination problems of this kind thinking may not occur at all; the *solution* of the problem may itself be routinized, so that there is a smooth transition into a different perception. Thus, given the happily stable environment in which we usually find ourselves, we learn the solutions of many of our problems (including, of course, the appropriate reserve routines) before we ever encounter the problems themselves. Hence, when we do encounter a problem, it usually consists merely in finding out which one of several reserve routines is appropriate in these circumstances. This is what education does for us—both the formal education that occurs in the schools, and the informal, accidental, partly unconscious education that goes on all the time. Parents and teachers—and the very conditions of the child's life in a stable society—select the routines he is going to need later on, and inculcate them against the time of their eventual need. To the extent that this selection process is successful—to the extent that the child's future needs have been correctly anticipated—we reduce the number of occasions on which anything can go seriously wrong. To put this another way: by forward planning (partly deliberate, largely unconscious) all societies manage to convert most of most men's problems into simple learning-problems, which are solved in childhood, instead of allowing them to develop into real crises later on in the individual's life.

But sometimes the environment changes in ways that society has not remotely anticipated: the background structures, which the adults patiently inculcated and which the children laboriously learned, are now inappropriate. What is then required is a *reorganization* of the background structure—a reorganization that is more or less extensive depending on the magnitude of the problem involved and the novelty of the experience in question. Reorganizing the background structure is quite different from simply adding a new item of information to an existing background structure without changing it materially. We may, if we like, call both processes *learning,* since in both cases the outcome is change in perception and behavior. But, if we do, it is important to distinguish between routine learning, where the process is essentially merely addition, and problematic, or insightful, learning where the process involves reorganization of the background structure, with correspondingly radical changes in what is experienced (i.e., in *E*).

Köhler's work with chimpanzees provides a good example of real problem-solving, that is, of problem-solving that involves reorganization of background structure rather than merely finding the appropriate item in an existing structure.[8] Köhler used chimpanzees' fondness for bananas to study these animals' ability to solve problems. When he put a banana outside the cage, out of arm's reach, the chimpanzees raked in the banana with a stick which Köhler had left in the cage. This was no problem: there was no hesitation. Even though, presumably, sticks and bananas had never before been related in their experience, they at once grasped the connection between the stick and the banana; or rather they grasped the relationship between the *length* of the stick and the *distance* the banana was away from the cage. This is a much more complex relationship than the relationship that was built up by the rats between black and food. Moreover, where the rats had to learn this relationship by repeated trials, the chimpanzees "took in" the relationship between the stick and the banana at once.

Köhler next put the banana farther away and provided the chimpanzees with two sticks. Neither was long enough to rake in the banana, but they could be fitted together (the end of one in the end of the other) to make a long stick. This *was* a problem; and even Sultan, Köhler's favorite chimpanzee, failed to solve it. He tried all sorts of schemes—for instance, he used one stick to push the other stick out until it touched the banana, but of course he still couldn't rake it in. After repeated failures Sultan had a temper tantrum, retreated to the back of his cage, and turned his back on the banana (exactly as the professor at Padua had refused to look through Galileo's telescope). It happened, however, that he carried the two sticks with him and, as he sat, he idly fiddled with them. By chance the end of one of the sticks slipped into the end of the

---

[8] W. Köhler, *The Mentality of Apes* (New York: Harcourt, Brace, 1925), pp. 130–133.

other: quick as a flash Sultan dashed across the cage and raked in the banana with his new, long stick.

Perhaps it will be thought odd to call this the solution of a discrimination problem. But this is what it was. Before he encountered the problem Sultan had developed a background structure by means of which he interpreted (saw) what *we* call "stick" as "banana-rake," just as the rats developed a background structure in which they interpreted (saw) what *we* call "black" as "food-here." The fact that Sultan continued to try to use this background structure in the changed environment (the environment that we call "too far away for either stick by itself") shows that he did not discriminate the new, changed situation from the old situation: he did the same sort of thing with the two (separate) sticks that he had done before with the one stick. But Sultan's accidental solution of the problem was accompanied by (indeed, consisted in) a new perception: the two sticks had suddenly become one, and *this* stick was long enough. That is, the same relation obtained between the longer stick and the present, greater distance, as had obtained earlier between the old, shorter stick and the shorter distance. Sultan's perceptual field was radically revised, for a perceptual field containing one long-enough stick is quite different from one containing two too-short sticks. Of course, the field was changed *for* Sultan rather than *by* Sultan. That is to say, it changed because of the accidental slipping together of the two sticks, not as a result of deliberately trying to solve it.

At the human level, the same sort of transformation of the perceptual field occurs whenever we laugh at a pun or solve an anagram. A pun consists in using a word in a novel way: we don't see the point until we are jolted out of our old way of understanding this word. And when this happens we perceive the word in a new way. Suppose, for instance, someone tells us a story about the two deaf men on a bus, one of whom remarks that it is Thursday and the other of whom promptly replies "So am I; let's get off and have a beer." Because "Thursday" and "thirsty" have wholly different meanings in ordinary discourse they seldom occur in close juxtaposition. Consequently, we think of them, as Sultan obviously thought of the two sticks, as being *two,* that is, as quite different. For this reason, at first hearing the exchange overheard on the bus just doesn't make sense: why should B propose having a beer when A says that the day is Thursday? There is shock (doubtless only minor); there is hesitation (doubtless only momentary); then resolution. The exchange now makes sense, but only because "Thursday" and "thirsty" have both been slightly changed: What were, before, completely disparate items, have become, in this particular respect, similar. We usually take *meaning* as the leading features of words and mark them as similar or dissimilar accordingly. By putting the words into violent juxtaposition, the punster forces us, briefly, to take *sound* as a leading feature, and this results in a radical reorganization, in terms of quite different similarities and dissimilarities. As with Sultan, this problem is largely solved *for* us, rather than *by* us. That is, just as Sultan was presented with the joined stick by the happy accident that the two sticks slid together, so we would probably never notice the similarity between "Thursday" and "thirsty" if they were not juxtaposed by the punster.

Now suppose we are working a crossword puzzle and come across the following clue for a six-letter word: "Repeating rifle used by Boers and us in latin sea." It is likely that "Mauser" will promptly occur to almost everyone, since this is the name of a rifle used by the Boers—and possibly also by us. But what about "in latin sea"? One would expect the clue to read, "Repeating rifle used in Boer war" or something of that sort, not "in latin sea." There is blockage; what ought to make sense, doesn't. What can "in latin sea" mean? Usually "in" means "contained in," "inside." Usually adjectives qualify the nouns they modify. Thus "salt sea" means "sea that is salt," "northern sea" means "sea that lies to the north." We might start out, then, on the hypothesis that "in latin sea" means "in the sea that lies in the latin region," and search for a sea (the Mediterranean?) that has something to do with the Latins or the Romans. But because the puzzle occurs in *The Reporter,* which goes in for puns and anagrams, we may take a harder look at "in latin sea." Suppose it means, not "sea that is latin," but "latin word for 'sea.'" Suddenly, the whole solution falls into place: We are being instructed to put "us" into "mare," the Latin word for "sea" (= mauser).

This is exactly the sort of transformation that occurred in the banana problem. Whereas Sultan now saw one long stick instead of two short ones, we now see two short clues instead of one long one. The "and" now functions differently. Originally we read the clue:

Repeating rifle used by Boers and us, in latin sea.

Now we read it:

Repeating rifle used by Boers, and us in latin sea.

Of course the transformation that occurs in a pun is trivial (even though it is a real transformation). An example of a truly radical transformation is Galileo's discovery of the moons of Jupiter. On the night of the 7th what Galileo saw in the night sky, as he himself tells us, were three fixed stars. So would anyone else have seen fixed stars, had he chanced to look through the telescope that night, for the received opinion (a part of the standard background structure in 1610) was the belief (1) that there are but seven planets, and (2) that everything else in the night sky is a fixed star. Since the seven planets were already accounted for, these new stars had, logically, to be fixed ones. Not that Galileo actually went through a process of reasoning; the interpretation was probably smooth (automatic). What he *saw* in his telescope were stars, just as, regardless of what was actually on the path, the man walking along it confidently saw a stick. But on the next night these fixed stars had moved. This is quite different from seeing a stick and then finding it slither away. What one says then is simply, "Oh, so it was a snake after all." There is a standard alternative background structure readily available that is brought into play at once, and that produces a new, smooth interpretation. But when the fixed stars moved, there was no standard alternative background structure. Hence there was no immediate, smooth alteration to a new perception, as in the perception of the snake. On the contrary, there had to be a radical reorganization of the perceptual field, more like that by which, in the banana problem, a new structure (one long stick) emerged.

And, as with puns and anagrams, there was an experience of nonsensicality and a drive to make it make sense. How can a *fixed* star move? Obviously it can't; this is a contradiction in terms and therefore sheerly nonsensical, not merely just puzzling, like the reply "Let's have a beer" to the remark "Today is Thursday." The only exit from this meaninglessness is reconstruction, like the shift from attending to meaning to attending to sound, and the consequent observation of similarity between the sound of "Thursday" and the sound of "thirsty."

Though the reconstruction required of Galileo is immeasurably more radical, the *principle* is the same; things that look different, that have always been thought of as being wholly different, are suddenly juxtaposed and then seem to be similar in one respect—but this happens to be the one respect that is essential for the solution of *this* problem. With the pun, it is the sound of "Thursday" and of "thirsty" that are suddenly seen to be similar; with Galileo, it is these pinpoints of light and the earth's moon that are seen to be similar. There may have been a projection in imagination of what the earth and its moon would look like if one were a long distance away, watching the latter turn about the former; or perhaps a projection in imagination of what the planets themselves would look like turning about the sun: in any event, a similarity was noted between (1) what one was actually seeing in one's telescope and (2) what one *would* see if, from an immense distance, one were watching the moon turn about the earth.

And here, just as with the pun, the solution of the problem was accompanied by a transformation of the perceptual field (*E*). Originally one saw a star imbedded in a sphere of fixed stars and a long way behind Jupiter; now one saw a satellite, relatively close to Jupiter and turning around that planet. The transformation is exactly like (though of course immensely greater than) the transformation that occurs in the meaning of "latin" as one suddenly sees the point of the crossword-puzzle clue, and the adjective abruptly stops functioning as "attribute" and begins functioning as "word for." In order for any such reconstruction of *E*—the experiential field—to occur there has to be (1) a fairly serious breakdown of some normal interpretation, (2) the failure of any of the standard, or reserve, structures to effect a smooth interpretation, and (3) a strong drive—either curiosity, or some practical need.

The first thing that happens when such a breakdown occurs is a contraction of the perceptual field, a reconsideration and review of what one is sure of. This kind of "pulling in of one's horns" must have occurred on the night Galileo saw that the stars had moved. On the first night of viewing, on the 7th, his perceptual field had contained fixed stars. If anyone had asked, "Are you sure?" his answer would have been, "Of course. Look for yourself," or words to that effect; there was nothing else the things he saw near Jupiter could be. On the night of the 8th, when the stars had moved, Galileo's answer to the question, "What do you see? What are you sure of?" would probably have been: "I see pinpoints of light in the night sky—I am sure of *that*. But what they are, I don't in the least know." On the night of the 10th he might have said, "I see pinpoints of light and I *think* that maybe (or "probably" or "almost certainly") they are moons of Jupiter." And at some subsequent time he and others (we ourselves, for instance) would say: "I see satellites of Jupiter. I am sure of it."

Contraction of the perceptual field may occur for other reasons as well; for instance, depending on our temperament (whether confident or cautious) and depending on our circumstances—on how much hangs on the identification in question. For instance, if we are sitting comfortably in our home in the mountains and someone asks, "What are those lights on the other side of the valley?" we may confidently reply, "Those are stars." But if we are piloting a plane through those mountains we may reply to the same question: "Those are pinpoints of light; they may be stars (in which case we are in the clear) or they may be houses (in which case we should be flying higher)."

So, in point of actual fact, there are relatively few people today who can confidently say as they look through a telescope, "I see a moon of Jupiter." Only an astronomer can say that. Most of the rest of us would have to report, "I see a pinpoint of light which I have been told is a moon of Jupiter, and I have no reason to doubt it." Even an astronomer, if he were of a really cautious temperament, might report, "I see a pinpoint of light—which is a moon of Jupiter, unless some radical revision of astronomical theory should someday be introduced."

Or again, if we happen to be in Westminster Abbey and someone points in a certain direction and asks, "What is that?" we may well reply simply, "The throne"; but if we are cautious, or if our interrogator is a philosopher and we know from bitter experience what philosophers are like, we may reply, "That is a chair which I have reason to believe is on occasion used as a throne." Thus the extent of E—an individual's perceptual field—depends on many variables, including contextual variables (such as being in an airplane, or being on the ground) which affect what parts of the individual's available background structure are actually applied to the interpretation of a given foreground.

I have now distinguished the types of elements that constitute a background structure and I have illustrated the radical differences in E that are produced by changes in these elements. As a result, the nature of what I call an interpretative process—the process by which a foreground is organized and structured by a background—may be sufficiently clear. But what, exactly, is being worked on, being interpreted, in such a process? What is F?

The short, and basically satisfactory, answer to this question is that F is just whatever it is, just whatever it is experienced to be. F is just whatever we encounter (experience) at the start of an interpretative process.

Thus, on occasion, F may be a snake, or a stick, or a long, narrow some-thing-or-other, or a booby trap to frighten the passerby, or whatever. F, then, is the starting point of an interpretative process—a process that may be smooth and rapid, or marked by hesitation and delay. E, on the other hand, is the terminus of an interpretation process ("Why, yes, it is a snake after all" or "Oh, only a shadow"). Of course, this E may quite possibly become a new F (this happens whenever further interpretation occurs), or this E may pass out of our perceptual field as we walk along the path and we may encounter some new F that requires to be interpreted in its turn.

As I say, this answer is basically correct. But since people are likely to think of the interpretative process on analogy with certain well-known physical processes, and since they are likely to be misled if they do so, I shall give a somewhat more detailed account of F. The misleading metaphor, or model, that may be applied to interpretative processes is that of some substance (say, crude oil) under chemical transformation (say, in a refinery). For those who are thinking about the interpretative process in these terms, B probably represents the various refining proc-esses, while E represents the various products—aviation gasoline, diesel fuel, etc.—that are relative to the particular refining processes employed. So far, so good. But those influenced by this metaphor are probably now looking for something in the interpretative process which corresponds to the crude oil in the model. They may now be asking, in effect, "Where is the crude oil? What is the stuff that is being processed by background structure?"

The answer is, there is no such stuff—the metaphor is misleading. To translate into the language we are using in this chapter: they are using the wrong sort of background structure (one containing a more or less vague model of a refining process) to interpret the present foreground (which happens to be the nature of the foregrounds). Therefore, try another, more appropriate, background structure.

However, at this point somebody may reply: "That is all very well, but still there must be *something* there to be interpreted. What is it?" The short answer to this question is: "That depends on the circumstances. It is whatever it happens to be, and has no special ontological status." Consider any perceptual field you like. Here is one that contains a chair; I think it's perhaps the throne. Here is another perceptual field which contains a long, narrow something; maybe it's a snake or maybe it's a stick. Here is another which contains a cat that may possibly belong to Mr. Smith. At any given time, with respect to any perceptual field, there is something that is experienced as being here and now (chair; long, narrow something; cat) and there is also "reference beyond" (maybe throne; snake or stick? Mr. Smith and his search yesterday). This "reference beyond" may be what is sometimes called *meaning:* thus we say, "That's a red light; it means that traffic has to stop." Or the reference beyond may be *usage:* "That's a chair; it is used during the coronation ceremony." Or the reference beyond may be *possibility:* "That white blob near the sofa may be the tail of a cat or it may be only a crumpled piece of paper."

But what is foreground now is not a lump of unstructured experience, waiting to be interpreted, as the oil is in the ground waiting to be refined. Foreground is not unstructured; it is *pre*-structured. It is a segment of experience which has been structured in previous interpretative processes. What was once background has been absorbed into (incorporated into) the foreground, as a result of repeated, successful acts of interpretation. I see a stranger in the street and infer that he is a doctor because of the bag he is carrying. (This may be a conscious process, involving careful weighing of evidence.) Then, later on, after I have come to know him well, I simply see my doctor. On the night of January 10, 1610, Galileo saw some pinpoints of light which puzzled him but which he took to be small bodies turning about Jupiter; now we see satellites of Jupiter. The first time I visited Westminster Abbey I saw a chair which I believed was probably the throne; now, after repeated visits, I see the throne.

People may agree that throne is indeed a product—the product, namely, of interpretation of what I see (the chair) by means of a background structure containing a particular item of historical and ritualistic information: anyone lacking this item of background structure could not possibly see a throne there. But if this much is admitted, I believe it must be allowed that the chair I experience is also a product.

Remember that, in this chapter, I am still concentrating on the subjective aspect of experience—that is, on what, as a matter of fact, we happen to experience. I am not yet even raising the question of what it means to distinguish what is "really out there" from what we experience. And, as far as *experience* goes, interpretation enters as much into chair as it enters into throne. The only difference is that in the former case (experience of chair) the relevant parts of the background structure have been fully incorporated, while in the latter case (experience of chair used as throne) they have not yet been. For just as the man who now perceives a throne doesn't *now* perceive a king sitting on it, so the man who now perceives a chair doesn't *now* perceive the chair's back and bottom. And just as the first man would not see a throne unless he remembered having seen a king sit on it, or is otherwise confident that kings have sat on it, so the second man would not see a chair unless he remembered having seen back and bottom, or is otherwise confident that it has back and bottom. Hence in the perception of chair, just as in the perception of throne, much is added from memory to what is now, literally, before us. Chair, as well as throne, is a product; the only difference is that in the instance of the chair, unlike that of the throne, the relevant background structure has been incorporated.

So, again, when I see a man and infer he is a doctor, man is the foreground that is being interpreted by a background structure containing the generalization "People who carry bags like this are doctors." (It does not matter, for present purposes, whether this generalization is valid. If it is not, then my inference may be mistaken; but there is no doubt that people's background structures do contain generalizations of this kind and that they do interpret foregrounds by means of them.) But my present foreground (man) is certainly not an absolute experience. For when I am looking at the man's face I am not at the same time looking at the back of his head; any more than when I see the man in the street I am also at the same time seeing him in his consulting room advising a patient. Yet I would not call this face that I see a man, unless I thought it had a back, any more than I would call this man that I pass in the street a doctor unless I thought he did advise patients. But I see a man (that is what I really do see) and only infer that he is a doctor. Why is this? Because the generalization "Things that have fronts have backs" has long since become fully incorporated, while the generalization "People who carry bags like that are doctors" has not yet been incorporated and may never become incorporated. But there was once a time in my life, doubtless, when "That is a man" was as much an inference as "That is a doctor" is now an inference. And there are occasions even now (for instance, in fog or if the light is bad) when "That is a man" is itself an inference from what is experienced, not itself a present experience.

To generalize: I say that what is experienced (E_1) at any time t_1

becomes foreground, at some later time t_2, for further interpretation (by a somewhat different background, B_2). Then this new experience (E_2) becomes foreground for still another interpretation by B_3 later, at t_3, and so on. Thus the foreground at t_3—for instance "now"—is not an absolute, or nuclear, experience; it is a product, pre-structured by earlier interpretative processes. Since this sounds rather complicated, I shall represent it schematically:

$$
\begin{aligned}
\text{Time } t_1 \qquad & E_1 = f(F_1, B_1) \\
\text{Time } t_2 \qquad & E_2 = f(F_2, B_2) \\
\text{Time } t_3 \qquad & E_3 = f(F_3, B_3)
\end{aligned}
$$

Every perception, then, is a product, the interpretation (structuring) of a foreground by means of a background; but this foreground, in its turn, proves to be a product—the product of some *prior* structuring of some simpler foreground by some simpler background; and this simpler foreground turns out to be a product—the result of the structuring of some still simpler foreground. But here the reader may interpose: Is this not an infinite regress? Must we therefore not presuppose a *something,* not itself a product, which is the absolutely pure, unstructured starting point of all these structurings and interpretations?

Many philosophers have answered this question affirmatively. They believe there are ultimate elements in experience and that these consist in colors like red, green, yellow; shapes of various kinds—circular, square, oblong; and so on. Some philosophers call these elements sense data and say that they are "given"—they are the materials (corresponding to crude oil in the metaphor) out of which the mind constructs the objects of experience.

This theory may have a certain initial plausibility. It allows for the facts of interpretation and construction to which I have called attention; yet it gives us something permanent and definite to hang on to—sense data. Thus when I say that I see a man approaching me in the street, what is really happening (according to this view) is that a certain flesh-colored sense datum is gradually getting larger. On the basis of my

knowledge of perspective, on the basis of certain informal incipient generalizations, such as "Things that have fronts have backs"—all derived
ultimately from past experience—I infer that the present sense data are
signs of certain other sense data; for instance, I infer that if I do what
is called "walk around to the other side" of the flesh-colored sense datum,
I will experience other (brown or black) colored sense data, and so on.
If all or most of these expectations regarding subsequent sense data are
fulfilled, I say that I was correct in thinking that a man was approaching
me.

Now the first thing to note about this view is that philosophers who
hold that there are these ultimate elements in experience tend also to
hold that these ultimate elements are also what is real out there: the real
world, according to this view, consists of atomistic colors, shapes,
sounds, etc. These enter experience via perception and, once there, are
manipulated in various ways by our minds. However, it is one thing to
say that there are ultimate elements *in* experience; this is a question for
psychologists, not for philosophers; and it ought to be answerable. It is
quite another thing to say that the only thing real about the man I
see approaching me in the street (i.e., the only thing out there apart
from me and my mind) is a collection of flesh-colored sense data. The
philosophers who hold this theory tend to wobble back and forth from
one position to the other, and the theory gains such plausibility as it
possesses only from this wobble. But, obviously, even if there are ultimate
elements in experience, this would not prove these elements to be real
independently of us, and still less would it prove that *only* they are real
independently of us.

And in the second place, as regards the question whether there are
atomistic elements in experience: the answer seems to be, Yes, there are—
under rather special conditions. However, it does not follow, because such
elements can on occasion be discovered in experience, that they have any
superior ontological status. The sense-data theory is, unfortunately, a
theory—that is, it is just one particular interpretation, one particular
background structure, which has been introduced for a specific metaphysical purpose. Specifically, what this theory does is to claim that the
conclusions of a particular theory of the physiology of sense perception
are a metaphysical absolute. Thus, on this view, "fixed star" is an interpretation; so is "satellite of Jupiter." When these, and all other interpretations are stripped away and we finally reach what is really there, apart

from all interpretation, we find merely tiny pinpoints of light in the night sky. But what the sense-data theorist calls "stripping away all interpretation" is only substituting for one interpretation another, very sophisticated one, namely, the interpretation of current physiological theory, and erecting *that* interpretation into a final metaphysical truth. If it seems more plausible than the interpretation that what is there are fixed stars (or satellites), this is because of the high prestige of physiology, and for no other reason.

Thus, the whole doctrine of sense data, far from being the ultimate, metaphysical truth it claims to be, is simply one interpretation among many: more sophisticated than most, but also relatively unusual and introduced to satisfy rather specialized metaphysical needs.

Now it is true that, under unusual circumstances, the actual foreground *is* reduced to sense data. We have already studied some of these circumstances: whenever there is a failure to fit, whenever some normally smooth interpretation falters, we pull in our horns, and a contraction of foreground (of what we are sure of) follows. How much contraction occurs depends on the degree of failure to fit: we may remain confident it is a snake and merely become doubtful whether it is a rattler; we may, however, become doubtful whether it is a snake at all, or even a stick. In general, we are guided (if only unconsciously) by a very sound maxim: "Don't give up any more than you have to; don't let yourself in for any more reconstruction than is necessary." This is the principle of least effort operating in the field of thought and of problem-solving. But even on occasions of extreme contraction, we never eliminate *all* interpretation. Even in this most problematic (doubtful) situation, we are still dealing with an interpreted (structured) object. Even when we are reduced to the level of sense data and start reconstruction from that point, we have not gotten back to some metaphysical ultimate. Instead, we have only provisionally introduced a rather unusual type of background structure, one that is of little use for ordinary purposes but that has often proved effective when we are confronted with a serious cognitive breakdown.

At all times, in any ongoing life, we can distinguish within experience between, on the one hand, what is present and, on the other, what is "reference beyond" (interpretation of this foreground in terms of "meaning," "use," or "possibility"). The line between actual foreground (*what is being interpreted*) and the interpretation of it is constantly shifting, depending on circumstances: on the state of our knowledge, on what we are sure of, on what elements in the background have been incorporated, and so forth. Thus, if the question "What does interpretation start with?" means "What is being interpreted now?" the answer is "What is being interpreted now is the foreground, and what (how much) this is depends on the circumstances." Occasionally, in very unusual circumstances, the foreground may consist (in part, never entirely) of sense data. Usually it is much richer and more complex. Nevertheless, however meager the foreground may on occasion be, it is a product, the result of an interpretation; this is true, as we have seen, even when the actual foreground temporarily contains some "bare" sense data.

But perhaps someone will reply at this point: "Agreed; we cannot find any ultimate elements which are the starting points now, in adult experience. You are right: everything in adult experience involves interpretations. Still, there must be ultimate starting points somewhere. It is in the baby's experience that we find the given." Let us try to deal with this argument.

Perhaps "feeling" or "sensation" are the best available terms to describe the experience of the baby, though it is difficult—indeed, quite impossible—to find a word that will designate the genetic starting point, since all our words designate experience that is already (at least to some extent) organized and structured. Whatever the baby starts with, we may be sure it is not *things*—not the shoes, ships, and sealing wax of adult experience, since the baby lacks the background structures to make such complex interpretations of what is occurring in his perceptual field. Nor does the baby start with sense data, for these too, as we have seen, are the products of highly complex analysis—they are terminals rather than starting points.

On the contrary, the most elementary experiences would seem to be the feeling of something which we may characterize (in our terms, of course; not the baby's) as "again." That is, there is recognition of an eddy in the flow: the sense, as this occurs, that it has occurred before. And with this feeling of "same," there is also, at the same time, the feeling of "different"—for if the second experience were literally and completely the same as the first it would not be felt as second, as "again." It would *be* the first, sheerly and without distinction. It is not the whole content of experience at any time that is felt to be the same ("again") as some earlier content: rather, some segment is felt to be the same (again), in contrast to a context that is different. And this means that, even in this simplest, most primitive, experience, discrimination is occurring. Parts of experience are selected and attended to—discriminated from other parts. Recognition, discrimination, awareness of sameness and of difference must occur together: they are aspects of a single process, the process by which the most minimal kind of order and structure emerges in experience.

Even at this rudimentary level, then, we find the same pattern of perception and cognition that occurs in more complex form at adult levels. There is a foreground (*this* felt segment) that is perceived, in the sense of being discriminated, however slightly, against the context in which it occurs. There is "reference beyond" (even if this only takes the form of the "again" experience; even if the reference is simply to a similarity that has occurred before). There is background (the few, fragmentary memories, the few simple expectations and habits of response, the rudimentary value attitudes which structure, and so make possible, both the discrimination of *this* segment and the reference beyond it to other similar segments).

"Segment" is of course a misnomer to characterize what first emerges in experience; what I am here calling "segments" are what, if we adults experienced them, we would characterize in our adult language as "warm-good-now"; "cold-bad-coming soon": experiences that are vaguely bounded, diffuse, indeterminate, and saturated with affect. To say this is to say that there is, as yet, no distinction at all between fact and value; no distinction between what is perceived (seen) and what is felt about what is seen; no distinction between what is subjective and what is objective. The distinction between self and not-self, like the distinction between this object and that object, like the distinction between fact and value, emerges within experience. The gradual development in the child's experience of objects, on the one side—shoes, ships, etc.—and, on the other side, of felt states—attitudes toward, lovings, fearings, wantings, etc.—reflects the development of increasingly complex and stable background structures (memories, generalizations, attitudes) which the young child is rapidly acquiring.

Thus the experience of the baby no more provides us with metaphysical ultimates than does the experience of the adult. What we find at all levels, from infant to grown man, is an identical, but increasingly complex, process—a process that can be fairly described as consisting in the interpretation of foregrounds by backgrounds of ever-increasing structural richness. Every actual foreground, which is being interpreted now, at some particular level, is the product of some earlier interpretative process. That is to say, what is now directly and smoothly perceived ("I see the throne") once involved inference, thought, and perhaps serious hesitation ("That's certainly an awfully old chair; I wonder why they keep it? Could it just possibly be the throne?").

At every level, from the baby to the adult, changes in background are constantly occurring, and these changes are reflected in changes in E (what is actually experienced). At every level, these changes occur in part as a result of unconscious assimilation from the social environment, in part as a result of accidental learning and trial and error, in part as a result of thinking.

For our purposes, the key element in this whole process by which backgrounds change is thought. Thought occurs in problem situations; and all problems involve a difficulty of discrimination. That is to say, a background structure by means of which we have been discriminating (organizing, interpreting) the field has broken down. When this happens, the perceptual field contracts more or less radically—perhaps even down to the level of sense data—but at least to some point we feel sure of. At this point we have eliminated false, erroneous, or too hasty interpretations; at least, we think we have. We are now in a position to rebuild. Rebuilding means reorganizing E (what we experience) into a new and viable pattern by means of a more or less extensively reorganized background structure. And this repatterning is always dominated by an interest—the interest in solving *this* problem—which causes some patterns that occur to us, perhaps many, to be rejected as irrelevant. For instance, the anagram NECCIES is an arrangement, or pattern, of letters that doesn't make sense. We want to find a pattern that *does* make sense. We may set about solving it by trying one arrangement after another, almost at random:

NECICES?	No.
NEICCES?	No.
NIECCES?	No.

And so on. However, unless we are very simple-minded indeed, we aren't likely to try *purely* random combinations. We know enough about English not to try any combination beginning with NC, since no English word begins in this way. Many English words begin with E; we might try combinations beginning with this letter. Other English words begin with C; try this. . . . Sometimes solutions are reached in this mechanical way; sometimes they are reached by more or less complex standard search procedures; sometimes they are reached by chance or accident (as with Sultan or in this anagram, if it happens that someone has just been talking to us about science). Some people are lucky, we say. But if the same person solves complex anagrams easily over and over again, we say it is more than mere luck; it is ability. And for truly complex problems like the fixed stars that moved, we say that it takes genius of the highest order.

What does this consist in? Perhaps it is an immensely rapid scanning process by which possible patterns are considered and rejected: Not this. Not this. Not this . . . and so on until the relevant one is reached. But certainly a successful outcome for this scanning process, if that is what it is, depends on the necessary elements being there to be scanned: Galileo could not have solved the problem of the fixed stars that moved if he had not read Copernicus' book. The awesome thing about this example is not that he had read that book; that might merely be good luck. The awesome thing is the selection, out of all the books he had read, out of all the items of information he possessed, of this particular bit. It is not different in *kind,* but of course it is immensely different in scale, from Sultan's selecting, out of all the items in *his* perceptual field, the one relevent item —the joined sticks.

If what I have said is correct, two important conclusions about problem-solving follow: (1) In problem-solving we never, strictly speaking, *invent* anything. Even the most radically novel and insightful solution is novel only in the sense of being a drastic reorganization of old materials. The items we need must be in our repertoire, as it were; the problem is to get at them. In order to solve the anagram about "latin sea" we have to know that one function of an adjective is to indicate the language in which we are to take the noun it modifies. If we did not know *that,* we would be helpless. But the point is that this usage is very infrequent as compared with the adjective's standard function of indicating a quality or property of the noun it modifies. To solve the anagram we have to be flexible enough to get past the standard usage; we have to be alert enough to find the buried, appropriate one. The smaller our repertoire, the easier it is for us to scan it; unfortunately, the smaller our repertoire the less likely it is to contain the items needed to solve the problem. Given a repertoire of any particular size, large or small, the test of intelligence is the ease, the rapidity, and the facility with which the scanning process is accomplished.

(2) It also follows that the heart of thought is analogy—seeing that this item and that other item, which initially, which usually, are quite unalike, are *after all* similar: seeing, for instance, that though this new (long) stick differs from the old (short) one in many respects, they are alike in the vital respect of being adequate to the distance the banana is away from the cage. Or again, seeing that though these pinpoints of light differ from the earth's moon in many (most) respects, they are like it in this one vital respect: through the telescope they look the way the earth and its moon would look if we were to look at them from a long way off. Thus, in problem-solving we bring together things that are being experienced now (stick, pinpoints of light) with things recalled (distance of the banana outside the cage; book by Copernicus), or with things imagined or conceived (appearance of earth's moon from an immense distance). The difference between a mechanically random scanning and the processes of genius is probably a difference of degree rather than of kind; thinking, of whatever quality, is a repatterning of background structure in the course of which new, relevant connections are formed.

But what brings it about that the requisite items turn up together, that we see the relevant similarity between them? This is a psychological question. From the point of view of psychology, the primary question is, *How* are these repatternings produced? What are the relevant psychological variables and how are they controlled? An answer to this question, if it were attainable, would enable us to make a great advance in educational practice. We could shift the emphasis from merely teaching children the routines that we believe they will later need to helping them learn to repattern their experience as problems arise. But since this is not a book on psychological theory or on educational practice, I shall not pursue this question here. There is, however, another, equally important, question which is highly relevant to that cultural conflict which is my central theme. Whatever the variables that produce them, massive repatternings do from time to time occur: witness Galileo. What repercussions do such repatternings have on the underlying metaphysical beliefs by which men live? To this question let us now turn.

III THOUGHT AND ITS OBJECTS: *Things*

WHEN I BEGAN this discussion of minds and their objects in the last chapter I pointed out that, because both minds and objects emerge as interrelated structures within experience, neither can be discussed without talking about the other as well. So far, I have concentrated on the subjective aspect of experience—on what, once the distinction between subjective and objective has been drawn, we experience as our awareness of the world. It is time now to turn to the objective aspect of experience—to give an account of the world of objects and events which we also experience ourselves as experiencing.

We all certainly experience objects as being encountered, and most people interpret this as the experience of "things" that exist independently of us and of our experience of them—that they are "out there" apart from us. Thus people may agree that what *I* experience (subjective aspect) is variable and dependent on my particular background structure, which is limited or inadequate in various respects as we have shown. But they will maintain that there is something *there* all the time, and that it is just whatever it is (either a snake or a stick, as the case may be), quite apart from what I happen to experience it to be. Indeed, people will say that my subjective experience (what I actually see) is correct only if it agrees with what is there. If I experience a snake and it turns out that a stick is there, then my subjective experience is false; only if I experience a snake when a snake is there, is my subjective experience true.

In a word, because I have deliberately confined myself to the subjective aspect of experience, everything that I have said so far could be reconciled with a metaphysical and epistemological dualism. Dualism would identify what I call the subjective *aspect* of experience with experience; it would go on to assert the existence of a separate reality (what I have called the objective aspect of experience) independent of experience. Now, so far as the basic dualistic stance goes, the nature of this supposedly independent reality is not specified. Different types of dualism have identified it in different ways. We shall consider some of these identifications—that what is independently real is intuited in some sort of special state of consciousness (pp. 71–72); that it is the shoes–ships–sealing-wax world we see and otherwise encounter in ordinary experience (pp. 73–74); that it is "what science says" it is (pp. 75 ff.)—and we shall find reasons for rejecting all of them. But it is not enough, of course, merely to show that the various dualistic formulas are unsatisfactory. The question is, can we do better?

Dualism is a plausible way to account for the out-thereness, the resistance, of the world beyond us, since it tells us we confront an independent and separate object. The basic question for this chapter is whether we can give an adequate account of these characteristics as being the "objective phase of experience" and formulate it in terms of our concepts of foreground and background.

Now, to make a beginning: out-thereness and resistance are characteristics we find in experience. They are characteristics of experience, but not all of our experience is marked by these properties. Some of it is not experienced as either subjective or objective—it simply occurs. Some is experienced as plainly subjective (I may say, "Well, that was *my* experience; the facts of course may be different"); some is experienced as doubtfully objective ("Is that a dagger that I see before me?"); some is experienced as plainly objective (I have no doubt at all that there is a sheet of paper before me now, that this sheet lies on my desk, that my desk is in my study . . .). But though I experience the paper and the desk as independent of me, as apart from me, as out there, these qualities and attributes are in experience. The desk is apart from me, out there, in experience; or perhaps I should say, the apartness of the desk, its independence, is a part of my experience: I experience it as apart, as out there. When I distinguish, as I on occasion do, between my experience of the desk and the desk itself, I am not distinguishing between experience and something altogether different from, outside of, and apart from experience. The basis for the distinction is in experience; it is the hardness, the out-thereness, the resistance of the desk (and these are experienced characteristics) that lead me to experience the desk as independent of me.

To put this still another way: What is experienced as independent is not experienced as outside of experience. How, indeed, could we experience anything as outside experience? What is experienced as independent is experienced as having a constancy and a consistency about it. Today my desk looks just about the same as it did yesterday when I left my study; if I put out my hand, I encounter it where I see it to be. On the basis of such procedures I distinguish between reality and illusion: I have learned from and in experience that certain experiences (such as seeing things in a poor light, or in a fog, or from a very obtuse angle, or when I am nervous or excited) are likely to be misleading. I have also learned from experience that certain other experiences (seeing things in a good light, on a clear day, from close up, etc.) are likely to be reliable, that is, present us with things as they "really" are. But these test procedures arise in experience, and so do the reliable experiences that result from them, that is, the experiences of what is there, in distinction from the merely subjective experience of what is not there.

In a word, the flow of experience contains a certain amount of (certain areas of) constancy, regularity, and stability; it also contains breaks, gaps, and instabilities. These stabilities and instabilities already characterize experience in babyhood, long before anything as complex as a self or a world has emerged. If there were not at least some repetitions and recurrences (i.e., some degree of pattern) the baby would die; even if it survived it would never develop a self or the kind of articulated experience discussed in chapter ii. But if there were no gaps, no breaks, no instabilities, the baby would never have occasion to think; it would never learn to distinguish between subjective and objective—for this distinction emerges only when expectations, based on previous experiences of pattern, are disappointed (e.g., when Macbeth expects to grasp a dagger as well as see it).

But where do the constancies, the regularities, and the patterns come from? The short answer is that we find them—in experience.

If this short answer does not satisfy, we can approach it differently. In chapter ii, we described the range of variation in experience (E) which results from changes in background (B). But this range of variation, clearly, is not unlimited. I may experience the thing in the path as a snake, or, given a different background structure, I may experience it as a stick; but I never experience it as an elephant or a house. I may experience that object in the Abbey as a chair or as a throne; I never experience it as a lion or a supernova. And so on. Of course, there is the matter of the stabilized (learned) foregrounds which have been built up slowly over long experience. Still, quite apart from the stabilized foregrounds, there is something that causes the foregrounds to develop in such-and-such ways, and to become stabilized in this form and not in others. In other words, there is something that "resists" interpretation and bends interpretation to conform with it. What is it?

Since differences in background structure clearly introduce variations from one individual to another, it might be thought that the way to get at what is out there is to get rid of background structure altogether. It may be tempting to say that what is there—in distinction from what under certain circumstances we happen to experience as being there—is what we experience without the mediation (or intervention) of any background structure at all.

But if we did not bring some sort of background structure to bear, we would experience exactly nothing at all. *What* we experience, both qualitatively and quantitatively, is a function of the degree of complexity, order, and richness of the background structure we have available for purposes of interpretation. A world uninterpreted by *any* background structure at all, so far from being a confrontation with absolute reality, would not even be the "buzzing blooming" confusion that, according to William James, is the infant's world. Accordingly, we can say: No background structure; no world, no reality, no anything.

Philosophers who claim to experience reality directly, without the mediation of some background structure, are simply unconscious of the background structure they are using. Because it is so familiar, so accustomed, so "obvious," they see *through* it without being aware of it at all. This phenomenon of "seeing through" is not confined to metaphysicians. It occurs whenever we read a printed page—for instance this one. If we are accomplished (accustomed) readers we don't attend to, or even see, the printed words—the actual black wiggles on the white sheet—we see through them to the meaning; this is why we often miss typographical errors. It is only if we are unaccustomed readers (e.g., reading a foreign language) or if we are held up by illegible printing or grotesque misprints that we become aware of the medium standing between us and the meaning.

In one of her essays—to give another example of "seeing through"—Jessamyn West gives an account of a letter she received from an admirer in Arizona. The letter-writer described herself as having been so absorbed in the account, in one of Miss West's novels, of a violent storm that, when she finished reading and got up to go out of doors, she took her raincoat with her, though it was a typically clear, beautiful desert night outside.[1] The philosopher who believes he is in direct contact with reality is like Jessamyn West's admirer: he is so absorbed in, so satisfied by, one particular *version* of reality that he fails to observe that it is only *a* version. It is as if one lived so continuously in the pages of one novel that one came to identify this novelist's outlook on life with reality. If, under these circumstances, one finally chanced to read another novelist, one might protect oneself from having to admit that one had been involved in a limited perspective, by roundly declaring that this new novelist was "only" a novelist and so quite untrue to "reality."

It is obvious that intuitionists' claims to direct contact with reality result in embarrassing puzzles. For instance, they differ widely about the character of this reality with which they suppose themselves to be in direct contact. The most diverse schools, from religious mystics to hardheaded realists, have claimed to have direct access to reality; it is easy to see that in each case the reality they experience is actually a function of some preferred background structure. Thus Bergson rejects the whole spatiotemporal view of reality as illusory and tells us that he experiences the inner nature of reality as an *élan vital* in a moment of direct experience. But *what* Bergson experiences in this allegedly direct intuition is a function of an extremely complex background structure constituted by a whole set of metaphysical beliefs and value attitudes.

Similarly, if another philosopher tells us that what is out there is sense data, that these are experienced directly, just as they are, and that everything else is the product of interpretation, we know how to reply. Sense data are not "givens" at all. They do indeed occur on occasion *in* ex-

---

[1] *The Reading Public* (New York: Harcourt, Brace, 1952), p. 27.

perience, but only as the products of complex interpretative processes (pp. 60–64).

Finally, perhaps someone will say: All of this metaphysical discussion is pointless. What is out there, what resists interpretation, is not sense data nor any other metaphysical ultimate; it is simply the snake (or the stick, as the case may be), the chair, the table—in a word, the ordinary objects of ordinary experience. For instance, the reason I never interpret what is in the path as a house or an elephant is that it is a stick; if on occasion I see a snake instead of a stick, that's because, after all, sticks and snakes are both long and narrow; they are sufficiently alike for me to mistake a stick for a snake, especially if it is dark and I happen to be rather nervous about snakes. And what about the Zulu? If the Zulu reports that he sees firewood, where you see a throne and I see a chair, the commonsense reply is that the Zulu sees the same physical object you and I see (the same shapes, colors, and arrangements of parts); it just happens that he doesn't know that an object of this shape and arrangement of parts is called a "chair" and is used to sit in, as I may happen not to know that this particular chair is used in the coronation ceremony.

This is probably what common sense would say. What is wrong with it? My answer is that nothing is wrong with it—at the level of common sense. But unfortunately this way of talking, like the intuitionists' way of talking, involves certain difficulties and paradoxes. For instance, what exactly is the chair that is there? or the snake? or the table? Common sense might at first answer: "It's the object we see when we look in that direction, the object we touch when we reach out our hand. That's what's there." But sometimes when I look in that direction, I see a snake, not a stick. "Oh, of course," replies common sense. "But that's because the light is bad, or you're nervous. The real, objective stick is what you see when the light is right, when you're calm and collected, and so on—not what you see under unfavorable conditions of viewing, but what you see under optimum conditions."

But what are the optimum conditions? And who decides what they are? For instance, optimum visual conditions are formulated by common sense as "not too far away and not too close." If you get very close, you lose detail and just see a sort of blur. How close is "close enough"? At this point, common sense might well reply: "Oh, but you're now talking the language of chapter ii. You are talking about 'seeing' in the sense of what is actually experienced (kind of blur). Here, in chapter iii, you ought to be talking about seeing in the sense of what is really there. The size you see, in the sense of *actually* experience, does indeed vary, depending on distance. But it varies in a regular and consistent way—and the reason it does is that the chair has a real size which doesn't vary at all. We ascertain this real size by measuring. You and I may be near the chair and see it as a large chair; the Zulu may be farther away and see it as a small firewood. But if you and I and the Zulu all put a foot rule against the chair, we get the same results. The ruler may look larger or smaller depending on our distance away—just as the chair does. But the numerical ratio between chair height and ruler length is constant— the chair remains four feet high regardless of how near or how far away you are."

Very well, we now have a standard procedure—measuring—for ascertaining the size that is out there (the "real" size), in distinction from the several variable actually perceived sizes. This real size is the size obtained by using the standard procedure. But suppose somebody comes along and says, "The chair is not really four feet long. You've used a ruler from the five-and-dime store, and it's inaccurate. If you measure more carefully, you'll find that the real size is 3.9 feet." This amounts to an improved standard procedure, and common sense may want to say that the real size (the objective size, the size that is there) is the size experienced when we use this improved procedure. And procedures for measurement can be refined as much as we like, by introducing carefully calibrated instruments. When we begin to do this, we run into certain complications, such as maintaining constant temperatures and getting a coincidence between the edge of the measuring stick and the edge of the chair. But additional procedures have been developed for dealing with these matters, and once more common sense may say that the real size is the size experienced when these now very refined procedures are carefully adhered to.

Again, if the object under investigation is very small we will use a microscope; if it is far away we will use a telescope. Obviously telescopes and microscopes of different power give us different amounts of detail. A cell we can't see at all with the "naked" eye looks very different under an electron microscope from the way it looks under even a very powerful lens. And what we see when the cell is stained in one way is very different from what we see when it is stained in another way. And *mutatis mutandis* for what we see through telescopes. With the naked eye we see a pinpoint of light; with telescopes of moderate resolving power we see a nebula; with the 200-inch we see a galaxy.

At this point we seem about ready to identify what is really there with what science says is there. Is this satisfactory? Shall we identify what is there with what we see with the 200-inch; or, if it is very small, with what we see with an electron microscope? No; not unless we are very naïve. For anyone who some few years ago identified what is there with what is seen when we use a lens would feel silly now that electron microscopes are available, and improved microscopes will probably soon be invented. And as for telescopes: what we come to see, once telescopes are mounted on satellites, will be very different from what we now see looking through the earth's atmosphere.

Perhaps someone may be disposed at this point to identify what is there with what we will see when we develop the best microscope and the best telescope. But what does this mean? The best microscope and the best telescope at any particular time are simply those beyond which we haven't as yet made any progress; and if you were to say that some particular instruments are not merely the best yet, but the best possible—then we would have to ask how you *know* there couldn't be better ones. And suppose you manage to answer this satisfactorily. It would still be true that what you experience by means of the best possible telescope and microscope would be merely whatever, as it happened, could be experienced by these instruments, which, best though they may be, are still limited. On the other hand, if you identify what is there with what would be experienced under absolutely ideal, in distinction from merely best possible, conditions, you will have to admit that what is there isn't ever actually experienciable—that is, you admit that your reality is unknowable.

Common sense may therefore want to return to what common sense proposed at the outset—that what is really there is just what we experience by the rough-and-ready procedures of common sense. But common sense itself has admitted that its procedures are corrigible, that they do not by any means always present us with objects as they really are—that it may, for instance, be mistaken about the size of the chair and that scientific procedures of precise measurement are better for ascertaining the size. Hence we are in something of a quandary: common sense itself admits that it won't do, and if we turn to scientific method as providing better procedures for ascertaining what is there, we seem to be committed to saying that it is impossible ever to experience what is there.

Thus—this is the one clear result of all this discussion—science and common sense both define reality in terms of, and relative to, certain procedures for viewing and otherwise experiencing. To the extent that we are satisfied—and surely, under some conditions we *are* satisfied—with commonsense procedures for viewing (getting the object in a good light, holding it close enough, having a calm mind), then what is there is just what we do see when our minds are calm, when the light is good, and so on—a stick, not the snake that we saw in the dark when we were nervous. However, if for any reason we are not satisfied with common sense and adopt other, more refined, procedures for viewing, then what is there is whatever we experience under these conditions—such-and-such a cellular structure for instance (that of wood), instead of such-and-such another (that of reptile).

Now a "viewing procedure" is simply a more regularized and formalized version of what in chapter ii was called a background structure. Let us proceed to distinguish, on the one hand, between actual foregrounds (F_a) and standard foregrounds (F_s), and between actual backgrounds (B_a) and standard backgrounds (B_s) on the other hand. An actual foreground (F_a) is what is actually now being perceived by somebody. Actual background (B_a) is what somebody recalls or believes in connection with what he is now experiencing. Thus actual foreground and actual background are precisely what we were analyzing in chapter ii, when we were discussing the subjective phase of experience.

Consider various occasions on which I may be walking along that path at night. If I happen to have certain purely personal items of information in my background structure and if I happen to be using these items, I may see a booby trap for the unwary, because I happen to know, what nobody else knows, that this is a plastic snake that I put there to frighten the passerby. Here I am using an idiosyncratic background structure. More often, however, I use the complex of generalizations and information that most men of my class and of my time possess, as a result of the education we have shared. Since you also use this same background structure we tend to see the same thing, a snake; if we differ, we resolve the question by applying viewing procedures acceptable to us both—we shine a flashlight on the object, we get a little closer (but not too close), and so on. What we agree is "really" there, in distinction from what we at first thought was there, is what we both see when we use these procedures. I shall call this set of memories, generalizations, and rough-and-ready viewing procedures the background structure of common sense (B_{cs}). What we see when we use this background structure, including the tests, criteria, and viewing procedures it contains, is the foreground of commonsense (F_{cs}). Suppose, however, that I am not a layman but an ophiologist. If I happen to employ the technical and specialized zoological background structure available to me, I see not just a snake, but a rattler of such-and-such a species. In this case, correlative to the standard background of zoology, is the standard zoological foreground—what is out there to the extent that we use and accept zoological generalizations, concepts, and viewing procedures.

A standard foreground, in a word, in distinction from an actual foreground, is what we would experience if, instead of using the actual background structure, whatever it is, that we happen to be using now, we were to use some one of the standard available background structures, including the standard background structure of common sense (B_{cs}), as one such available alternative. It follows that at any time there are several different standard foregrounds in any society, not to mention the different standard foregrounds in different societies at different times. This may at first hearing sound odd. But it is, as we have seen, just the position that common sense itself reached in its efforts to formulate an account of out-thereness. After all, it was from common sense itself that we heard about the table for "naked" eyes, the table for chemistry, the table for physics, and so on.

But why, if it sounds odd to talk about standard foregrounds and backgrounds, and if (as I maintain) this is just what common sense means anyway, do I insist on employing my foregrounds-backgrounds language? Why not continue to talk in commonsense terms about "out there," "real," and so forth, or in dualistic terms about "independent objects"? The answer is that while commonsense language is not at all inappropriate for commonsense purposes, both it and the independent-object language have the disadvantage of suggesting (seeming to commit us to) that dualistic metaphysical stance which has caused the whole conflict between the sciences and the humanities. Substitution of a new language, in which the conflict does not occur, shows that it is not fundamental but results from a linguistic confusion (see p. 27). It is therefore not at all redundant to translate what everybody "knows," and what we are customarily content to describe in commonsense terms, into fore-ground-background language. By making this translation I can (1) ac-count for the objectivity of experience as described in the commonsense language of "out-thereness" and in the dualistic, "independent-object" language, and yet, (2), avoid the metaphysical paradoxes of common sense and of dualism.

Now to begin. So far I have pointed out that the view I am putting forward involves a plurality of standard foregrounds, each of which is relative to (a function of) some standard viewing procedure. For in-stance, in addition to the rough-and-ready procedures of common sense, there are procedures involving the use of high-speed centrifuges, others using electroencephalographs, still others using cloud chambers and accelerators, not to mention those using microscopes, telescopes, and thermometers. Thus it is possible to write the following functional rela-tionship:

$$R = f(F_s, B_s),$$

where $R =$ what is the case,

$F_s =$ what is out there now (i.e., standard foreground),

$B_s =$ what is true about what is out there now (i.e., standard back-ground).

It will be seen that R is a variable, just as E is a variable in

$$E = f(F_a, B_a),$$

where F_a and B_a are some particular individual's actual foreground and actual background. But where each individual's E varies in response to changes in that individual's private memories, hopes, and fears, R varies only in relation to changes in the accepted beliefs, theories, and hypotheses of the recognized experts. Thus, at any given time, R constitutes a norm for evaluating the various E's of the individual members of that society: an individual's actual experience is adequate (true) to the extent that it conforms to R.

In our earlier discussion (p. 44) of the various senses in which an individual discrimination process may be inadequate, I defined three distinct types of inadequacy and then remarked that a discrimination process might be inadequate in a fourth sense, namely, in the sense of failing to correspond with what is out there. I said then that I would leave discussion of this type of incompletion to chapter iii where we would be tackling factuality, objectivity, and out-thereness. Now that we have reached this point, we can see that this fourth type of incompletion, or inadequacy, turns out to be identical with the third type, for what is out there at any time t is what is experienced through the accepted background structures at time t, that is, the background structures of the recognized experts at that time.

Thus there is a relationship between (1) F_a and F_s, and between (2) E and R, such that F_a is said to be "true" (correct, reliable, adequate) to the extent that it corresponds with F_s, and E is said to be true (correct, reliable, adequate) to the extent that it corresponds to R. When we are judging the truth of F_a we are concentrating on what is actually in the perceptual field now; when we are judging the truth of E we are considering not merely what is in the perceptual field now but what is the case about—that is, what is true of—what is there. My perception may be correct (agree with the standard foreground, what is there), but my background structure may contain misinformation which leads me to make a mistaken inference regarding the properties or relationships of what is there. Thus I may see a chair when a chair is there (F_a agrees with F_s), but I may also mistakenly infer that it is a throne, because of something I read in my guidebook which happens to be false (misinformation in B_a). In this event, though F_a agrees with F_s, E does not agree with R, since E is also a function of B_a which differs from B_s.

There are also important relationships between (3) F_s and B_s and (4) B_a and B_s which we may consider briefly. First, as regards interactions between standard foreground and standard background: the line between standard foreground and standard background shifts backward or forward, just as the line between actual foreground and actual background shifts forward or backward to incorporate more or less of the background in the foreground (pp. 62–63). But whereas the shift from actual background to actual foreground is a shift from what is inferred (that this chair is a throne) to what is actually seen (a throne), the shift from standard background to standard foreground is a shift from (1) what is the case about—that is, true of—something to (2) what is there. For instance, suppose someone picks up a stick while walking in the woods and uses it as a pointer. If I am asked "What is that?" I reply, "That is a stick being used as a pointer." But suppose that the stick has been trimmed and polished a bit and is sold in a shop specializing in educational supplies. Then, in reply to the same question, I say, "That's a pointer." And now if a boy scout were to take two of these pointers and rub them together to start a fire, I would unhesitatingly say, "Those are pointers being used as sticks."

These are incorporations of standard backgrounds in standard foregrounds, not merely of actual backgrounds in actual foregrounds. That is, these are not merely changes in what I happen to see; they are changes in what everybody would agree is there. In the first example, I don't say, "I saw a stick and inferred it was being used as a pointer" (which is the sort of language that expresses what we regard as the subjective aspect of experience); I say flatly, "That was a stick being used as a pointer." Similarly, in the second example, in the shop, I don't say, "I see a pointer," I say, "That's a pointer." There are, however, transitional instances, where incorporation is not yet complete but is in process of occurring. Suppose our friend does not merely use the stick as a pointer while he is walking in the woods; suppose he takes it back to town with him, carries it into his lecture room and uses it there repeatedly and habitually as a pointer. When asked, "What is that?" one student may reply, "That's a stick being used as a pointer." Another might reply, "That's a pointer." The difference in language between "That's a stick (F_s) being used as a pointer (B_s)" and "That's a pointer (F_s)" reflects the fact that a standard background has been incorporated by the second student but not yet by the first.

The amount of actual background incorporated in actual foreground is a function of various psychological variables, among them the rapidity with which habits are learned. The amount of standard background incorporated in standard foreground is a function, in addition, of such sociological variables as the complexity of the communication net in the culture, the variety and types of mass media, and so forth. But to go into these matters here would take us far beyond the subject of this book.

One point, however, is worth mentioning since it bears on a famous philosophical issue, the doctrine of internal relations. Those who maintain this doctrine hold that everything is related to everything else. It follows that there are no unit (or complete) facts at all; nothing except the Whole (usually written thus, with a capital) is complete or completely real. Those, on the other hand, who hold that there are unit facts complete in themselves must deny that relations are internal. This long dispute can now, as it seems to me, be cleared up. Both parties are in a sense correct, but each emphasizes only one aspect of the situation, the aspect that the other party is ignoring. To translate into our terms: they are debating whether there is a sharp dividing line between F_s (the "thing" itself) and B_s (the thing's context). The answer is that at any particular time there is a sharp line (in this respect the anti-internal relations people are correct) but the line is variable and dependent on circumstances, including the amount of information we possess (in this the pro-internal relations people are correct). The anti-internal relations people correctly emphasize that we always do draw a line between thing and its context; the pro-internal relations people correctly emphasize that the line is not ontologically significant. But both parties unfortunately believe that their dispute concerns a deep metaphysical issue (and this is what makes it so acrimonious), while it is only a culturally determined distinction; for example, it is affected by differing preferences, such as those for order, system, and theoretical completeness (see pp. 186–187).

Finally, as regards (4), the relations between actual background and standard background: This is a two-way street. First, the standard foreground tends, over a period of time, to influence the actual foregrounds of the individual members of the society ($F_s \rightarrow F_a$). We may call this assimilation. It occurs in the following way: as children learn the standard backgrounds of their society, these become the actual backgrounds in terms of which they interpret their experience. The normative character of the standard background is shown by the fact that individual perceivers commonly feel they ought to see (or otherwise experience) whatever the experts say is there, and by the fact that, over a period of time, they usually come to see (i.e., actually experience) what they feel they ought to experience (F_a comes to conform to F_s through the absorption of B_s into B_a). Thus actual background (B_a) at any given time is to a large extent a function of standard background (B_s). And standard background is just the set of generalizations, memories, beliefs, and value attitudes that have met the tests of survival in that society and that therefore are taught in the schools and indoctrinated in many subtle, and in some not so subtle, ways. Because of these strong pressures to adopt the standard background, we tend to evaluate aspects of experience that do not conform as irrelevant, eccentric, insignificant, or "merely" subjective (see below pp. 94–95). But these aspects of our experience are not any more, or more especially, *ours* than those aspects that do conform to the standard foreground. The relevant distinction is not between what is public and what is private, but between what conforms and what does not conform to the current standard foreground. And the extent to which a man's actual experience actually does, or does not, conform to the standard foreground is a function of how fully and completely he has absorbed into his own background structure the predominate concepts, memories, and values of his society. It is just from among those individuals whose foregrounds do *not* conform to the standard foreground that the innovators, the *creative* members of their culture, are drawn.

Thus there is a reverse process, which we may call "creativity" in contrast to "assimilation," by which some individual's actual experience causes a modification, over a period of time, in the standard background structure and so in the standard foreground $(F_a \rightarrow F_s)$. Most scientific discoveries are instances of this process—Galileo's discovery of the satellites of Jupiter, for instance. Over time, the new beliefs and generalizations, which originally were merely Galileo's private convictions, became accepted widely in Western society.

These distinctions enable us to define common sense somewhat more precisely. So far in this chapter we have said that common sense believes the world contains (among other things) shoes, ships, sealing-wax, snakes, sticks, chairs, and tables; further, common sense believes that these *are* what, under such-and-such conditions of lighting, etc., they are experienced to be. We have also discussed the relationship between commonsense procedures for viewing and scientific procedures for viewing. There is, we said, an "out-there" for common sense and there is an "out-there" for physics (also for chemistry, for biology, and so on), which can be conceived to be a more exact and detailed discrimination of the out-there of common sense. But, so far, this has presupposed that common sense's world is constant over time. Actually, common sense varies over time just as the various scientific R's vary over time. Using the terminology introduced, we have to define R_{cs} in terms of certain cultural and temporal parameters: thus R_{cs} for culture C and time t, and so on.

R_{cs} at any given time (say t_2) was probably the advanced scientific "out-there" of some earlier time, t_1: what was a daring hypothesis in 1650—that all bodies gravitate—was a commonplace in 1950. And what is advanced scientific thinking at t_2 (e.g., current hypotheses about space travel) may become a commonplace at t_3. But the advanced hypotheses at any time (say, t_2) stand or fall depending on whether they are confirmed by "the whole body of empirical fact," including facts that were themselves only advanced hypotheses at t_1). In other words, a hypothesis that is proved by its conformity to fact becomes a law, and as such a part of the body of fact to which future hypothese must conform.

Thus the standard foreground (R; what is the case) changes over time as a result, among other causes, of creative insight and problem-solving by individuals. Not only does R change over time; it also follows that there will be different R's in different societies (whenever there are fundamental differences in standard backgrounds as between cultures) and that there are likely to be at least several R's in the same society at the same time (R_{cs}, the R of advanced physical theory, the R of biological theory, and so on).

At this point someone may say: "This talk about standard foreground is all very well. I can quite see that a standard foreground of the kind you describe does develop in a society, in the way you say, and also that at different times and in different cultures there are different standard foregrounds. And it is also true that we often evaluate our actual experience in terms of the current standard foreground. All of this is true and even not without significance. But it is beside the point here, since you still have to distinguish between standard foreground (any and all standard foregrounds) and what is there, what is real. For (1) though there may well be a great deal of variation from one actual foreground to another, you greatly exaggerate the variation between standard foregrounds. These tend, over time, to converge, and what they are converging toward, even though we don't yet know what it is, is what is real. Moreover, (2) your standard foregrounds, which, after all, are only social norms, can never account for the resistance, the hardness, the factuality, of the things out there. Tables, chairs, electrons, positrons, or whatever are all independent of us in a way that a standard foreground, which is merely the reflection of some standard interpretative process, can never be."

I shall reply to these objections in turn. But first a general remark applicable to both: I certainly don't deny the experiences to which the objector points. The question is how they are to be interpreted and whether they need to be interpreted as the objector interprets them. Is there not some other background structure in terms of which they will make sense, and perhaps even better sense?

(1) There is no doubt that, as we look back through time, a remark-

able amount of convergence has already been achieved—not only convergence in the sense that primitive peoples are becoming acculturated and that more and more societies everywhere are adopting the standard background structures of contemporary Western culture, nor merely in the sense that, as a result of mass education and the mass media, these same standard background structures are becoming to an ever-increasing degree the actual background structures of all members of the society, not just of a few "intellectuals."

Though convergence in these senses is important, convergence is even more important in the sense of the tendency of the various specialized sciences to conform to each other and so to present an increasingly unified conception of nature. The different standard foregrounds obtained under different conditions of viewing are more or less consistently related to each other. It is often possible, for instance, to predict, on the basis of what certain viewing procedures yield, what certain other, as yet undeveloped, viewing conditions would yield; and then, when the necessary instruments have been invented, to confirm the prediction. Moreover, the experiences we have under the more exact conditions of scientific viewing can be conceived as the further discrimination of detail which is "there" all the time, but merely not detectable under the less refined conditions of commonsense viewing. For instance, when we look at a fly under a microscope we see in more detail the wings which we already saw with our naked eye; as we increase the power of the microscope, at every stage we see more detail (e.g., the cellular structures) than we saw with a microscope of less power. When we turn from microscopic analysis to chemical analysis, or from chemical analysis to physical analysis, we seem to pass to a closer study of substructures within the larger structure which was the object of the grosser analysis. With our ten-cent store ruler we may be able to say only, "The length is somewhere between $3\frac{7}{8}$ feet and $4\frac{1}{8}$ feet." With better instruments we can say, "It is between 3.966 feet and 4.033 feet." With still better instruments we can narrow it down farther, and so on. As we increasingly refine our instruments for measuring time or distance, we obtain more exactly discriminated measures, but within parameters established by the procedures of common sense.

So far, so good. But the fit among all these standard backgrounds is far from smooth. There may be a failure to fit, for instance, between the standard foreground yielded by carbon-14 analysis and the standard foreground yielded by geological analysis of strata, or between the aphasia (standard foreground) yielded by neurology and the aphasia (different standard foreground) yielded by psychoanalysis. And so on. Moreover, apart from failures to fit as between different specialized standard backgrounds, there may be a failure to fit between any or all of these special background structures and the standard background structure of common sense.

Thus convergence is only a tendency in things, not a present achievement. That is obvious, surely. However, perhaps someone will want to add that complete convergence is the ideal, or limit, toward which the sciences are tending, as 0 is the limit of the series 1, ½, ¼, ⅟₁₆. . . . But this analogy is misleading. Complete convergence is an ideal, not merely in the sense that it is not actual yet, but in the sense that it can never be actual—not unless we suppose that there is an actually possible (attainable) state of affairs in which there is nothing more to be known, a state of affairs in which everything that *is* is known and in which everything fits everything else perfectly. And what such a state of affairs would be like, we simply have no idea.

If we want to use the term "ideal" at all, we had better call convergence an operative ideal. By this I mean that hope of convergence does affect present decisions to adopt or to reject some particular theory or hypothesis. It is an actual ideal, not in the sense that it is an actually possible state of affairs in some (remote) future time, but in the sense that it is an idea that affects theory construction now. But it is perhaps better to call convergence an article of faith—a very strongly held article of faith. As such, it is itself a value imbedded in our current background structure, a value that causes us to prefer foregrounds showing signs of convergences to those lacking these signs.

(2) What about the objection that a standard foreground is only a social norm and so cannot account for the resistances we encounter, for the factuality of fact? Certainly we do encounter resistance—this, too, is a characteristic of experience. And though the pressures generated by a social norm are very powerful, nobody will want to attribute the resistance of factuality entirely to a social norm. When I walk through a puddle, I don't get my feet wet as a result of a social norm. A man doesn't die of thirst in the Sahara because drinking "simply isn't done"

in the desert. The resistance I encounter if I try to jump through the ceiling is not imposed by my absorption of a standard background structure that happens to contain, as one item, the gravitational constant. On the contrary, observation of such phenomena as my inability to jump through the ceiling is the basis for the law of gravity being an element in this background structure.

Not only are there resistances with respect to perception (I see either a snake or a stick, but not an elephant in the path); there are also resistances to policy (however much I might like to, I cannot jump through the ceiling or continue to live without water). There is something that checks desire, that constitutes a restraint on desire—both the desire to believe what we want to believe and the desire to do what we want to do. This is one of the earliest, and one of the most profound, of human experiences; and it is the principal element in our conviction that there is a world out there, independent of us. It is also one of the principal elements in our ethics and our religion—the sense of our insufficiency, our incompleteness, our finitude. If we want to call what checks desire—especially the desire to believe what we want to believe—a fact, then facts are what is out there. But what exactly are facts? Or rather, what is the most appropriate language for talking about them? That is the only issue between us. My position is simply that I have a way of talking about what you call "the facts" in my foreground-background language; and that my way of talking—in terms of "resistances"—does not involve us in the paradoxes that your way encounters.

In a word, though I maintain that a standard foreground involves the application of a background structure containing a culturally adopted norm, I agree that it involves more than such a norm. There are, we have already observed, regularities in experiences—patterns, constancies, and stabilities that we encounter. Every standard foreground, to become standard, has to take account of and accommodate itself to these regularities. But the regularities are sufficiently loose—this is the point—to allow several alternative standard foregrounds to be accommodated within them.

The regularities are, of course, the basis of the resistances we encounter —getting wet "goes with" walking through puddles; death always follows prolonged lack of water. As Dewey has remarked: "The environment does enforce a certain minimum of correctness under penalty of extinction. That certain things are foods, that they are to be found in certain places, that water drowns, fire burns, that sharp points penetrate and cut . . . : Such prosaic facts force themselves upon even primitive attention." [2]

Yes, of course. At any given time there is always something, usually there is much, that we cannot change; we simply have to conform or risk defeat. But the specific things to which at this time we have to conform do not remain eternally resistances; over time, we may be able to change them. We may modify the facts, as well as, or instead of, our desires. We find ways of using the very regularities that resist us in order to evade the consequences of these resistances. We invent armor to protect ourselves against sharp points; we use asbestos suits to prevent fire burning us. Thus the prosaic facts to which Dewey refers often turn out, in time, not to be facts at all.

To quote Dewey again: "Extravagantly fantastic notions are eliminated because they are brought into juxtaposition with what actually happens." Of course. But one generation's dreams may be another generation's prosaic facts. And these prosaic facts may in their turn be rendered obsolete and replaced by still another generation's wild dreams. It used to be a fact that men could not work at night; they lived by day and slept by night. Whole cultures have been built on the "inexorable" pattern by which night follows day. We still cannot make a short day longer, but we extend the day by the use of electric lights. The pattern of night following day has become a virtually inconsequential regularity in our lives, and it is certainly no longer a hard fact of life that men must sleep by night and fish and hunt by day.

At any given time, then, there are resistances; there is the hard factuality of fact at *that* time. And nobody at that time can tell for sure which of these various hard facts can be modified. It is always an open question whether to take the facts we have encountered, and that are resisting some policy of ours, at their face value and accommodate ourselves to them as best we can, or whether to try to alter the facts so as to bring them into conformity with our long-range program. To put this in military terms: it is always an open question of strategy whether to change our tactics or to abandon the campaign and launch our attack elsewhere.

---

[2] This and the following quotation are from *Reconstruction in Philosophy* (Boston: Beacon Press, 1957), pp. 10, 11.

The history of culture is strewn with the forgotten bones of those who lacked the courage, or the imagination, or perhaps just the good luck, to make the right decision when confronted with such a choice.

Nor is it merely a matter of finding ways to avoid policy defeats (we want to work at night) by using one set of regularities (those characterizing electromagnetic phenomena) in order to circumvent some other regularity (that night follows day). The patterns that we encounter and that are the basis for our experience of resistance, are, at the cognitive level as well as at the action level, indefinitely modifiable. They have a way of gradually becoming more complex, of proving to contain subregularities within them, and then, suddenly, of changing their form and becoming simple again. For instance: men early found a basic pattern in the sequence of day and night. Further observation showed that the pattern was not so simple as it seemed: some days proved to be longer than others, but this change in the length of the day also conformed to a pattern. That there was a stellar pattern was not immediately obvious, but eventually it was found that the movement of the stars conformed to a pattern of circular movements through the sky. As further observations were made, epicycle after epicycle had to be added which complicated the pattern, until, at a stroke, the heliocentric hypothesis provided a different and vastly simpler pattern. And all of this change took place within the broad parameters of a basic day/night pattern.

At every stage in this process the scientist faces a strategic question—whether (1) to reinterpret the facts so as to conform to the existing theory of what the pattern is (as was done at each stage when a new epicycle was added) or (2) to accept the facts as they are and abandon the theory (as was done when the fact of a fixed star's movement was accepted and a whole astronomy was discarded). This corresponds, at the level of action, to the option between (1) clinging to a policy come hell or high water and setting out to circumvent the barrier by following a more circuitous route, and (2) abandoning that goal and deciding that one really wants something else altogether different.

The point is that at the cognitive level as well as at the level of policy one can never tell *in advance* which alternative strategy to adopt. It is always possible to say of the fact that contradicts the established theory that it is an experimental error, or a failure of observation, or the result of a statistical quirk. On the other hand, it may just be the key to a major breakthrough in our undertsanding of nature. For instance, in the late 1920's and early 1930's physicists began to report a very curious behavior of electrons. "Falling back into their source," "curving the wrong way," "coming up from the floor," "moving backward" were some of their descriptions of what they observed on their photographic plates. All of these descriptions reveal the physicists' puzzlement; the electrons were doing exactly the opposite of what one would expect. Some physicists held that the odd tracks were "spurious" or "dirt effects"— this amounted to a strategic decision to hold on to the theory that such particles were only negatively charged; it involved reinterpreting the observed facts to fit the accepted theory. In 1933, however, Carl D. Anderson published a photograph of such a track which he interpreted as a "positive electron." This amounted to the opposite strategic decision: to accept the facts as observed and revise the theory to fit them, that is, to introduce the concept of a positively charged electron, or positron.[3]

T. H. Huxley once said that the great tragedy of science is "the slaying of a beautiful hypothesis by an ugly fact."[4] This makes it all much too easy. It wasn't, for instance, just a matter of Professor Anderson slaying the established theory by confronting it with his photographic plate, for the whole question was, What *were* the facts? What did the marks on the plate mean? Thus the really critical question is whether the ugly fact that seems to destroy a theory is really a fact. Everybody who reads detective stories, or even newspapers, knows that criminals sometimes leave false clues that are calculated to slay any beautiful theory that they committed the crime. The detective always has to decide whether the clue is a fact or a booby trap. Though nobody lays booby traps for the scientist, he faces much the same sort of problem.

If the seemingly ugly fact is really a fact, it is wrongheaded to persist in one's theory in the face of it; but if the ugly fact is a booby trap, it is equally a mistake to surrender the theory. It is always easy *ex post* to

---

[3] I have followed the extremely interesting account by N. R. Hanson, "Discovering the Positron," *Brit. Jour. Phil. of Sci.*, XII (1961), 47, 194–211. Professor Hanson remarks that "several microphysicists saw, but did not observe, positron tracks prior to 1930" (p. 197). In the terminology I have introduced, they interpreted *F* (the tracks on the photographic plate) by means of the old, standard *B*. The resultant *E* was either a "backward-moving electron" or else a "spurious" track. On the other hand, on using a novel background structure (which subsequently became standard), Anderson's *E* was a "positive electron."

[4] In "Biogenesis and Abiogenesis," his Presidential Address to the British Association for the Advancement of Science, in *Discourses Biological and Geological* (New York, 1896), p. 244.

say that so-and-so went wrong by persisting too long in some theory which was clearly (i.e., "clearly" to us now) becoming outmoded. It is easy on the other hand to think of those whom we praise for precisely this same sort of persistence, since it finally turned out ("turned out" is, of course, only something *we* know about now) that the theory was correct. Kepler, for instance, represents both the strengths and weaknesses of persistence. His persistence in believing in his law connecting the planetary orbits and the five regular solids was wrongheaded, we say, since it proved to be a dead end. But his persistence in the conviction that the planetary orbits were simple curves, despite his repeated failure to formulate the paths exactly, is praiseworthy, since this proved fruitful. It is always easy, after the campaign has been won or lost, to say whether it was a mistake to "fight it out on this front if it takes all summer." This proved a sound program for Grant before Petersburg in the Civil War, but exactly the same tactics applied by Haig and the other Allied generals in the 1914–18 war were almost disastrous.

Naturally, there are maxims recommending both procedures. On the one hand, facing up to the "stubborn and irreducible" facts is put forward as the highest duty of the scientist and the citizen; on the other hand, "Nothing is but thinking makes it so." On the one hand, "It is as fatal as it is is cowardly to blink facts because they are not to our taste." [5] On the other, "False facts are highly injurious to the progress of science, for they often endure long; but false views . . . do little harm." [6] It would seem that there is a basic personality difference here between (1) those who are predisposed to accept the factuality of things-as-they-are— both at the level of cognition and at the level of action ("Don't kick against the pricks"; "Facts are facts and flinch not")—and (2) those who are predisposed to emphasize chance, choice-points, might-have-beens, and serendipity. We cannot, I think, say that either of these two dispositions is intrinsically better than the other. We can only say, in individual cases, that this one worked out better or that the other did; and even this can only be said *ex post*.

Certainly no one who is not neurotic wants to question the existence of facts. But to insist too strongly (how strongly is "too strongly"?) on the hardness, the factuality, the stubbornness of facts overlooks human

---

[5] J. Tyndall, "Science and Man," in *Fragments of Science* (New York, 1897), Vol. II, p. 360.

[6] C. Darwin, *The Descent of Man* (New York, 1896), p. 606.

resourcefulness, our capacity for improvisation, for improvement, for creative advance. The language of common sense and the language of dualism alike tend to ignore these latter aspects of experience (which are just as much aspects of experience as are the resistances and frustrations we encounter) and so commit us to an acceptance of the status quo, both at the level of policy and at the level of cognition. One of the advantages (so it seems to me) of replacing talk about "facts" with talk about "check-points that limit standard foregrounds" is that the latter sort of talk, however cumbersome, enables us to give adequate weight to objectivity and factuality without ignoring creativity and flexibility.

To put this another way: factuality is always with us, restricting our policies and confining our theories, but the exact parameters of the factual are problematic. There are always check-points in experience that frustrate and resist us *now;* but how much of a check-point this particular check-point is—whether we should accept it, circumvent it, or attack it head on—is itself a question. Thus, while factuality—the inevitable presence of resistance, of frustration, of out-thereness—may be a metaphysical ultimate, the *particular* facts we encounter are not metaphysical ultimates: they are indefinitely modifiable in experience, and the exact dimensions, extent, and nature of their factuality is problematic. So facts, too, turn out to be ideals, or limits—ideals that modify, regulate, restrict our standard foregrounds within limits, though the limits are never exactly determinable nor permanent nor ultimate.

I maintain, then, that the concept of standard foreground allows for, and accounts for, the resistances we encounter in experience—for the out-thereness, the hardness, the independence we encounter in experience. There are a plurality of standard foregrounds, not only the different standard foregrounds of different cultures at different times, but a variety of standard foregrounds in the same culture at the same time—the standard foreground of common sense, the standard foreground of physical theory, the standard foreground of biological theory, and so on. We cannot choose between these standard foregrounds merely on the basis of their hardness and independence, since all of these variations in foregrounds take account of, and occur within, the general framework of regularities that we find in experience.

But is there not some other ground for preference? Obviously common sense is better for some, perhaps most, purposes. It is idle to measure the floor of a room in centimeters if we are buying paint by the gallon.

If we are shopping in the supermarket it is enough to distinguish cabbages from lettuces by "naked-eye" viewing procedures, without ascertaining their molecular structures. Some people might admit that the foreground of common sense is better, in the sense of "more useful for purposes of getting and spending," but maintain that the foregrounds of the special sciences are better in the sense of being "truer and more accurate," as the measurement of length made with calipers is more precise than measurement with a foot rule from the five-and-dime. And they might add that what is better in the sense of truer is also better for practical purposes, too. In the long run, things are more useful if they are true and accurate than if they are not.

Does this give a basis for choosing between the various standard foregrounds with which history and the diversity of cultures present us? Are not the standard scientific foregrounds of the mid-twentieth century truer, and in this fundamental sense better, than the standard foregrounds of (say) the Middle Ages and of primitive men? If a Zulu sees firewood where we see a chair, we may write this off as more of a confusion than a mistake. He sees the same chair (physical object) we see, most people will say; he just doesn't know that objects of this shape are used for sitting and not for replenishing fires. But what if the Zulu is walking along the path with us, and while you and I are arguing over whether the object out there is stick or a snake, he says, "You're both wrong; that's my grandfather." Surely, if the Zulu were to say this (and this is the sort of thing primitive people do say), it is he who is mistaken. And it is not the sort of mistake I make if I judge the chair to be four feet high and it turns out to be 3.9 feet high. It is not as if the thing out there turns out to be the Zulu's great-uncle on his mother's side, instead of his grandfather. No; when the Zulu says, "That's my grandfather," he is sheerly and completely mistaken.

There are, however, one of two complications about this: for instance, when the Zulu says (in his language) something that we translate as "That's my grandfather," it isn't self-evident that he means exactly what we would mean if we were to say (in our language) "That's my grandfather." Moreover, even if he does mean more or less what we would mean, it isn't self-evident that he means this literally. For instance, if a woman looks at another woman's very large, ornate hat, and says, "My dear, the Taj Mahal!" it isn't likely that she means this literally (p. 116). It isn't likely that she thinks the building in Agra has somehow got itself transported from India to her friend's head. In other words, it isn't the sort of completely nonsensical mistake we tend to attribute to the Zulu when we hear him say "That's my grandfather." And it may be that he isn't making this kind of mistake any more than the woman is making this kind of mistake.

Still, even taking all of this into account, no one would want to claim that savages (or men in classical times, or in the Middle Ages) gave anywhere nearly as accurate versions of what is out there as current common sense and current science give. And this seems to be the main point that people want to make when they say that current conceptions are truer than those of earlier times.

But such considerations show only that current versions are better (i.e., truer), not that they are best (i.e., completely true). Indeed, there are reasons (p. 75) for holding that no version is best, and that the best possible version, even if it were attainable, would still be only a *version*. Again, what does a proof of "truer" amount to in this kind of case? It is easy to show that the current explanations are truer than (say) medieval explanations, if we mean by "true" (as *we* do) accurate, predictable, and empirically verifiable. It is also easy to see why we regard these as important criteria: modern technology, with the air conditioners, television sets, and automobiles that modern men so greatly prize—not to mention the nuclear bombs about which even admirers of technology feel ambivalent—depends on the achievement of precision and predictability. Our whole culture would be radically different without them. Thus deeply imbedded in the widespread contemporary conviction that the scientific world view is truer than (say) some primitive cosmology, is a value attitude, namely, commitment to the fundamental value of prediction, control, mass-production technology, and all the rest.

This is to say that criteria of explanation—and the truths, the versions of reality, they validate—emerge in experience, and are modified and refined in experience, both as a result of the resistances encountered and also as a result of a whole complex of underlying attitudes, not by any means merely from a respect for the "truth."

An example is the fundamental difference between the schema of explanation in vogue in the Middle Ages and that in vogue today. I am not talking here about differences in particular explanations (though Heaven knows these are different enough); rather, I am talking of differences in those basic criteria in terms of which particular explanations are judged to be satisfactory or unsatisfactory. In the Middle Ages, and indeed in classical times, too, the basic criterion of explanation was teleogical (see p. 12). Any puzzling occurrence was explained by showing the good state of affairs (purpose, end, goal) that was promoted or achieved by the occurrence in question. When one was shown the end it fulfilled, one was no longer puzzled: one said, "Oh, yes; now I see why that happened."

Of course this schema of explanation is still used in respect to certain occurrences (Why did the pitcher throw the ball to first?—To put the runner out. Why did the butler murder the dowager duchess?—Because she had discovered that he was a bigamist and an embezzler), but only in a very limited way. If people nowadays are asked why St. Paul fell from his horse on the road to Damascus, most of us do not reply, "Because God wanted to save his soul." Instead, we reply, "Because he had an epileptic attack," or "Because his mother weaned him too soon," or whatever. That is, the puzzling occurrence is explained by showing it to be an instance of some empirically observed regularity, for example, the pattern of epileptic symptoms. Hence, where the Middle Ages looked for goals, we look for rules (regularities). We regard an occurrence as satisfactorily explained when we can show that it is a particular instance of some function of the general form, $y = f(x)$. For instance, if anyone asks why a rock has fallen d feet at the end of the t-th second, we reply by saying that, given $d = gt^2/2$, where g is the acceleration of gravity, and given that the rock has fallen for t seconds, the distance fallen will be such-and-such: the facts in this particular case conform to, are only an instance of, the regularity expressed in $d = gt^2/2$.

Thus different explanatory schemas become imbedded in the standard background structures of different societies. An explanation (any particular explanation) simply fails to satisfy unless it has the accepted form, unless it conforms to the explanatory schema that the society has adopted. If it does not, people do not say, "That's a poor explanation"; they say, "That's no explanation at all." (There is a very great difference between saying "No; that's not your grandfather. That's your great-uncle on your mother's side," which one might say to a young child about an elderly relative he sees infrequently; and saying "No; that's not your grandfather at all; that's a snake," which we might say to the Zulu.)

Now my point is simply that medieval men and primitive men would feel about contemporary, scientific explanations what modern men, imbued with different values, feel about theirs—that they are not explanations at all; not that they are bad (deficient) explanations of the right sort. It is one thing to compare two particular explanations formulated in terms of the same schema of explanation and to say that one is better (truer) than the other. It is quite another thing to compare two particular explanations formulated in terms of *different* schemata of explanation and make the same sort of evaluation. The question is, What does the latter evaluation amount to?

Just as the scientific schema of explanation (dominated as it is by ideals of prediction and by hopes of convergence) is closely connected with other matters that the contemporary culture values highly (such as mass-production technology), so the medieval schema of explanation was closely connected with matters that the men of that time valued highly, such as a sense of the sacred, a sense of the presence and immanence of forces and powers. Does it make any sense to try to prove that the modern explanatory schema is better than the medieval schema on the grounds that medieval men would not have been satisfied with theirs had they known about ours? No; it does not. Given the whole configuration of their culture, they would still opt, if they had an option, for a sacred universe instead of a predictable one. They would opt for a predictable one only if they were somehow, while still living in their culture, *us,* that is, people with our particular configuration of values and attitudes, including the high value we assign to predictability.

Does it make any sense, then, to say that, whatever as a matter of fact they might have opted for, they ought not to have been satisfied with their explanations? Again no. For to say that they ought to have preferred our explanatory schema over their own means that they ought to have preferred a predictable over a sacred universe. And how could you prove that they ought? Only by showing that what you get with a predictable universe (e.g., mass-production technology) is better than what you got with a sacred universe (divine immanence and presence). And any attempt to establish this will turn out to be circular. You will find that at some point your proof is assuming the very values you are seeking to validate.

So far we have been discussing differences in R (what is the case) which have emerged within a common Western culture—differences resulting from the contrast between medieval and contemporary explanatory schemata. But there are even more profound differences of background structure that mark off Western types of R from non-Western R's. We Westerners organize our experience into things—objects in space and time—and this interpretative process has become so "smooth" that we regard any other organization of experience as wrongheaded and unnatural. Yet radically different organizations of experience do occur, not only among primitive peoples but also, it would seem, in the background structure of nuclear physics.

First, as regards the thing-type background structure: Each thing (this is simply to enumerate some of the high-order generalizations in this type of background structure) is held to be an enduring and distinct entity—to have a continuous identity (each is itself and not another thing) despite the fact that in some respects it is like other things and, in still other respects, like a different set of things. Each object occupies its own part of space and is marked off from the rest of space by a surface. What is inside the surface is the thing; what is outside is not the thing. Every object at any given time is somewhere—and all of it, at that time, is there; all of it, as it were, is inside of itself—inside its surface, however complex and however extensive this may be.

On the assumption that things are ultimately and finally real, rather than merely the products of one particular sort of background structure, philosophers of earlier times sought to give a "rational account" of things; for example, they invented the notion of an underlying substance, an essence which "has" various properties, and to which "accidents" occur. And further, since philosophers have widely assumed that to be real at all is to be a thing, great efforts have been made to explain God, value, and the self as things. Thus it has been supposed that the self is a self-identical continuing entity, with an epidermis (as it were) that marks it off from everything else, in the way in which a table is marked off by its surface from the books and papers on it. And, further, it has been supposed that whatever is not a distinct thing (for instance, "feelings") must be states of some self, and so private and subjective, rather than objective and "out there." And this in spite of the fact that *in experience* (as distinct from a particular theory about what the self ought to be) the self does not look like a thing at all. So far from having an essence that is self-identically the same through time, the self, in experience, is disrupted, discontinuous, and (sometimes) subject to radical alteration (e.g., in religious conversion). So far from having a sharp boundary that marks it off from what is not-self, my self seems to entwine itself in the affairs of other people and in "causes" (ego ideal; ego identification).

Nor is it only metaphysicians who fall into the trap of over-generalizing this thing-type of background structure into a universal reality-principle. For instance, we tend to think of organizations and institutions (e.g., General Motors Corporation and American Telephone and Telegraph) as if each had an epidermis, like a cabbage or a billiard ball, clearly marking it off from its environment. Hence we ask where one institution leaves off and another begins, or we ask whether, in such-and-such a case, we are dealing with one organization or with several. And we expect the same sort of answer we would get if we were to ask how many billiard balls there are on the billiard table. Similarly, if we are not careful, we are likely to think (at least laymen are) of the nuclear particles—positrons, mesons, neutrinos—as if they are tiny billiard balls. This tendency to extend the billiard-ball model illegitimately into other areas of experience may be called "the epidermis fallacy." But the use of this type of background structure to organize experience is not a fallacy when it works. And it *does* work at the level of common sense, for our common-sense encounters with life.

This, then, is what we may call the "thing-type" background structure. If it seems inevitable, necessary, and a part of the nature of the world, this is only because we are too provincial to be aware of other, alternative types of background structures.

Much work has been done in recent years on what is sometimes called the "primitive mentality," and also on the child's mentality, on the mentality of psychotics and neurotics, and on the mentality of animals.[7] All of these provide examples of background structures radically different from our adult Western-type. While these radically different background structures do not directly concern us, a brief look at them will bring into attention the characteristics—and the limitations and the peculiarities —of the type of background structure we *are* chiefly interested in.

The primitive mentality, the child's mentality, and the neurotic mentality are all similar in important respects: for instance, all three are "syncretic" where the adult Western is "discrete." Discreteness is the familiar (familiar to us, that is) property by virtue of which things are perceived as separate and distinct. Syncretism, in contrast, is the characteristic of

---

[7] Heinz Werner, *Comparative Psychology of Mental Development* (New York: International Universities Press, 1957. See pp. 53, 152, 59–61, and 135–141 for Werner's discussion of the points summarized in the following paragraphs.

mental contents that are merged without sharp differentiation. In the normal Western adult, syncretism is experienced only in reverie or in dream, where, for instance, the same person may at once be uncle and brother. But what is unusual and marginal for us is apparently the normal mode of perception for primitive man. It would seem to follow that for primitive man the Aristotelian law of non-contradiction does not hold: *A* can be both *A* and not-*A* at one and the same time.

Further, the syncretic mentality (or type of background structure) does not distinguish sharply, as does the adult Western, between the subjective and objective. According to Werner, the primitive (or child, or neurotic) with his syncretic mentality does not make this distinction. For this type of mentality, objects are primarily "things of action."

Again, primitive perception is said to be diffuse, where ours is articulate; indefinite, where ours is definite; rigid, where ours is flexible; labile, where ours is stable. It follows that objects which we would regard as remaining the same, change for primitive man, as their situation changes. For primitive perception objects are meaningful only insofar as they are integral parts of the contexts in which they function.

Much more detailed studies of primitive mentality, based upon analysis of vocabulary and grammar, have been made by, among others, Benjamin Whorf.[8] For instance, Whorf points out that in Hopi one says, "I drank a water," while in what he calls SAE ("Standard Average European") one says, "I drank a glass of water." In connection with what Whorf calls mass nouns that designate unbounded continua, we use a container-formula ("bottle of milk," "stick of wood," "piece of cloth"); as a result, deeply built into our SAE pattern of thought is a dualism between a formless mass and a form. It is this feature of SAE thought, Whorf believes, that has predisposed Westerners to make the philosophical distinction between "form" and "matter" and to organize their experience in terms of "substances" enduring unchanged through time. The Hopi, on the other hand, because they have no mass nouns designating unbounded continua, because all their nouns have an individual sense and both singulars and plurals, because, in fact, they *can* say, "I drank a water," have happily avoided the whole nest of metaphysical problems

---

[8] Benjamin L. Whorf, "The Relation of Habitual Thought and Behavior to Language," reprinted in John B. Carroll, ed., *Language, Thought and Reality, Selected Writings of Benjamin Lee Whorf* (Cambridge: Technology Press of Massachusetts, 1956), pp. 134–159.

clustering around the concept of substance: their world, in contrast to the SAE world, is a world of "eventings," not a world of things.

Further, the Hopi do not have the imaginary plurals that occur in SAE. Where we say "They stayed ten days," the Hopi say, "They stayed until the eleventh day." And once again, this verbal difference reflects, and is the expression of, a radical difference in background structure. The Hopi background structure lacks the concept of time as an even, continuous flow, moving steadily through the present into the past. Rather than thinking of a quantity of distinct days, the Hopi think of there being successive appearances of the same day. Because we think of time as we do, we put much emphasis on "saving time," on keeping accurate records of time, and, more generally, on regularity, scheduling, and routine. Because the Hopi think of time as they do (of there being successive reappearances of the same time), they put much emphasis on "preparing"—on prayer and on ritual.

Similar studies, of Navajo language and culture, have been made by Hoijer, who argues, for instance, that Navajo verbs function very differently from our verbs: "Navajo emphasizes movement and specifies the nature, direction, and status of such movement in considerable detail." [9] And these emphases are reflected in Navajo culture—in the fact, for instance, that the Navajo are "fundamentally a wandering, nomadic folk, following their flocks from one pasturage to another," and in the fact that, in their myths and legends, "both gods and culture heroes move restlessly from one holy place to the next, seeking by their motion to perfect and repair the dynamic flux which is the universe."

Perhaps these examples are sufficient to indicate the kind of contribution that anthropology and psychology can make to philosophy. Western philosophers, it would seem, base their discussions of reality too exclusively on one type of background structure—their own Western type. Clearly, if anthropological and psychological studies have any validity, we must admit that the Hopi and the Navajo—and primitive men in general—live in a world in which what is the case (R) is markedly different from what is the case in our world. It is not merely that they attend to other things from the things we attend to. That they do is, of course, true—for obvious reasons the Eskimo attend to snow very much more closely than we do, and have many words designating various con-

---

[9] Harry Hoijer, "Cultural Implications of Some Navajo Linguistic Categories," *Language,* XXI (1951), 111–120.

ditions of snow where we have but one. No; it is not merely like the different experiences of two men walking along the same path, one attending chiefly to the trees and plants, the other chiefly to the animals, they both encounter. Rather, the difference is more like the difference between two paths. For the Hopi and the Navajo do not merely attend to different things from the things we attend to; they do not attend to *things* at all, but to eventings. The basic patterns of the background structures by which they organize their experience differ radically from ours, being syncretic where ours are discrete, diffuse where ours are articulate.

Our conclusion, accordingly, must be that while objects (things) are objective, they are not coextensive with what is objective. We have to distinguish between objects and objectivity. Being an object is not the only mode of being objective. Organization of experience in terms of objects is one form of standard background structure, but it is not the only one. We cannot prove that one of these standard backgrounds is better than the others. To do this would require an independent set of criteria, and there are no such criteria. Every criterion we could use is built into, and a part of, the background structure whose superior value we want to prove. Hence every purported proof of superiority is only rhetorical. Each purported proof is a form of patting oneself on the back —an operation in which one part of a standard background is singled out for favorable evaluation in terms of other parts of the same background.

Does this commit us to a "vicious" relativism? Of course not. I am not denying the objectivity of objects; I am not saying that objects emerge only in *my* experience. I am saying that objects *and selves* emerge in experience. I am not saying that the objects that we see when we open our eyes, that we reach out and touch, that resist us and impel us, are illusory. Nor am I claiming that it is just as true to say that the object in the path is somebody's grandfather as it is to say that it is a snake. No; not at all. To do so would be absurd. I am simply making some recommendations about the sort of language to use in describing the objectivity, the out-thereness, the resistances that we encounter in experience.

The vocabulary that common sense employs to talk about objectivity includes such words as "of course," "sure," "obvious," and "fact." Common sense says, "Of course that's a snake, not the Zulu's grandfather." It says, "Why, that's obviously a stick." It says, "The plain fact is that what was in the path was a snake." And so on. Common sense is so impressed by the factuality of fact that the language it prefers may be fairly characterized as "fact-that" language.

In recommending against the use of fact-that language, I don't mean that it is never appropriate. On the contrary, for ordinary purposes it is obviously the natural language to use. Thus in most contexts I am sure that what is in the path is a snake, not a stick, still less a grandfather; and there is no harm in saying so. On the other hand, there are at least five strong reasons for recommending against fact-that language as the one, definitive language for all contexts whatever:

(1) Many people have a tendency to be cocksure, to draw too firm conclusions from insufficient evidence. Fact-that language encourages this tendency. If I am in the habit of saying such things as, "Of course that's a snake in the path; I am sure of it," I may testify in court in the same way: "Of course that's the man I saw running away from the scene of the crime; I am sure of it." Nevertheless, I may be mistaken. And my mistake may cause great harm.

There is a continuum of states of mind which passes from "completely uncertain," at one end, through "only the vaguest idea," "believe on the whole," and "nearly convinced," to "absolutely convinced" at the other end. People differ widely as regards both the kind and the amount of evidence that produces these different states of mind. People also differ about how broad a spectrum of states of mind they are prepared to label by such terms as "of course" or "it's a fact that." That is, two people might agree to use the expression "it is a fact that" only in cases beyond reasonable doubt, but they might differ greatly about what they thought was a reasonable doubt.

Since this is a messy—not to say dangerous—situation, there is a good deal to be said for confining our use of socially and morally important terms like "sure" and "certain" to cases that cannot be falsified, that is, limiting our use of "sure" to such cases as "I'm sure that a feline is not a dog" or "I'm sure that a square is not round." If this recommendation be adopted, then, even though one is sure, in the vague, commonsense sense of "sure," that the object on the path is a stick and not the Zulu's grandfather, one will nevertheless resist saying "I'm sure that this is a stick, not the Zulu's grandfather," for this statement is falsifiable.

(2) Uncritical use of fact-that language not only tends to make us "sure" on occasions (e.g., in testifying in law courts) where we may well

be mistaken; it also tends to make us the unconscious victims of a narrow ethnocentrism. To let oneself say easily, "Oh, of course that's not the Zulu's grandfather; that's only a stick" may sound harmless, but it very easily becomes equivalent to, "Anyone who thinks that's his grandfather is just a poor damned savage." And this in its turn all too readily translates into: "I don't have to take much account of him or his interests." In a word, fact-that language tends to commit us to a complacent acceptance of ourselves and our culture—our present selves and our present culture—as "best," as the be-all and the end-all of time and history.

(3) Fact-that language, by concentrating on and emphasizing the hardness and objectivity of facts, is likely to result in a corresponding lack of attention to the affective components in experience, which, as contrasted with the "facts," are then written off, or down, as "subjective," "mere feeling." Thus someone may look at a thermometer and exclaim, "Why, it's not so hot as I thought!" This is unobjectionable if the person who says this means only that the column of mercury in a glass tube is lower than he had predicted it would be. But the chances are he means, "Why, I shouldn't have felt as hot as I feel." And this is to derogate the experienced (felt) heat, as compared with the measured heat. In some contexts, of course, what is important is the heat obtained by the standard viewing procedure of looking at a thermometer, but in other contexts what is important is the heat obtained by the "viewing procedure" of feeling how hot one feels. The person who says, "Why, I shouldn't have felt that hot" has fallen into the metaphysical trap of supposing that one particular background structure has a superior ontological status.

Or again: a man dominated by fact-thatism is likely to distinguish sharply between the following sentences:

> "That's a large upholstered chair."
> "That's an inviting chair."

He is likely to comment, "The former sentence reports a fact; the latter is different. The chair isn't really inviting, as it is really large and upholstered. You only feel it's inviting because you are tired." The implications of this distinction, like the implications of "Why, I shouldn't have felt that hot!" are unfortunate. If it were merely a matter of chairs being inviting it would be trivial. But it is a matter of a fundamental attitude that depreciates vast segments of human experience.

(4) By emphasizing the hardness and objectivity of fact, fact-that

language encourages our natural tendency to resist innovation, novelty, and scientific discovery. Fact-that language does not take account of the fact that facts, hard though they be, change through time. Every fact has a natural history of which most of us are largely unaware, because, time-bound and culture-bound as we are, we remain submerged in the small section of this history that is nearly contemporaneous with ourselves, a section so short that, during it, probably only minor changes have occurred in the facts.

But if we broaden our perspective we will see that the history of most facts is a series of crises. And each of these crises follows a pattern that is a sad commentary on the rigidity of men's minds, and on the damaging consequences of fact-thatism. Each crisis occurs because some innovator disturbs the settled facts. What he declares to be fact (e.g., that those stars moved) conflicts with what the rest of us know (are "sure") is fact: that the stars are fixed. Since it is a fact that they are fixed and since, as we like to say, "facts are facts," it follows that the innovator is either a fool or a knave. The standard pattern of response to what disturbs us is to destroy it if we can. Therefore the innovator is forced to drink hemlock, or is crucified, or is put in protective custody (for his own good, of course). Somehow the disturbing element is eliminated.

But then, gradually, imperceptibly, men discover that the offensive new theory works, that it opens up a range of experience previously closed. Without being altogether aware of what is happening, they find themselves adopting it and interpreting their experience in terms of it. They may disguise this shift from themselves by continuing to use the old language (e.g., the language of "attraction"), but if so, they now employ it with a radical shift of meaning. At this point they are likely to canonize the crucified one.

Next, the very success of the new theory ruins it; it becomes a new sacred doctrine, a new "fact-that," which must not be questioned and which resists the next innovation in exactly the same way that, a few generations earlier, it had been resisted by the older dogmatism that it eventually replaced. Thus the history of culture is the history of an occasional novel insight, of ferocious attack on it and resistance to it, of its gradual acceptance into common currency, and, finally, of its gradual collapse into dogmatism.

(5) Fact-that language encourages resistance to innovations, not only in the sciences, but also in any other area of experience in which radical

innovation is proposed. Not merely cognitive norms (e.g., the Ptolemaic theory) but moral, religious, and esthetic norms break down. It may be (as with Galileo) the shock of seeing fixed stars move, or (as with Röntgen) the shock of finding a photographic plate affected by an electric current in a vacuum tube that is the incentive for innovation and reorganization of background structure. But it may be (as with Plato) the shock of seeing a good man juridically murdered. Or it may be the esthetic shock of discovering that shadows are not always black, or that discords are powerfully expressive. In any case, there is a breakdown of a standard background structure because it fails to discriminate effectively the new situation: For instance, the immensely old background structure that organized the social system into a rigid hierarchy, a privileged upper class and a completely valueless slave class, failed hopelessly to deal with an insight into human equality—an insight that came to be formulated in the shocking and revolutionary formula that "all men are made in God's image and are the children of one Father"—an expression that most people still find shocking and revolutionary whenever anyone expects them to take it seriously.

Of all the breakdowns that have caused men puzzlement, frustration, and distress, the most far-reaching is the one that is the subject of this book. Beginning with Galileo, Kepler, and the other early physicists, the history of the last 350 years has been the steady discovery in physics, in psychology, in anthropology, of new data that are uninterpretable by the old background structures, while the traditional humanistic and religious insights are uninterpretable by the new types of background structures. There is a radical difference between an interpretation of experience in terms of the traditional structures (man a moral being in a morally significant universe) and an interpretation in terms of the new set of backgrounds (man a cloud of heedless molecules). This failure to fit at the highest levels of generality has meant (1) in the intellectual sphere, the fragmentation of knowledge into separate compartments, and (2) in the moral sphere, stress and tension, resulting from the conflict between current beliefs and the traditional world view.

It is certainly desirable to find a way, not only to relieve this particular tension but, generally, to enable men to face change—cognitive, moral, social, esthetic change—rationally and effectively. One of the major hindrances in the way of such a rational attitude is fact-thatism—not only the metaphysical stance of dualism but the fact-that language which at once reflects and encourages that stance. If we are persuaded that there are a number of unchanging, independent fact-thats out there (which is what fact-that language encourages us to believe), we are likely also to believe that we are acquainted with at least some of them. Hence it is not surprising, when our beliefs are challenged, that we react with fear and fury. However, once we abandon this metaphysic and come to interpret our experience in terms of variable backgrounds and the foregrounds that are relative to them, the situation looks very different. What had seemed a profound metaphysical question about the nature of "Reality" becomes simply the problem of ascertaining how to make life more viable, simply the problem of ascertaining which of two background structures is the more effective (by whatever criterion of "effectiveness" we have adopted) for dealing with experience as it comes to us.

✻   ✻   ✻   ✻   ✻

Since the argument of these two chapters has been long and involved, I shall summarize the main points.

I began by introducing a new vocabulary for talking about cognition and perception, because the old language (in which minds over here are supposed to confront independent things over there) leads to unnecessary metaphysical difficulties, including the seemingly insoluble puzzle about how to find a place for values in a world of facts.

Though this new vocabulary may look peculiar and even paradoxical at first sight, it is justified if it resolves this puzzle—of course, without introducing new difficulties on its own. It is justified, that is, if in this new language we can say everything that could be said in the old language—about "objectivity," externality, and so on—and say it better.

The basic terms in this new vocabulary are "experience," "foreground," and "background."

"Experience" is the term I use to designate what is encountered—the initially undifferentiated flow as it flows. Experience is initially neither objective nor subjective. It is that in which increasingly complex distinctions come to be made, including the distinction between what is subjective ("my experience") and what is objective ("what I experience").

As regards "foreground," an actual foreground is whatever happens to be somebody's perceptual field (what somebody actually sees or otherwise perceives). A standard foreground, in contrast, is what is there. An individual's actual foreground is evaluated as adequate or inadequate (true or false) in terms of the current standard foreground.

As regards "background," an actual background structure is whatever somebody believes to be the case about what he perceives (the complex of memories, generalizations, and attitudes by which the foreground is currently interpreted). A standard background, in contrast, is a complex of "accepted" (approved) generalizations, laws, information, viewing procedures, and explanatory schemata.

Several types of standard backgrounds may be distinguished, depending on the kinds of very high-level generalizations and values that characterize them. Each standard background constitutes the cognitive norm for some society at some particular time, and each changes as the culture itself changes. One of these background structures is the thing-type that is prevalent in our culture—that is, the kind of background structure in which experience is organized into distinct, self-contained, and self-identical objects.

Since the standard foreground (what is there) is functionally related to the standard background, it will vary from one culture to another; and in the same culture it will change through time, depending on the information, generalizations, and attitudes included in the standard background of that culture.

In any culture at any particular time, people tend to identify "Reality" with the standard foreground of that culture at that time. Only in this way—by arbitrarily identifying "Reality" with some one preferred standard foreground (e.g., Western-now, or science-now)—can the notion of an independent, autonomous world of things ("fact-thats") out there be made to seem plausible. As soon as we recognized that this identification is arbitrary, the whole notion loses its plausibility.

In contrast to the old notion of a single reality (a world of things out there), my formula leads to the notion of a plurality of realities, each relative to, and expressive of, certain basic attitudes and needs. Accordingly, since the world of fact ("things") is not the only reality, we do not have to make a place for value in it. Values are expressed through, and realized in, a different type of background structure.

IV LANGUAGE AND REALITY

It PROVED impossible, in chapters ii and iii, to talk about the nature of reality without at the same time talking about talk about the nature of reality—that is, without evaluating the various vocabularies in which philosophers have chosen to discuss the nature of minds and their objects. Thus, at the end of the last chapter I raised some objections against using fact-that language as the language for talking about reality, and I maintained that my foregrounds-backgrounds vocabulary is more satisfactory. Indeed, in one way or another, I have been involved in questions about language from the very start; it is time therefore to consider directly the nature of language and the criteria of its satisfactoriness. Otherwise my argument for my particular vocabulary remains incomplete.

Accordingly, this chapter on language occupies a pivotal place in the whole argument. To some extent I shall be covering the same material as in the preceding chapters. Not that it is impossible to think except in language nor that it is impossible to be in contact with an objective world except linguistically. Still, much thinking is linguistic both in the sense that language records (fixes the solutions that thought works out) and in the sense that many problems are either linguistic in character or have a linguistic phase. This applies not merely when we are solving crossword puzzles or writing books; it also applies whenever we are curious about what exactly we are experiencing. When we are puzzled about something and ask (ourselves or others) "What is it?" we do not feel satisfied about the thing that is puzzling us until we can fix it verbally; fixing it verbally is not something we do *after* we solve the problem; it is a part of the solution. Accordingly, problem-solving, discrimination, and interpretation of foregrounds by backgrounds will all turn up again in this chapter. But I hope that reviewing these concepts in a different frame of reference will illuminate the earlier discussions, while they in their turn should supplement and cast light on the present undertaking.

Two more preliminaries: First, I am not concerned here with how language arose in the evolution of the species, nor about how it develops in the individual. I am giving not a genetic but a functional account; and I assume, therefore, a store of available symbolism already at our disposal. I am not asking how we acquired this store of symbols; but what we do with it now that we have it. Second, though I happen to be concentrating on verbal symbolism, there are many other types of symbols (gestures, paint and pigment, musical tones, etc.), and what I say about verbal symbolism is applicable to the other types.

Now, in order to talk about language and the relation between language and reality, I propose to use a drive-reduction model; but before I introduce the model, I shall give a simple example. Suppose, for instance, that a man is beginning to get hungry. There is a period, short or long, during which the drive builds up; then it discharges into action: the man goes to a favorite restaurant, where he expects to get a good steak; after eating, the drive is satiated—he becomes quiescent until this, or some other, drive builds up to a point where he begins again to act.

Though this is, of course, much too simple for any actual human behavior (for men are never simply hungry), adequacy of representation is not the point here; I am simply introducing some explanatory concepts in a systematic way—concepts that I am going to use in another connection. The next concept, *displacement,* will complicate the model a bit. Suppose, on arriving at the restaurant where he expects to dine, the man finds it closed. He must then find a substitute object. It is important, if drive is to be reduced, that the substitute object be similar to the original object in a relevant respect (it must be a restaurant, if possible in about the same price range, and with as good a cuisine). I shall say that any such substitute object (e.g., the second restaurant) is a *symbol* of (or, "for") the original object (e.g., the unavailable restaurant). This may sound like an odd use of "symbol," for most people probably associate this term only with objects like the stars and stripes (symbol of the United States) or the swastika (symbol of Nazism). But these symbols are substitute objects, too. In each case we tend to act in the same way in

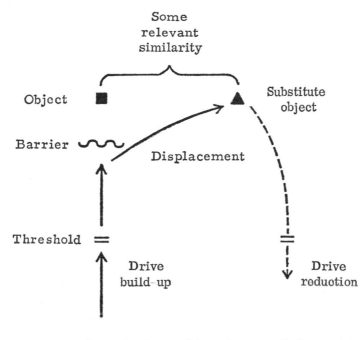

The substitute object is a symbol
of the original object

the presence of the symbol (e.g., swastika) that we act in the presence of that of which it is the symbol. Nazis reverenced the swastika as they reverenced their Third Reich; anti-Nazis felt the same hatred for the swastika that they felt for Nazism itself. The symbol is a symbol because it serves to reduce whatever drives the original object itself reduced. Thus the root idea in symbolism, whether the symbol happens to be a restaurant or the flag, is the idea of a substitute object that replaces the original object of a drive. The more obvious sorts of symbols (the flag, and written and spoken languages) are thus sub-classes of the more general class, substitute objects. Symbols in the narrower sense are simply objects that happen to have become *standard* substitutes; that is, they function to reduce drive, not merely occasionally for a hungry man in search of a good steak, but regularly and systematically for whole societies.

So far, the model applies to any drive whatever—hunger, thirst, sex, sleep, aggression, withdrawal, and so on. Now I shall apply the model to a specific drive that I shall call *curiosity*. In the case of the hunger drive, I presupposed (in my artificial example) both that the man knew he was hungry and also that he knew what restaurant served the best steak; further, I presupposed that when this restaurant turned out to be closed, he knew of an adequate substitute restaurant. But, actually, of course, we often do not know what we want: either we don't know what drive is moving us, or, if we know this, we don't know how to satisfy it. Often, in fact, we are confronted with something—a smell, a sound, a visual experience—that is unclear in some respect; and we want to get it clear. We want to know what it is. (Is this a dagger that I see before me? Is that a handkerchief or is it a piece of paper? What is the point of the joke those people are laughing at?). When we want to clear up something that is ambiguous, unclear, or diffuse in our experience, I shall say that the operative drive is curiosity.

Whenever we are curious, there is a barrier of some sort—for instance, the light may be dim, or the object that interests us may be partly hidden, or the voice that is speaking is too faint—that is preventing the smooth reduction of this drive; and there is displacement to a symbol, or substitute object. With men, the symbol is usually verbal, but it need not be; and in animals, of course, it is not.

There is a good deal of evidence to show that animals—rats, for instance—are curious. Rats learn more about their mazes than they need to learn in order to reach the feeding box at the end of the maze. Tolman and others who have studied this kind of latent learning talk about the rats developing "cognitive maps"; that is, rats develop a schema of the spatial relationships of their mazes as they run through them to reach their feeding boxes.[1] We may suppose that a rat who has acquired such a map is now at some choice point. He is curious; he says to himself (in effect), "Where exactly am I? Is this the choice point where the left turn leads to a dead end? or is this the one where it leads directly to the

---

[1] Edward C. Tolman has given a good summary of his own and other experiments in "Cognitive Maps in Rats and Men," in *Psychological Review* (July, 1948), which is reprinted in his *Behavior and Psychological Man* (Berkeley and Los Angeles: University of California Press, 1958), pp. 241–264.

feeding box?" The problem is solved by displacement to the map. The map, however sketchy and rough-and-ready, is a symbol in that it represents, schematically, the spatial relations of the maze.

So, too, on occasion men may displace to cognitive maps, instead of to explicit verbal symbolism. As I walk around a strange city—say, Florence —I pretty soon begin to locate the relative positions of the Arno, the Duomo, the Uffizi, and Santa Croce, though doubtless only with a vague notion of distances and of compass directions. And I can learn this as I walk about the city, without relying on the standard symboblism of a city plan. Then, hesitating on a street corner, like the rat at its choice point in the maze, I can displace to my rough cognitive map and take the turning that leads me back to my hotel in time for lunch.

Accordingly, the fundamental factor in the reduction of curiosity is displacement to some sort of symbolism, not necessarily verbal in character. To put this differently, curiosity about something-here-now ("What is it?") is reduced when the puzzling thing is matched to some recalled other-there-then ("Oh, yes! Why, it's a so-and-so"), which may or may not involve verbal symbolism. If I'm puzzled about some odor-here-now, I may be able to satisfy my curiosity by giving it a name, "Chanel No. 5." But since our vocabulary for odors is very limited, it's likely that I will displace to some more or less extensive array of odors, whose circumstances I can recall ("like what I smelled at the beach at low tide"), but to which I cannot assign a name.

In both sorts of situation there is a more or less prolonged, a more or less rigorous, scanning of several sets of possible similars in order to see which the puzzling object is most like. Suppose two people are having a discussion along the following lines:

> *Hamlet:* Do you see yonder cloud that's almost in shape of a camel?
> *Polonius:* By the mass, and 'tis like a camel, indeed.
> *Hamlet:* Methinks it is like a weasel.
> *Polonius:* It is backed like a weasel.
> *Hamlet:* Or like a whale?
> *Polonius:* Very like a whale.

There are two points of importance here. First, the barrier is a matching problem: There is a set of individually different objects all of which we are willing to denominate "weasel" because their differences fall within a range of tolerated differences. There is another set of individually different objects which we denominate "whale," and a third set which we denominate "camel." The cloud is like the set of weasels in one respect (it is "backed like a weasel"); it is like the set of whales in another respect; and like the set of camels in a third respect. The problem is to select the relevant similarity from this array of similarities all of which, at the outset, are possibly relevant.

Second, something more than a pure, disinterested curiosity affects Polonius' decision regarding the relevant similarity. If he ends by deciding in favor of the whale-similarity, this is surely not because the whale-similarity is objectively the most relevant; it is because he wants to agree with Hamlet. Here, then, what we may call a courtier drive is at work, influencing the outcome, that is, affecting the way in which curiosity is satisfied. Of course, sometimes this is conscious and deliberate: the courtier drive may not affect the conclusion Polonius reaches, but merely what he says to Hamlet, whom he wants to please. But I am not talking about this kind of situation. The interesting kind of situation is the one in which this drive unconsciously affects the outcome—one in which Polonius honestly comes to believe that the cloud is most like a whale and does so because he (unconsciously) wants to agree with Hamlet. I am not saying, of course, that whenever this courtier drive is present it always has a determinate effect on the outcome; I am only saying that, at the margin, when the field is diffuse and ambiguous, it may have a determinate influence. I have called this the courtier drive, but it is not limited to courtiers. It is probably present, at least to some degree, whenever a student is talking with his teacher, whenever a professor is talking to a dean, whenever a dean is talking to the president of his college. There is also something we may call an anti-courtier drive, often causing children to dissent from, rather than to agree with, the opinions of their elders, especially their parents.

Clearly, then, our model requires a further modification. So far, for the sake of simplicity, I have assumed that only one drive is operating at any particular time. Usually, however, several drives are operating; together they constitute what we may call the "drive complex," or "drive pattern" at that time. For instance, when a man is hungry he is not merely, or barely, hungry: he is hungry for a certain range of foods cooked in a certain range of ways; he may also want to economize (or to impress his guests), to avoid illness by meeting such-and-such standards of cleanliness, and so on. All of the drives that are present in the drive complex along with hunger modulate the shape of the hunger drive and so affect the nature of the object (in this example, restaurant) on which the hunger drive is satiated.

The situation is exactly parallel when curiosity is the primary drive (when we are puzzled about what something is, or is like): here, too, other drives are present in the drive complex and affect what reduces the drive, that is, what we decide the object is. Suppose, for instance, I am standing on the deck of a ship, puzzling about some object on the horizon—is it a cloud or a mountain? In some respects this puzzling object must be like the set of individually different objects we denominate "cloud"; otherwise it would not have occurred to me that it might be a cloud. In other respects it must be like the set of individually different objects we denominate "mountain." Which is it more like? Which is the relevant similarity, the similarity to the set of mountain-items or the similarity to the set of cloud-items? Thus we have a matching problem exactly like the matching problem in the Hamlet–Polonius discussion.

I am not saying that in this cloud-mountain example we do not have standard procedures for resolving the puzzle (e.g., using binoculars, looking at a chart, or going nearer). I am only saying that there are, or may be, situations where ambiguity remains after all the standard procedures for resolving doubt have been exhausted. I am saying that, at the margin, when the field is very ambiguous and when the other drives in the drive complex are very strong, they may have a determinate influence. For instance, if I am very much concerned about a prolonged drought and very anxious for rain, I will probably pay more attention to the cloud-like characteristics of the thing on the horizon than does a spectator who is quite unconcerned about rain.

There is a second way in which the complexion of the drive pattern affects what is experienced. The field which we experience at any given time is not uniformly diffuse nor uniformly clear. There is usually a center ("focus") of relative clarity fading off into a more or less diffuse fringe, a penumbra—felt as "there" but not sharply experienced. Moreover, this focus shifts from place to place. You are now reading this page, attending, perhaps, to the exposition. But the desk on which the book rests, the lamp beside the desk, the walls of the room beyond the lamp, noises outside the house—any of these, which are now diffusely felt as a part of the whole present experience, may come into focus. For some reason attention now shifts to the noise. Of course, until this happens, it has not yet been experienced distinctly as *noise,* but merely as a diffuse part of the whole. Attention shifts because we have become curious; we now notice that we have been hearing a noise for some time and ask ourselves, "What is it?" There is a more or less rapid matching process in the course of which we scan an array of recalled sounds for relevant similarities, and as a result we identify the noise verbally (silently to ourselves, or audibly to others) as "fire siren" or "town clock striking midnight," or whatever. Thus people with different drive patterns will not only find different relevant similarities between whatever is in focus and the standard available symbols; it is also likely that different aspects of the field will be in focus.

Since we are presupposing displacement to verbal symbolism (instead of, like the rats, to cognitive maps), it follows that the language that seems to us appropriate for describing reality—the language in which we reduce our curiosity about this or that area of the field—will be affected by the total configuration of our drive complex at the time our curiosity happens to be aroused by what is out there. For instance, in Britain the highway code provides that the driver of a car on a public road must be in possession of a valid license. A car driven by a man without a license was involved in a collision in a parking lot. The driver was tried and convicted. He appealed, arguing that the law did not apply to parking lots. The appellate court therefore had to decide whether a parking lot is, or is not, a road. The judges decided in favor of the defendant.

It is obvious that operating here was not a pure, disinterested juridical intelligence searching out and noting the similarities and dissimilarities between roads and parking lots. There are similarities, certainly—a parking lot is like a road in that cars are driven on it and parked on it. There are also dissimilarities—it is a broad, open space, not a long narrow strip; in this respect a parking lot is like a meadow. Which is it *more* like? Which is the more relevant similarity? A disinterested intelligence would be left in suspense; only an interested intelligence could say. And the verdict of an interested intelligence depends on the configuration of its interests. The appeal judges must have seen that there would be inconveniences to the public however they decided the case: if they decided that parking lots are not roads, the result might be an increase in accidents on parking lots due to exempting drivers there from the need to possess licenses. If they decided that parking lots are roads, the result might be to curtail the public's use of meadows and other open spaces. These judges weighed the latter inconvenience as more serious than the former, and this is why they concluded that parking lots are more like meadows than they are like roads. Who can doubt that another panel of judges—an American appellate court, for instance—might have been more impressed by the dangers to life and limb from careless

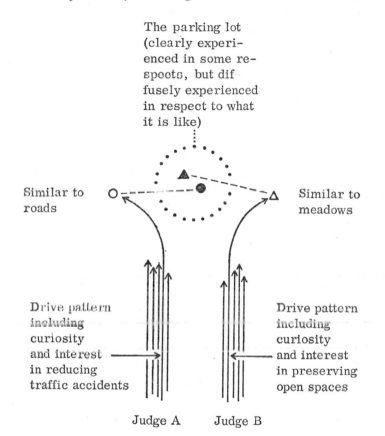

The parking lot
(clearly experi-
enced in some re-
spects, but dif-
fusely experienced
in respect to what
it is like)

Similar to roads

Similar to meadows

Drive pattern
including
curiosity
and interest
in reducing
traffic accidents

Drive pattern
including
curiosity
and interest
in preserving
open spaces

Judge A   Judge B

drivers, and would have decided that parking lots are like roads? With a different complex of drives, the similarity to roads would have come into focus, instead of the similarity to meadows.

These considerations explain why so many disputes and arguments are inconclusive. For debate is often not over the facts of the case (the facts are that a parking lot is both like a road and also like a meadow, and these facts are agreed to), but over how to weigh the facts. And here differing interests come into play. Diplomatic disputes are often of this kind, and diplomatic language may be described as designed to reconcile differences in interest by providing a form of words that takes (or seems to take) all interests into account. For instance, during the Punta del Este Conference in 1962 the United States was eager to obtain a large majority (if possible, unanimity) for a resolution condemning the Castro regime. The text of the resolution stated that "this incompatibility excludes [the government of Cuba] from participation in the inter-American system." Apparently all parties agreed about the incompatibility, but, unfortunately for United States' aims, six of the largest and most powerful of the Latin American republics objected to "excludes" and proposed substituting "is contrary to." Although at the outset, the President of Uruguay had declared that "Our beautiful Spanish language will save the conference," this prediction was not fulfilled: "is contrary" seemed to the United States too weak a description of the incompatibility, and "excludes" seemed too permanent to the Six. Hence unanimity was not achieved.[2] The divergent interests that made the various parties weigh the incompatibility differently presumably included, for Secretary Rusk, a concern with (an interest in) Congressional opposition to "having anything to do with" communism in any form.

So far we have been considering cases in which the problem is to select from a more or less limited array of possibly appropriate descriptions (e.g., cloud, mountain; road, meadow) the most appropriate one. We have seen that interest plays a part in this choice. In the Punta del Este case, we have also seen an attempt made, without success, to find another, new descriptive phrase that would be more acceptable than any of the standard ones. Let us consider in more detail an example of this latter kind, where a new description emerges.

Suppose that someone is trying on a hat. She is studying it in a mirror. There's a pause and then a friend says, "My dear, the Taj Mahal." Instantly the look of indecision leaves the face in the mirror. All along she has known there was something wrong with the hat; now she sees what it is.[3]

Though "Taj Mahal" was not a wholly new word in the vocabulary of either woman, it was certainly not a part of the repertoire of standard

---

[2] Douglas Cater, in *The Reporter,* March 1, 1962.

[3] John Wisdom, "Philosophy, Metaphysics and Psychoanalysis," in his *Philosophy and Psychoanalysis* (Oxford: Basil Blackwell, 1957), p. 248.

descriptions of hats. Nevertheless this description cleared up for the prospective buyer what had been an area of diffuse experience: the feeling
that something, she didn't know what, was wrong with the hat.

Why did "Taj Mahal" function in this way to allay curiosity and the
other drives (e.g., mild anxiety) that were operative at this occasion? The
answer, I think, is that "Taj Mahal" called attention to what, for this
woman at this time, was *the* relevant similarity: the hat was like the Taj
in being too grand by far.

Professor Wisdom himself would not accept this interpretation. According to him,

All this happens in spite of the fact that the hat could be seen perfectly clearly
and completely before the words "Taj Mahal" were uttered. And the words
were not effective because they referred to something still hidden like a
rabbit in a hat. . . . To call the hat the Taj Mahal is not to inform someone
that it has mice in it or will cost a fortune. It is hardly to say that it's like
the Taj Mahal; plainly it's very unlike and no less unlike now that this far-
fetched analogy has been mentioned.

I disagree. To me it seems misleading to say that "the hat could be
seen perfectly clearly and completely before the words 'Taj Mahal' were
uttered." I should say that some aspects of the woman's field of experience were clear (i.e., that it was a hat that she had on her head, that it
was of such-and-such a shape and color); but other aspects of her field
were not clearly perceived. There are always such diffuse areas in a field;
it is just a question of whether we ignore them or whether they nudge us
enough for us to try to bring them into focus and whether, if we try,
we succeed in doing so.

In the first place, Wisdom seems to confine himself to (what I would
call) the visual aspect of the field. The field as a whole—what is being
experienced—contains, but is not limited to, what is being experienced
visually. The "too grand by far" aspect of the situation could be in the
field without being something one *sees*. And in the second place, Wisdom
assumes that anything is either in the field or else it is not there—as the
mice are either in the hat or else not in the hat. But surely something can
be in the field (visually or otherwise), and yet not clearly there. Thus
"too grand by far" was there, not in the sense that it was clearly recognized but in the sense that it was nudging the woman with the feeling
"something wrong—what?"

The words "Taj Mahal" functioned to call attention to this obscurely perceived "too grand by far." Their function was to bring this diffuse experience into focus. Wisdom is correct in calling it an "analogy": I should say that satisfaction of curiosity *always* takes the form of analogy —the diffuseness of the this-here-now is clarified by seeing its similarity to (its analogy with) something else. But it is a mistake to say, as Wisdom does, that the analogy is "far-fetched." If it were far-fetched it wouldn't clarify the experience, as Wisdom admits it does.

But perhaps just at this point I can formulate a diplomatic compromise which will be acceptable to Wisdom. I shall agree with him, then, that the analogy *is* far-fetched, but add that this is so only because in most contexts we are uninterested in this particular similarity. In most contexts it is the dissimilarities between the hat and the Taj that are relevant. But there is *one* point in which they are similar; despite all their many differences (Taj made of marble, hat made of straw; Taj in India, hat in London), both the Taj and the hat are "too magnificent by half." And in the present, rather unusual context, this point of similarity is highly relevant precisely because it clarifies the woman's puzzlement about what is wrong with the hat. Hence, though usually far-fetched, the analogy is not far-fetched now.

One more point in connection with this example. Here it is a spectator, not the puzzled person, who formulates the clarifying description. This is an instance of what I shall call "other-communication." But the formulation could just as well have been made by the puzzled woman to herself, nobody else being present ("self-communication"). In both circumstances the descriptive phrase *functions* in the same way.

Thus there are two points here: (1) the difference between allaying curiosity by relatively routine procedures ("It's a cloud, not a mountain.") and allaying curiosity by relatively novel descriptions ("The Taj Mahal, my dear!"); and (2) the difference between self-communication and other-communication. Much communication is both other-communication and also routine. To say this is to say that one of the chief functions of language is to communicate something we already know to somebody who, we have reason to believe, doesn't know it but wants to know it. Suppose the pen of my aunt is on the table, I see it on the table, and someone asks me where it is. I have only to say, "The pen of my aunt is on the table." There is no problem at all unless the other person doesn't speak English and, despite Mr. Berlitz, I have forgotten that "plume" is the French word for "pen." But even in such a case, the communication problem, the problem of finding the right word ("plume"), is only the problem of finding the correct translation for something on which I am already focusing in English. Translation problems of this kind may on occasion be difficult; they may arouse sustained curiosity and even anxiety. But here we already know, in *some* language, what we want to say. That is, the part of the field we want to communicate is focused, not diffuse. What is diffuse is only the French equivalent of what we already hold firmly fixed by means of our English vocabulary.

Much of the time, of course, we don't even have translation problems. When we are dealing with standard objects in standard situations and with standard needs (say, the need to know where my aunt's pen is), there is a relatively smooth verbal flow.

Sometimes, however, the problem may be different. Though we may still describe it as the problem of finding the right word, the problem is now to find the right word for ourselves—not merely to find the right word in order to translate something we have already fixed verbally. And until we find what seems to us the right word, we don't know exactly what it is that we are experiencing; we remain puzzled and curious —nudged by that elusive part of the field. The woman who was puzzled over what was wrong with the hat is a case in point. Though the right word came fairly easily, it was clearly a matter of innovation, not of translation. A much more profound example (but different only in degree, not in kind) was Galileo's discovery of the satellites of Jupiter. Before he could communicate to others what he saw (translation problem), he had to decide for himself what he was seeing (problem of self-communication). Like the woman who exclaimed, "My dear, the Taj Mahal!" Galileo saw a far-fetched analogy. In Galileo's case it must have been the analogy between (a) what he actually observed in the telescope and (b) what he realized the earth and its moon would look like, if they were seen from a great distance. Possibly he projected himself in imagination a long way from the earth and imagined himself looking at it through a telescope; then the moon would appear as a small pinpoint of light, first on one side of it and then on the other, and when it was passing behind the earth, the pinpoint of light would disappear altogether. At this point Galileo may well have exclaimed to himself, "My God, the moon!" The problem was solved as far as he was concerned; he had satisfactorily fixed and clarified the field of his experience. But he still had a problem in other-communication. Suppose he were to say to the professors at Padua, "Those are fixed stars that move." Every right-thinking person would point out the absurdity: It is a contradiction to assert that something stationary is moving. Or suppose he were to say, "Those are satellites of Jupiter." People would reply, "That's also absurd; everybody knows that 'satellite' means 'moon,' that there is only one moon, and that it turns about the earth. It is ridiculous to talk about satellite in the plural or to assert that it revolves around Jupiter."

It is as if the woman trying on the hat were very literal-minded, so that, when her friend exclaimed, "My dear, the Taj Mahal!" she were to reply, "Whatever are you talking about? This can't *be* the Taj; for it's in India and here we are in London; it's made of marble and this is made of straw." But observe that a far-fetched analogy may become, over time, a new literal meaning. This did not happen with "Taj," but it might have happened: It might have caught on, and first in slang and then in good usage people would have come to talk about a "Taj effect." It did happen, of course, with "moon": the far-fetched analogy of 1610 was eventually accepted as good usage, even in academic circles. By 1665, at the latest, "satellite," which had once meant, and meant exclusively, "earth's moon," had come to mean (i.e., to mean literally, not merely figuratively) any "small or secondary planet which revolves around a larger one." And much more recently, as a result of developments with rockets and missiles, the term has undergone another expansion. In most respects, certainly, a rocket is very different from a "small or secondary planet": it is a machine, it may have men aboard, it is launched from the earth. . . . If the analogy does not seem far-fetched, this is only because the one similarity (revolves about a larger planet) is regarded by everyone as more relevant than the many differences. Hence in this case the expansion from analogy to a new literal meaning occurred relatively smoothly and easily.

Whenever we encounter something novel in experience, something that none of the standard available descriptions quite fits, we can allay our curiosity only by misusing one of these standard descriptions—by twisting and distorting it into a new and "far-fetched" use, which exploits a hitherto unseen similarity. This applies as much to self- as to other-communication.

Whether or not one of the standard available descriptions satisfies us depends not only on the novelty of what we are experiencing but on the degree of our curiosity, and also on the context. Suppose my field now contains an area which I will call "pain." Let us suppose that this area is not now sharply focused; it is diffuse, in the fringe. (Of course, I can't talk about it without focusing on it, and to call it a "pain" is already to focus it as a particular level of clarity. But, as Sweeney said to Doris and Dusty, "I gotta use words when I talk to you"; so I shall refer to this as yet diffuse and unfocused area as a "pain.")

Now suppose someone asks me, "How are you?" This question is enough to direct my attention to the diffuse area, to begin to bring it into focus. There is available a set of standard descriptive phrases: "fine," "rotten," "wretched," "poorly," "very poorly." . . . I choose, from this repertoire of available phrases, the one that most nearly matches the new focus. But the context in which the question is asked has a bearing on how precise a matching I demand of myself. For instance:

(1) "How do you do?" asked by a stranger as we are introduced, may not result in any focusing on the pain at all; I may merely respond automatically ("Quite nicely, thank you") without asking myself how I feel.

(2) "How are you?" asked by a friend or acquaintance may produce focusing up to the level of "back ache," or "a little nauseated," or "crick in the neck." (I am talking here about self-communication; this interior monologue may or may not issue in a reply.)

(3) "You have been looking wretched lately. How are you, really?" asked by a close friend in a solicitous tone of voice will probably produce a more searching matching process. (Once again, here I'm talking about self-communication primarily.)

(4) "Can you describe your symptoms a little better?" asked by the doctor one is consulting professionally commits one to a higher level of precision in matching, and so on.

Usually (not always, of course) the diffuse experience can be brought to any desired level of articulateness and clarity, the level in question being determined by the social context and, of course, by the strength of our own curiosity drive. Usually, again, the context is such that we are content with a fairly low-level matching; our curiosity is satisfied at the point where we have matched merely to "happy" (instead of "sad"), or to "fine" (instead of "wretched"). This is why so much communication (both self-communication and other-communication) is a super-ficial, ready-made affair consisting of passing along bits of current coinage.

But occasionally, at least some of us set ourselves higher standards of precision in the matching process. Perhaps the doctor is pressing us hard for a description of our symptoms; perhaps something about the experience itself has aroused a sharp curiosity. In any case, we are no longer content with routine matching. Even now, we may still find one or another of the standard available descriptions of pain is satisfactory; but, if there is a novel element in our field and we look at it long enough and sharply enough to see that it is novel, we may feel that none of the standard descriptions is adequate—we are now at a "loss for words" and have to look for an analogy. So a man suffering from a hangover for the first time and casting about for a way of describing his discomfort might come up with, "I feel as if I had slept in my mouth."

Such a novel verbal condensation of the experience may come quickly and all at once, as with the women in the hat shop and (presumably) with Galileo. But it may be a long process of trial and error. We project a phrase hypothetically (audibly or in interior monologue), and compare it with the partially focused area that has aroused our curiosity. It is focused enough for us to say, for instance, "No; that's not it at all. That's not what I meant at all." Or "That's not quite right, but it's on the right track." So we try again. And perhaps again and again.

This may seem a paradox. How can we reject a version as inadequate unless we already know what we want to say? On the other hand, if we do know what we want to say, why don't we say it at once? The explanation is that experience is not either sharply focused or else utterly diffuse; there are degrees of clarity. The initial version, though inadequate as a resting place for curiosity, may have further clarified the partially clarified area. As a result we know better what we want to say, though we still haven't said it; and our second version, or sketch, may therefore be more adequate. But if we set ourselves a very high standard, it may be that no version we succeed in producing ever quite contents us. There is nothing so difficult, nor anything so rewarding or so distinctive of man, as this process of self-communication or self-clarification.

Yet other-communication is so much more obvious that when people talk of "communication and its problems" they are usually thinking not of self-clarification but of what I have called "translation." However, other-communication is more obvious only because, so much of the time, we are content with a very low level of precision in the matching process. When routine matching satisfies us, self-communication (the process of fixing the diffuse experience verbally) occurs so easily that we are unaware of it. All our attention is then attracted to the relatively trivial, secondary problem of communicating what we already know (possibly, however, only at a very superficial level of "knowing") to somebody else. But self-communication is basic, since we have to find out, through self-communication, *what* we are experiencing—at whatever level of precision happens to satisfy us—before we can communicate it to others. To say that self-communication is basic should not be construed to mean that it is always temporally prior to other-communication. Both types of communication often occur together, and as a matter of fact, one of the most fruitful modes of self-communication is dialogue. In dialogue two people, each of whom may be primarily interested in self-communication, help each other by exchanging criticisms.

The existing language, with its grammar and vocabulary, is both a help and a hindrance in self-communication. That it is a help is more obvious perhaps than that it is a hindrance. The greater our linguistic resources, the more likely we are to find out exactly what it is we want to say. But the existing language is also a hindrance, because it tends to freeze expression into set channels and so standardize what we experience. From this point of view, the greater our linguistic resources, the more likely we are to depend on them and the greater the difficulty, therefore, in freeing ourselves for fresh and novel experience.

This latter characteristic of language can be observed in the degeneration that occurs when a young child first goes off to school and begins to substitute current clichés (whether those of slang or of "proper" usage) for the vivid personal language he had earlier constructed for himself, before he knew any better.[4] Thus a little child who, on seeing the Alps for the first time, exclaimed in excitement, "Big dirt!" was making (and marking linguistically) a real discovery. And an adult who corrects him ("No dear, not 'big dirt'—'Mountain.'") is merely providing him with a little ready-made pigeon hole which is likely to operate only to bypass further experience. ("What's that over there?" "Oh, just another mountain.")

---

[4] C. E. Montague's *Rough Justice* (London: Chatto and Windus, 1926) is full of examples of this kind.

So far I have been concentrating on one primary function of language—its use to satisfy curiosity, to clarify and focus diffuse regions of experience. From this point of view, self-communication is primary: after all, it is our own curiosity that we are satisfying. There are many other uses of language, however; in some of these, other-communication becomes primary. In these uses, communication is directed outward to others, not to help them clarify their experience or to convey information, but to influence their behavior. Sometimes the manipulative intent of language is openly displayed—as in a top sergeant's "At ease!" Sometimes, as in propaganda and advertising, the speaker attempts to disguise his manipulative intent. More interesting, however, are instances where the speaker hides his manipulative intent even from himself:

(1) Two elderly American women who have just arrived in London are dining in a crowded restaurant. They point to the brown crystalline sugar on their table, which they have never encountered before, and address themselves to each waiter as he scurries past, "Where do you get this adorable sugar?" On the surface this seems a straightforward attempt to influence behavior; they are trying to get the waiters to stop and tell them where they can buy the sugar. Is this all? I think not. It seems to me unlikely that these ladies really wanted to purchase any sugar. I think it more likely that they felt isolated in the strange English city and wanted to establish a link to the life about them. Why, then, did they not say (still manipulative language), "Please, talk to me," to the waiters as they passed? Well, of course, the first answer is, that's just "not done." But it is doubtful if the ladies admitted to themselves that they were lonely; this would be to confess that the trip was a failure, that the relatives back home who had advised against it were right after all. It was essential to mask, especially to themselves, the need they were seeking to satisfy. Notice, incidentally, that in other circumstances this indirect manipulative strategy might work very well. At the rail of the ship that brought them to Southampton they might exclaim to the stranger standing beside them "Oh, do look at that dolphin!" And, one thing leading to another, a mutual friend—or even a cousin in Charleston or New Orleans—might soon be discovered and a link established.

(2) A child is whistling as he walks down a dark path at night. Asked, "Why do you whistle?" he replies, "To keep the boogie man away." Can we take this at its face value? I think not. Whistling or making a noise

would be good strategy if the child expected to encounter some small creature likely to be more afraid of the child than the child was afraid of it. To give warning of approach permits timely withdrawal and so prevents a clash by accident. But a boogie man is not a small, timid animal. Instead of being warned off by the whistling, he will be alerted to the child's approach and the readier, therefore, to pounce. And the child ought to be able to see this for himself. Therefore, if he is not stupid, "to keep the boogie man away" is not his reason for whistling—any more than finding out "where to buy that adorable sugar" was the women's reason for asking where the sugar could be bought.

What drive, then, is the whistling reducing? We know that the buildup of tension is relieved by all sorts of activity—thumb-sucking, for instance; nervous ticks, fidgeting about. It may be, then, that in the total economy of the child's life whistling is primarily a tension-reducing outlet. But the child is ashamed to admit (both to himself and to us) that he is afraid; hence he produces a "good" (i.e., socially acceptable) reason for whistling.

So, if the rats could talk and we were to ask them why they jumped high and to the right, it is likely they would reply with some "good" reason (such as, "We hoped to frighten the experimenter and force him to feed us"), rather than admit to themselves or to us the extent of their frustration and anxiety.

Thus there are many occasions when language performs a double function—to some extent it is relieving tension directly, as it were, by the mere physical fact of its occurrence, as fidgeting might. But it is also satisfying what we may call a rationality need—the need to give a respectable account of what is going on, and the need to give this account not only to others but to oneself most of all. For someone who experiences the rationality need, whistling relieves tension satisfactorily only if he manages to give it a facade of rationality by making it appear to be a matter of deliberate policy.

(3) If this sounds overly elaborate when applied to a child's whistling, another example is the way the great powers threaten one another with "massive retaliation" and "nuclear annihilation" whenever it looks as if the cold war might grow hot. This is a kind of whistling in the dark in both of the senses just described—at once a calculated act of strategy (whether good strategy or poor strategy is not the question here) designed

to warn off potential enemies, and also an expression of the almost unbearable tensions to which foreign ministers and chiefs of state are subjected.

(4) When Freud first proposed that men as well as women suffer from hysteria, he was rebuffed by the Viennese medical society to whom he presented this thesis. The term "hysteria," the doctors pointed out, is derived from *hystera*, the Greek word for "womb." Therefore hysteria is obviously exclusively a female disease.[5] This may seem a ridiculous way to argue—especially to us now, *ex post* (compare p. 90). But apart from the fact that the "facts" about hysteria were not so obvious in 1886 as they are today, the statements of the Viennese doctors probably fuctioned in a complex way. Freud's observations constituted a serious threat to their whole way of looking at and treating mental illness. Challenges of this dimension are profoundly disturbing to most people since they require fundamental adjustments and re-orientations. Hence we should understand the doctors' reply as part (unconscious, of course) of a strategy of resistance, which, like the strategy of the professors at Padua who refused to look through Galileo's telescope, sought to exorcise the disturbing fact by denying that it existed. This strategy could be successful in the doctors' case only if it masked itself, however lamely, as a rational argument. The doctors did not want to chop off Freud's head or lock him up, even if they could. Being scientists themselves, they were bound to feel that they had to "prove" that he was mistaken; and their argument "showed" his mistake to be so gross that it was safe to conclude he must be either a fool or a knave and hence that they were justified in refusing to permit him to practice in their hospitals. Thus language that, on the surface, looks as if it were performing some rational function, and looks to the external observer as if it is performing it badly, is perhaps performing some other function in the economy of the speaker, and performing it well.

So far as the rationality drive is present in an individual's drive pattern, language that serves primarily to reduce some other drive will nevertheless have to meet some minimum conditions of reasonableness or plausibility; it may, for instance, adopt the mask of giving information ("There is a dolphin off the port bow") or of requesting information ("Where do you get that adorable sugar?"). From the earliest times and in the most

---

[5] Ernest Jones, *The Life and Work of Sigmund Freud* (New York: Basic Books, 1953), Vol. I, p. 231.

primitive groups we can see it operative. For instance, if a savage believes that Great Mumbo can bring or withhold rain, he may say, when his prayers are unavailing, "Great Mumbo is angry" or "Great Mumbo is busy about more important matters." Belief in one's ability to establish and maintain contact with the power that controls the rain doubtless reduces anxiety regarding the ever-present threat of drought in arid lands; the subsidiary belief that Great Mumbo is angry or absent satisfies the need for a rational explanation—at the savage's level of rationality—of his failure to maintain the contact, and so sustains the anxiety-reducing function of the primary belief. Thus primitive cosmogonies have much the same function as ad hoc hypotheses in the sciences—they make it unnecessary to abandon the primary belief or hypothesis.

A cosmogony is a narration of some god's activities; it is, in fact, sacred history. As such it is, at least in part, a response to the demand for plausible explanations. But what about a narration of the activities of a fairy prince or princess? Is this a kind of fictive history? And if so, what is its function? A child reading *Snow White* or *The Wonderful Adventures of Nils* is curious about whether the witch's wicked design is frustrated or whether Nils returns to human size. Some people might say that since the child presumably does not distinguish between fictive facts and actual facts, his interest in these adventures is intellectual curiosity, pure and simple, like that of the adult reading Gibbon's *Decline and Fall* in order to ascertain some facts about the Roman empire.

To me this does not seem plausible. When a child listens to *Tom Sawyer*, he is certainly curious about the (fictive) facts. But he is more than "merely" curious; his curiosity is powerfully reinforced and colored by the way he enters into the story and participates in the adventures, the dangers, and the triumphs of the hero. Something missing, it may be, in his everyday life is completed and made good in the story.

This is also a large element in adult interest in fictive narrative—in the novel, for instance. Of course we are curious (as the child is curious) about what is going to happen next, and curiosity plays a larger part in our interest in some novels (e.g., the detective story) than in others. But curiosity alone does not explain the extraordinary interest once evoked by some novels (e.g., *Werther*), nor why they are no longer read. We must suppose that there was some powerful interest (other than curiosity) present in late eighteenth-century society and almost wholly absent now, which the events described in *Werther* complemented. And even our interest in detective stories is not wholly curiosity. It seems likely, for instance, that the attraction of the novel of violence (e.g., Spillane) is related to the routinization and mechanization of modern urban life. Similarly, the stories in women's magazines of the little shop assistant or secretary who marries the boss's son are all too obviously designed to appeal to readers whose lives lack the glamor and romance of these heroines.

As for historical, in distinction from fictive, narrative: people sometimes say that this biography of Caesar, for instance, or of Napoleon, is "as good as a novel." They enter into the career of these historical (i.e., "real") persons as they enter into the careers of those fictitious ones. The selectivity displayed by biographers in their choice of the subjects they write about, and by readers in their choice of the biographies they read, reflects complex interests other than "pure" curiosity. Though we may indeed be curious about what happened next in the life of Henry Tudor, curiosity alone does not explain why we read his life instead of the life of Henry of Luxembourg.

It is possible, therefore, to think of narratives as forming a spectrum, ranging from the utterly fantastic, to the impossible-but-plausible, to the impossible-now-but-who-knows-when, to the not-yet-but-probably-some-day-soon, to the wholly-actual-now. Science fiction, the historical novel, fictionalized biography are some of the intermediary segments of this spectrum. Thus it is correct after all to say that the child's interest in *Snow White* and the adult's interest in Gibbon are similar. But they are similar, not because the interest is pure curiosity in both cases, but because in both—and along the whole spectrum of narration—a complex blend of interests is at work. The complexion of the blend varies from case to case, but there is an element of curiosity (e.g., about what is going to happen next) even in the most fantastic of narratives, and there is some element of identification or complementation in the interest anyone, whether author or reader, takes in the most prosaic, factual historical narration.

To put this differently: language serves a great many different functions—for instance, to mention just a few, it may satisfy curiosity, convey information, complement personal deficiencies, relieve anxieties, obviate loneliness. And the quality, tone, and vocabulary of any segment of language (say, Gibbon's chapter on "The Progress of the Christian Religion," or the passage in Grimm about Snow White being roused by the young prince) reflects the particular pattern of drives, whatever it happens to be, that is being reduced by this particular segment of language.

It is important to keep in mind this relationship between actual language, as it is written and spoken, and multiplicity of function, since many linguistic philosophers tend to ignore it. There is, indeed, a tendency not only to assume that language serves relatively few functions but also that corresponding to each of these functions, there is a separate and distinct language. Thus, it is currently fashionable to classify language into two basic functions, "cognitive" and "non-cognitive," with each of these main functions further divided into various sub-functions. For instance, Professor Herbert Feigl has proposed the following classification:[6]

COGNITIVE MEANINGS (Informational function)	NON-COGNITIVE MEANINGS (Emotive expression and appeal function)
Purely formal	*Pictorial (Imaginative)*
Logico-arithmetical	*Emotional (Affective)*
Factual (= Empirical)	*Volitional-motivational (Directive)*

Though Feigl is careful to say that "no evaluation of the functions of language as such is implied" in this two-fold classification, I do not think he has escaped evaluation. For instance, putting "pictorial" and "emotive" together as sub-functions under "emotive expression and appeal" means that he weighs the similarities between these two sub-functions as more important (significant) than their differences. Moreover, the very term "non-cognitive" is a kind of evaluation of these functions as relatively unimportant. The use of a negative term here is itself an instance of the way interest is involved in and affects a seemingly matter-of-factual classification. For Feigl has made his classification in order to be able to eliminate the so-called non-cognitive functions from further consideration. He dismisses them, it is true, with a fine compliment: "Some of the highest refinements of our civilized existence depend upon the emotive overtones of spoken and written language. However. . . ." Still, they *are* dismissed. Also the expression "emotive overtone" itself has an overtone: the description of the emotive aspect of language as an overtone suggests the main business of language is informational, and so contains an implicit evaluation.

---

[6] In Dagobert D. Runes, ed., *Twentieth Century Philosophy* (New York: Philosophical Library, 1943), p. 379.

In saying this I do not mean that classifications should not reflect interests nor that Professor Feigl's interest is mistaken. Quite the contrary. For, first, I believe that classifications inevitably reflect interests. Different classifications are made in the interest, as it were, of different interests. They clear up (introduce order into) some area of relatively diffuse experience: they do so by bringing out the points (the foci) that the classifier regards as important, that is, that interest him. And second, it would be ridiculous to say that Professor Feigl ought not to be interested in the cognitive aspects of language. His classification is constructed in such a way as to bring these aspects into focus, and there is no reason why he should not bring them into focus.

What, then, am I complaining about? Not about Professor Feigl's classification nor about any particular classification, but about two unfortunate and accidental by-products of the extremely useful operation of classifying. The first is a tendency to confuse utility with superior metaphysical status. A classification is merely one way of organizing material, a way that reflects some interest of the classifier. But if I share this interest I am likely to assume that the distinctions made by it are more real than those made by other classifications of the same material. It is as if, because certain letters all end up in a pigeonhole labeled "unknown at this address," I were to suppose that they were all addressed to "Unknown" and had the same contents. For a particular purpose it is convenient to send these letters to the dead-letter office and then forget about them, just as, for another purpose, it is convenient to group together certain linguistic functions as "non-cognitive," in order to concentrate on those that are "cognitive." But it is a mistake to suppose that the letters, or the functions, so labeled are any less real and significant than those which happen to hold our attention.

A second unfortunate by-product of the operation of classifying may be called the fallacy of ideal types. Because it is convenient for purposes of analysis and discussion to distinguish sharply between categories (pigeonholes), we tend to assume that the things thus categorized are also sharply distinguished. It is as if we were to assume that the geographical distribution of population corresponds to the distribution of pigeonholes in a post office. For purposes of efficiency, the post office department sends letters, however addressed, to the nearest post office. Accordingly, if there were no post offices between (say) New York and New Haven, there would be two contiguous pigeonholes, one labeled "New York" and the next labeled "New Haven"; and letters addressed to Greenwich, Stamford, and Bridgeport would be popped either into "New York" or to "New Haven," depending on which of these cities was nearer. Now if someone were to maintain that it follows from these arrangements that nobody whatsoever lives between New York and New Haven, that everyone without exception is an inhabitant of one or the other of these cities, this would be an instance of the fallacy of ideal types.

Now, taking together these two mistakes that grow out of the operation of classifying and considering the classification of language functions in the light of them, we see that, while it is useful for some purposes (e.g., for purposes of analysis and discussion) to isolate a purely cognitive function, there is no such actual function. It is not true that some particular segment of discourse satisfies a (pure) cognitive function, that this other piece of discourse satisfies a (pure) emotive function, that this third piece of discourse satisfies a (pure) appeal function, corresponding to the sharply distinguished functions in the classificatory scheme. On the contrary, every particular segment of discourse—this poem, this novel, this juridical decision, this paper addressed to a learned society, this classificatory scheme, this discourse about discourse that you are now reading —serves several different functions, satisfies several different needs. And every particular segment of language has the particular character it happens to have because it is satisfying several functions. Thus "Where do you get that adorable sugar?" has the character it has because it is satisfying at one and the same time both a rationality need and a need to reduce loneliness.

To point this up, let us look once more at "Great Mumbo is angry," as an answer to the question "Why does rain magic not bring rain?" (It does not matter whether this question is asked by a skeptical spectator or whether it articulates a lurking doubt of the dancer himself.) Many linguistic philosophers would agree with me that "Great Mumbo is angry" expresses the dancer's anxiety about the failure of his magic; they might also agree that, besides expressing anxiety, it tends to reduce anxiety, so far as the dancer believes it. But these linguistic philosophers might add: "Of course, 'Great Mumbo is angry' is only a pseudo-explanation. It is meaningless since there is no way to verify the hypothesis that Great Mumbo is angry. Whatever the savage believes about it, the statement is purely expressive."

Here we must proceed with caution. Linguistic philosophers who hold that "Great Mumbo is angry" is purely expressive for the savage would admit that it could under certain circumstances be cognitively meaningful to an anthropologist who records it on a field trip. The anthropologist might, for instance, have formulated a theory about primitive religions from which he has predicted that whenever rain magic fails, divine anger is offered as an excuse. Great Mumbo's anger may not be verifiable, but "Great Mumbo is angry" (the savage's assertion) is verifiable, since operations can be defined for producing this auditory experience in the anthropologist.

Now if an anthropologist formulated a theory of this kind, and if he made the prediction specified, hearing a savage exclaim, "Great Mumbo is angry!" would be a satisfaction. It justifies the theoretical construction into which he has put many long hours of hard work, just as hearing "Great Mumbo is angry" is a source of satisfaction to the savage who was puzzled about why the rain magic failed. In a word, if the statement is related to the savage's anxiety about a drought, it may be also related (and in much the same way) to an anthropologist's anxiety about completing his field work and getting his Ph.D. There is such a thing in the sciences as a crucial experiment; for this anthropologist everything might just possibly hang on hearing the savage make this statement. Accordingly, when he hears it he too may feel relief: "Now I know I shall be able to finish my dissertation in time!"

Finally, if the anthropologist's anxiety about his degree is acute, if it is imperative for him that the crucial experiment take place so that he can pack up and go home, it is not inconceivable that he may mis-hear what the dancer says. Suppose the expression translated as "Great Mumbo is angry" is *Akatawa Mumbo* and suppose that *Akatama Mumbo* means "I am angry with Great Mumbo." The anthropologist may mis-hear the latter (which would ruin his thesis) as the former (which saves it). As a thirsty man may mis-hear "Is it Thursday?" as "Are you thirsty?" and think he is being offered a drink. Or as a man who is worried about drought may see a cloud on the horizon when others, who are not, see a mountain. Every one has had experiences of this kind, which result from interpreting a foreground by means of background structures dominated by our private hopes and fears. And, however much the anthropologist may be aware of this danger and take methodological precautions, he may not render himself immune to it.

It follows that the difference between the meaning of "Great Mumbo is angry" for (1) the savage who says it, and for (2) the anthropologist who records it, is a difference in degree, not a difference in kind. For the savage and for the anthropologist alike, "Great Mumbo is angry" has an expressive-emotive-affective function, as we have just seen. The difference here depends on the amount of anxiety present in the drive complex; and if we assume that usually there is less anxiety in the scientist's drive complex than in the savage's, it is possible to think of circumstances in which there may be a very high degree of anxiety in the scientist's.

Again, "Great Mumbo is angry" functions cognitively both for the anthropologist and for the savage. That it functions cognitively for the scientist is obvious, since we have presupposed that the sentence verifies some anthropological hypothesis. But if the cognitive aspect of meaning is defined, not in terms of some specific set of criteria for explanation, such as the verification test (see p. 93), but in terms of the presence of curiosity in the drive pattern, then "Great Mumbo is angry" functions cognitively for the savage as well as for the scientist. Of course, much more than curiosity is involved for the savage dancer: he desperately wants his magic to work. Still, he not only wants it to work; he *expects* it to work. And any failure of expectation arouses curiosity, at least to some slight degree. The dancer's feeling may be predominately one of anxiety, but to some degree he is also puzzled: what usually happens, hasn't happened. Why?

Thus for the savage, "Great Mumbo is angry," in addition to allaying anxiety, also allays curiosity. Indeed, it would not allay his anxiety unless it also allayed his curiosity, that is, unless he regarded it as a good explanation (see p. 126). It has to make sense to the dancer in terms of the overall, theoretical system in which meteorological phenomena are accounted for in his society.

If our linguistic philosophers were to say to the dancer, "But you cannot verify Great Mumbo's anger," the dancer might reply as follows: "You have put the cart before the horse. I don't have to verify his anger; I experience it directly. And because I do experience his anger directly, it verifies my hypothesis about why my magic failed. I am as good an operationalist as you are."

He would be just as convinced of Mumbo's anger and of his direct experience of it, as the anthropologist might be convinced, on some occasion, that the president of his university was angry with him. He experiences "signs" of presidential displeasure—loud voice, red face, clenched fists—not as signs, but directly as anger, because he makes a smooth interpretation from a certain background structure containing an (implicit) theory about rages. So with the savage: the failure of rain is a manifestation, not merely an external sign, of Mumbo's anger, as presidential table-pounding is a manifestation of presidential anger. Of course, the linguistic philosopher will say that the implicit theory in the savage's background structure which enables him to experience the failure of his magic as a direct manifestation of Mumbo's anger is mistaken. But then the president's physician may say that the anthropologist's implicit theory about presidential rages is mistaken; the physician may interpret the president's red face as a sign of hypertension instead of as a manifestation of anger.

I am not concerned here with whether the savage's explanation of the failure of his magic is correct, nor with whether the anthropologist's explanation of primitive ritual (or, for that matter, of presidential behavior) is correct. I am simply pointing out that, whether the explanation contained in the statement is good or bad, the statement *functions* as an explanation—for the savage as well as for the scientist. It functions cognitively in both cases, because in both cases it reduces curiosity. It is likely that curiosity is a much stronger component in the scientist's drive pattern than in the savage's, but, since it is present in both, the difference is a difference in degree rather than a difference in kind.

It should be plain now, why it is a mistake to take the various linguistic functions as having separate, independent existence. Actual language would function purely only if men experienced separate, encapsulated, departmentalized drives. But every actual need-situation constitutes a particular pattern of drives. Language functions differently in *this* situation to reduce *this* pattern of drives, from the way it functions in some other situation to reduce some other pattern of drives. If the savage dancer were "purely" anxious, then exclaiming "Great Mumbo is angry" would operate just as if he were to reduce his anxiety by running about or shouting—the words uttered would not be language, any more than hopping to one's feet when one sits on a tack is language. But we have seen reason to believe that the dancer is curious as well as anxious, and that he has set himself certain standards (doubtless rudimentary ones by our lights) which explanations must meet before they reduce his anxiety. On the other hand, if the anthropologist were a disembodied cherub animated by a pure curiosity drive, then "Great Mumbo is angry" would be a purely cognitive (informational) sentence, to the extent that it solved some theoretical puzzle about primitive ritual, like the final piece in a jigsaw puzzle, which completes the picture when it drops into place. But the anthropologist is not a disembodied cherub; he is a husband, a father, a prospective Ph.D., and a man—perhaps, as a man, he even feels anguish about the future of man in the infinity of nature.

In this artificial example the form of words ("Great Mumbo is angry") remains the same whether the "mix" of the drive pattern is one in which curiosity is a minor component and anxiety a major component or one in which curiosity is a major component and anxiety a minor component. In real life, however, as situations change and as the mix of the drive pattern alters, differences in language are likely to appear which reflect these differences in drive complex. For instance, as curiosity becomes more predominant, language is likely to become more guarded, more circumspect, more neutral in tone. On the other hand, as other drives (e.g., anxiety) become predominant, language will change in response to the new configuration and become colored, highly charged, even passionate. Hence it is possible to infer from an inspection of any particular segment of actual language what was the drive pattern of the speaker or writer. Or, with a prior knowledge of this general relationship, it is possible, given a knowledge of an individual's drive pattern, to predict what sort of response a given type of language will evoke in him. This, of course, is just what manipulative users of language—orators, advertisers, propagandists—often do with great skill.

Many philosophers might agree that actual language reflects a complex of different drives, but they would insist that there is, or at least there ought to be, a special language in which only curiosity drive is present. Not that these philosophers would put their position in this way; they would prefer to talk either about ideal languages or else about the pursuit of truth—a pure, unadulterated search for truth.

This philosophical tendency results from a combination of an ideal-types way of thinking with an intellectualistic bias. The former encourages philosophers to believe that curiosity (truth-seeking) is, or could be, a distinct drive; the latter causes them to look down their noses at all other drives. However, these philosophers do not merely overlook activities that may be just as important as truth-seeking. Concentration on this one function to the exclusion of others distorts the account they give of that function itself. Focusing attention on what would satisfy a truth-seeking drive if there were such a pure, unadulterated drive, has led to a very artificial concept of truth (i.e., what would satisfy this drive). This holds as much of the positivists as it does of their opponents the rationalists, whose opinions in all other respects diverge radically.

F. D. Ramsey, for instance, maintained that in a perfect language each thing would have its own name. Therefore, if "in the sense of a sentence a certain object occurred, [it] would also be shown visibly by the occurrence of the name of that object. . . . Thus in a perfect language all sentences or thoughts would be perfectly clear." [7] And Brand Branshard has explicitly declared, "Thought is that activity of mind which aims directly at truth." [8] Of course, positivists and rationalists are deeply divided over what "truth" is. Ramsey's metaphysical beliefs led him, for instance, to hold that truth is readily attainable, by marking linguistically the relations observed between spatio-temporal events or data, while Professor Blanshard's metaphysical beliefs lead him to conclude that truth is never completely attainable, since it is what would be wholly systematic and consistent. Nevertheless rationalists and positivists agree that there is, or ought to be, a special language for truth-seeking; further, they regard this language as somehow more important, more serious, than languages "adulterated" by other drives.

What can I say about this, apart from what I have already said about "ideals" (p. 75), and about "best" (or ultimate) criteria (pp. 93–95)? To begin with, that there should be a "the Truth" is obviously important to many people. This widespread devotion to a pure, unadulterated truth is, indeed, a good example of the way in which the basic values and attitudes imbedded in men's background structures affect the versions of reality to which they give their allegiance. Granting that many people share this basic value, the specific conception they have of "the Truth" depends on a number of other variables. Among philosophers, for instance, it depends on the presence or absence of certain metaphysical be-

---

[7] *The Foundations of Mathematics* (New York: Harcourt Brace; London: Kegan Paul, 1931), pp. 283–284. I don't mean to suggest that positivists are the only philosophers who have yearned for a perfect language. There are Leibniz and Locke and Plato, for example.

[8] *The Nature of Thought* (New York: Macmillan, 1939), Vol. I, p. 51. See above, p. 37.

liefs. It may express itself in a language in which terms such as "ideal language" appear, or it may express itself in a language in which terms such as "coherence," "systematic," and "necessity" appear. Among others, however, this basic attitude may take a much less amiable form. In some cases belief in "the Truth" (and the concomitant conviction that one has, personally, latched onto it) is so strong and so central that considerable anxiety is felt about it; anything experienced as a threat to this belief is regarded with the deepest hostility. Those who question it are burned at the stake, locked up, or at the very least called ugly names.

This latter was the fate of William James and the pragmatists when, half a century ago, they defined truth as "what works." They wanted to correct the exaggerated emphasis on cognition (truth-seeking) in what they called the traditional philosophy. But it was perhaps imprudent of them to tamper with such a highly charged word as "truth"; it might have been better strategy to say that the truth is what satisfies our need to understand. This way of putting it recognizes (what pragmatism's way of putting it tended to obscure) that there are problems primarily cognitive in nature; but, at the same time, by emphasizing need—with the implication of there being many different needs—it also brings out that the fact that truth-seeking is not the only, or even chief, use of thought.

Indeed, in this respect the pragmatists didn't go far enough. They were so busy attacking the traditional overemphasis on cognition that they tended too lump all other uses together as being simply "for the sake of practice guided by sense apprehension." [9] This is too narrow, if "practice" means, as Dewey meant and as Lewis seems to mean, primarily problems growing out of our traffic with nature. It does not account for whistling-in-the-dark language, nor for the interest children take in Cinderella, nor for the interest adults take in Gibbon, nor for the Viennese physicians' insistence that hysteria is exclusively a disease of women.

Finally, the pragmatists, like the traditional philosophers they criticized (like the positivists, too, for that matter), still tended to think of there being distinct, separate, encapsulated languages of various kinds, each performing its own special use.

---

[9] C. I. Lewis, *An Analysis of Knowledge and Valuation* (La Salle, Ill.: Open Court, 1946), p. 146.

Thus the pragmatists not only irritated the philosophical Establishment of their time, which was perhaps inevitable. They also tended to confuse the issue. Will I fare better? Probably not, since the issue itself is complex and passions on various sides are strong (see p. 141). However, what I am trying to do is to strike a balance between an anti-intellectualism that reduces all problems to practical ones and an excessive intellectualism that assigns an exalted status to pure, cognitive problems. Against the former tendency I maintain that there are criteria for explanation other than (beyond) the criteria for the merely successful solutions of practical difficulties. Against the latter, I maintain that criteria of explanation vary and that they are affected by thought's other uses.

This is why I defined truth-seeking in terms of need-reduction. It is helpful to regard truth-seeking as a drive to understand—to reduce curiosity, to clear up confused and diffuse experience, because, when we think about it in this way, we get the truth off any sort of special pedestal, while at the same time affirming its importance and centrality in the whole human economy. Further, to define truth-seeking in terms of need-reduction is to emphasize that it is not a separate (pure) activity. For needs are not like golf clubs in a golf bag waiting to be used, or like rocks in a pile waiting to be picked up. When we say that the need for food is universal in man, we do not suppose that there is a little encapsulated nugget of "food need" stuck in every man waiting to be deployed, and separate from a need for health, a need for relaxation, a need for sleep, and so on. The need for food, as it emerges and develops in an individual life, is through-and-through characterized by the experiences of that life, including both the resistances it encounters and the other, ongoing needs of that individual. As a result, one man's need for food is fully satisfied by a broiled steak served in such-and-such a way and accompanied by such-and-such a wine, while another man's need for food is satisfied by raw fish, served in such-and-such a different way. So, *mutatis mutandis,* for the need for truth.

And what about the relation between need reduction in general and language? Certainly not all the needs we experience are reduced by behavior that takes a linguistic form—the need for food is a case in point. But, generally speaking, in man language enters to some degree into the satisfaction of many needs. I am not thinking here merely of cases where we use language to get something else that will satisfy the need (as when we telephone to the Auto Club to come and fix a flat tire); I am thinking of cases where the language used is itself an essential element in the whole activity that reduces the need. For instance, a dog may satisfy what appears to be a need for fellowship and companionship by putting its head in its master's lap, and a baby may satisfy a similar need by cuddling—though it may also "coo." With an adult, physical contact is usually accompanied by language—for example, exclamations of affection—and the need may not be fully satisfied without language.

Relating stories of Great Mumbo's prowess or of his temper tantrums, trying to decide whether a parking lot is a road, recounting the adventures of a folk hero, working a crossword puzzle, drafting the text of an agreement to expel Cuba from the O.A.S., writing a chapter on "Language and Reality"—here is a great diversity of activities whose common characteristic is that needs are being reduced by the use of language. Many and various are the needs being reduced; many and various, therefore, are the uses of language. And in every instance the language employed reflects the configuration of the operative drive pattern: it would not satisfy unless it did reflect the component needs. Truth-seeking is a primary drive in some of the cases just listed; it is a component in all of them—to the extent that, whatever else is needed, the speaker or writer is also feeling curious. What he is experiencing is relatively diffuse, and he wants to get clear about what it is. He may believe that, if only he could get clearer about it, he would satisfy that other need, but he also wants to get clear about it precisely because he is also curious.

In the light of this discussion of language-in-general, let us return briefly to the criticisms, at the end of chapter iii, of fact-that language. Fact-that language reduces curiosity (satisfies the truth-seeking drive) at a particular level of discrimination. It is the language we use when we want to discover for ourselves what the facts are (self-communication) or when we want to inform others of them (other-communication). Truth-seeking occurs, here as always, in a particular configuration of other drives, so that the truth is conceived as consisting in propositions about "things," that is, more or less discrete objects interacting causally with one another. Accordingly, the drive is satisfied, curiosity is reduced, providing that the discrimination process is carried through far enough to disclose determinate objects in determinate relationships—a world of shoes, ships, sealing wax, cabbages, and kings. To say, as people do, that the language in which these discoveries is formulated is "true" is to say that our curiosity has been satisfied by what we have found. Note that the form the truth-seeking drive takes under these circumstances is far less stringent than it might be. Under other circumstances, of course, it might not be satisfied by anything less than formulation in some "ideal language" or in talk about a necessary coherent Whole.

What, then, is my criticism of fact-that language? I certainly do not criticize it because it enables us to formulate the facts. The need to ascertain the facts, both in order to satisfy our curiosity about the world and to solve our policy problems, is fundamental in the human economy. The trouble with fact-that language is not that it is, but that it seems to be, purely factual. Because it looks so innocent, because it seems to be only reporting the facts, it unintentionally deceives its users. They forget that fact-that language, like all languages, formulates the truth only in a specific context of values, attitudes, presuppositions and metaphysical beliefs. There would be no trouble with fact-that language if it were, if it *could* be, purely factual. And of course there *is* no trouble with it so long as we know what we are doing when we use it and recognize the stance to which it is committing us.

And what, finally, about the language in which this chapter is written? What I just said about "all languages" applies as much to the language in which this discourse about discourse is written, as it does to fact-that language. The difference (and this difference is *all* the difference) is that this language knows that it is limited and restricted by the interests (drives) that animate it. To put this another way: the models introduced earlier in the chapter are self-applicable. Assuming, for instance, that somebody turns his attention to the relationship between language and reality, this part of his field begins to come into focus. He may be clear about some aspects of the relationship (for instance, language is one thing, reality is another), and relatively unclear about others. Part of the field is diffuse. He is curious; he wants to understand. Now, the relationship between language and reality is complex—quite as complex as the relationship between the Castro regime and Communism, much more complex than the relationship between a parking lot and a road. Accordingly, which aspects of the language-reality relationship a man focuses on depends on what drive pattern is operative, and this in turn depends on a whole set of value attitudes, presuppositions, and metaphysical beliefs. The particular language that a man finds satisfactory for talking about the the relationship between language and reality will be a function, in part, of the appropriateness of this language for dealing with (clarifying for him) those particular areas of the field on which his interests cause him to focus.

For instance, in the last chapter I maintained that fact-that language gave an unnecessary emphasis to out-thereness. A term such as "checkpoint" (p. 91) seemed to me just about right for calling attention to the fact of factuality while at the same time keeping in focus the chanciness of experience and reminding us that resistances can be overcome. I chose a language that gave "due weight" to the various aspects of the field (in this case, the hardness and objectivity of experience), as I weighed these aspects. Others, with different interests and with different aspects of the same field in focus, will doubtless weigh them differently.

Thus what I said about the problems of the diplomat who is trying to formulate a text of a treaty to which all parties will agree applies equally to the various vocabularies in which philosophers have tried to formulate the relationship between language and reality. Their different interests will be reflected in the language they prefer, as the different interests of judges in a court of appeals may be reflected in a dispute over whether a parking lot is or is not a road.

The language in which this chapter (and the book as a whole) is written reflects my leading interests. Those who do not share these interests will find the argument pointless. ("Verbal," "logic-chopping" are terms people use to describe language that articulates distinctions that may be extremely important to others, but which correspond to nothing of interest in their own field.) On the other hand, those whose interests are opposite—for instance, who strongly value a "Truth"—will not find the argument pointless; they will find it wrongheaded, pernicious, or deplorable—for these are terms people use to characterize arguments that threaten or ignore their interests. For instance, at one point I wrote that I was trying to strike a balance between excessive intellectualism and excessive anti-intellectualism (p. 138). Stating my position this way was an attempt to put my argument in a favorable light with the reader, since in this country most people favor compromise, balance, and the middle of the road. But some people will be put off by this description, since they do not think that the truth necessarily, or even very often, lies between two extremes. And of course people who adopt a position that I regard as extreme will not accept my version of where the balance lies. How much intellectualism (or anti-intellectualism) is excessive? What seems to me excessive, will seem to a rationalist the only tolerable position. So I do not expect to please everyone: it would be naïve to hope that this particular language—whether beautiful or not—"will save the conference," in the sense of achieving substantial agreement all the way round.

No one, for instance, will find this book useful who is not interested, as I am interested, in the seeming conflict between the sciences and the humanities; no one will find it interesting who is not concerned about current veneration of fact-thats and current derogation of the languages of poetry, of art, and of primitive peoples. But there are surely large numbers of people who share these concerns. These people are at least focusing on the areas in the field to which the language of this book is relevant. It is not unrealistic to hope that this language may help some of them become clear about the field and so not only satisfy their curiosity but also reduce the anxiety which, as I believe, many people feel—even those who claim to be uninterested (for a display of indifference is often a device for masking anxiety).

At this point someone may retort: "If reducing anxiety is what concerns you, why a book with a complicated technical vocabulary and an involved argument? Why not wine, women, and song—or, for that matter, why not whistling in the dark? Doesn't it follow from your own argument that anything that reduces anxiety is as good as anything else?"

Well, I don't think this does follow. As I have already said (pp. 100–101), relativism isn't necessarily vicious. If there is anyone who actually holds that everybody's opinion is just as good as everybody else's, that view might fairly be called vicious relativism. But I can't think of anyone who, seriously, holds such a view; and in any case it overlooks the fact of context—the fact that our specific evaluations and appraisals are always made in a context of more or less articulated and agreed-on values. Indeed, both the extreme relativists, if there are any, and the absolutists overlook context. The former conclude that no valid comparisons are possible because they suppose each individual to be in a social and cultural vacuum. The latter believe in the possibility of absolutely valid comparisons because they identify some particular context (possibly their own) with ultimate truth. Comparisons are possible and valid so far as we share a context; the context supplies the norms by which we appraise particular evaluations.

For instance: if it were *merely* a matter of reducing anxiety, then anything that reduced anxiety would be as good as anything else. But in real life, it usually isn't just a matter of reducing anxiety. People aren't merely anxious about the conflict between science and the humanities; they are also puzzled about it—just as the savage dancer was not only anxious about the prolonged drought but puzzled about why his magic failed. That is, they want an explanation; their anxiety is reduced only if what is offered to them seems to them to be "true." This is why some ways of reducing anxiety are better than others.

Of course, puzzlement occurs at varying levels and in varying degrees. Primitive peoples apart, many men today have such low-level criteria for the satisfactoriness of explanations that they are content with vague reassurances to the effect that God is still in his heaven and all is therefore right with the world. This book is not addressed to them; nor is it addressed primarily to professional philosophers. For though the language is fairly technical and the argument fairly abstract, they are not so technical or so abstract as they might be, as they would be if they were addressed to professionals. The language is not (to use Feigl's terminology) "formal" or "logico-arithmetical." It is (hopefully) "informational," but it also frankly has an "appeal" function. I want people to change their attitude toward language—including, of course, the language in which this book itself is written.

The attitude that needs to be changed is very widespread and very deep-seated. It consists in the belief that language is either non-cognitive (in which case it may be pleasing, but is neither "true" nor "false") or else it is cognitive, in which case it is either true or false, and, if it is true, this is because it faithfully mirrors the facts. Thus the attitude that I believe to be unfortunate rests on a certain belief about the relation between language and reality: reality is supposed to be out there, separate from us, just whatever it happens to be. Language either has nothing to do with reality—being merely expressive of subjective feeling—or it is purely and simply informational.

People who hold this view of the relation between language and reality are likely to become trapped in a linguistic prison of their own construction. They identify the particular version of reality that happens to be articulated by the language of their choosing with "Reality." Any alternative version is felt as a serious threat, and anxieties and hostilities develop. Such a state of affairs can be personally tragic for the threatened individual; it is also socially deleterious, since it interferes with an effective and resilient response to novelty. And all of this is greatly exacerbated by the rapidity of change in the period in which we live.

Thus the conflict between the sciences and the humanities is only one, though a very important one, of the discrimination problems whose solution can be made easier by a more sophisticated attitude toward the relation between language and reality. On this view, the notion of there being a reality apart from any and all languages is an idle concept—it is an unknowable thing-in-itself. Every language formulates a version of reality, a version in which value attitudes, presuppositions, metaphysical beliefs are imbedded. To adopt this view certainly does not free us from the limitations of language, but at least it frees us from the fatal illusion of freedom.

* * * * *

In this and the preceding two chapters I have set out a strategy for tackling philosophical problems of all kinds, based upon my conception of how language and reality are related. In the following chapters I shall apply this strategy to a number of problems that grow out of the conflict between the sciences and the humanities. Although I am confining myself here to this specific, but very thorny, set of problems, I would maintain that this linguistic method of analysis has a much wider range of use; indeed, I should say that there is almost no problem whose solution cannot be facilitated by it, since there is a linguistic component in all problems.

However, before plunging into applications, it may be helpful to review the argument of this long chapter and to relate it to chapters ii and iii, in order to provide a brief retrospective view of the position as a whole.

In chapters ii and iii, I developed a new vocabulary—my foregrounds-backgrounds language—for dealing with certain epistemological paradoxes that remain intractable so long as we employ a vocabulary based on metaphysical dualism. In the present chapter I reformulated the theses of those two chapters in terms of a drive-reduction model. Language, I said, is a type of behavior. As such, it is an expression of, a response to, certain (variable) needs of the organism as it operates in its environment. Alternatively, language is goal-directed activity; its character in any particular situation is determined by the specific goals to which, in that situation, the organism happens to be directed.

One result of employing this model is that, instead of talking about "truth," I talk about the reduction (or satisfaction) of curiosity. To be curious is to experience some segment of the field as being more diffuse than we would like it to be. Curiosity is satisfied when this diffuse region is clarified by displacement to symbolism, not necessarily verbal in character. Thus language behavior is a sub-set of a very large set of behaviors—those involving displacement to a substitute object.

But curiosity never operates alone, in splendid isolation; it always occurs in a complex, or configuration, of other drives—drives that have a bearing on what will satisfy curiosity. For instance, language that satisfies a drive complex in which curiosity is a primary component and anxiety (say) is a minor component will differ from language that satisfies a drive complex in which anxiety is primary and curiosity is minor.

It follows that what a man decides is true—for instance, that a parking lot is more like a meadow than like a road—will be affected by the drive pattern, including curiosity, that was operative when he became interested in what a parking lot is like. Further, we can read back from the language in which he reports his belief to the nature of the operative drive pattern.

Another result of our use of a drive-reduction model for studying language is that the sharp dichotomy some philosophers draw between the cognitive and the non-cognitive functions of language is seen to be a serious oversimplification. Rather, there is a "mix" of cognitive and non-cognitive elements in all language. For instance, there is not a difference in kind, but only of degree, between the language of a primitive savage and the language of an anthropologist who describes the savage's language. Similarly, it is an oversimplification to say that the anthropologist's world—in which Mumbo is a fiction—is "real," while the savage's world—in which Great Mumbo is angry—is "merely" fictive.

That is, I reject the notion of a single Reality (with a capital "R") and propose to replace it with the more viable notion of a plurality of realities (lower-case). Every such reality—the savage's as well as the anthropologist's—is a stable world resulting from interactions between the various resistances encountered in experience and a linguistically fixed and stabilized standard background. But these backgrounds vary, and each of them—the anthropologist's as well as the savage's—contains value attitudes that affect both the reality experienced and the language in which this reality is described.

V THE SCIENCES AND THE HUMANITIES

So far I have discussed the nature of thought, which I described as the process of reorganizing a foreground by means of a background structure whenever some previous interpretation has broken down, and the relation of language and reality. I can bring these discussions together, and lay the ground for our next forward move, by now formulating explicitly the relationship between language and background structure. An actual background (B_a) can now be defined as the symbolism to which an individual actually displaces curiosity and other drives. A standard background (B_s) is the standard symbolism available to that individual. This will sound odd, even false, if symbolism is narrowly identified with verbal symbolism, for certainly not everything in the background structure is verbalized. But of course I have defined symbol much more broadly. In my view (p. 109), any sort of behavior whatever may be, or become, symbolic, to the extent that curiosity, along with other drives, is displaced onto it.

Thus the important distinction is not between what is verbal and what is non-verbal, but between what is symbolic and what is non-symbolic. For, on the one hand, much non-verbal behavior is symbolic and, on the other, verbal behavior may be non-symbolic. As an example of the former: there is a language (non-verbal but symbolic) of gesture

—grimacing, frowning, yawning, pointing, shrugging, and shaking a finger all communicate information, make suggestions for directing conduct, clarify what is diffuse. On the other hand, exclaiming "Ouch!" when one accidentally puts one's hand on a hot stove is an instance of verbal behavior, but it may be non-linguistic; it may merely relieve feeling, as running about or flapping the burnt hand may also relieve feeling. What makes behavior symbolic, and so linguistic in character, is thus not that it is verbal, but that it represents something to some-body—either to the actor himself or to some observer. Of course, to the extent that running about (or for that matter, saying "Ouch!") is a constant or frequent accompaniment of high feeling, it will become symbolic; what was originally merely a causal relationship will become, over time, a symbolic one, since the running that is regularly associated with the high feeling will eventually come to represent it.

To say that running about represents high feeling is to say that there has been laid down in the background structure of the runner (and/or the spectators) an incipient generalization connecting running and high feeling, and that this generalization is available for interpreting observed occasions of running. A spectator sees a man running, is puzzled, and asks himself, "Why is that man running about?" Answer, reducing curiosity: "Oh, of course; he's excited. That's why." And this same generalization may reduce curiosity on the part of the runner himself, if he pauses long enough to ask, "Why on earth am I running about in this way?" Naturally the generalization used on such occasions may very well not be verbalized.

Not only may parts of a background structure be unverbalized; a background structure (actual or standard) need not be verbalized in any respect. Obviously background structures can be acquired without the assistance of words. For instance, several different tourists walking independently through Florence and none of them using guide books, may acquire similar background structures which enable each of them to get back to their several hotels for lunch (p. 111). Here we have an incipient standard background structure, not yet made explicit and fixed in the overt symbolism of a map or in verbal directions like "Turn left at the Piazza della Signoria." And obviously, background structures of a considerable degree of complexity can be passed on from one generation to another without the support of verbal language. Instinct and imitation play important roles in this connection.

Obviously again, even highly verbalized background structures, such as those used by adult Westerners, contain non-verbal elements—for example, certain unformulated but very basic generalizations, certain non-verbalized but very powerful value attitudes. Probably some of the most important elements in any background structure always remain inarticulate and non-verbal. This, indeed, is one of the reasons why people tend to take them for eternal truths, instead of recognizing their relativity to the background structure of which they are a part.

Though it is important always to bear in mind the differences between verbalized and non-verbalized background structures, these are not the differences with which we are primarily concerned in this book. Nor are we chiefly concerned with differences in background structure of the sort that are reflected in such linguistic differences as those between (say) English and German. English and German are certainly different languages; that is to say, there are differences in background structure which are reflected in the different vocabularies and grammatical constructions of English and German. For instance, "Kaiser" doesn't translate smoothly into "emperor"—those who preferred to talk about "Kaiser Wilhelm" in World War I, instead of "Emperor William," had a good intuitive sense of a significant difference. And what are we to do with "Deutsches Reich," "Österreich," and "Dritter Reich"? What English term will translate the whole nexus of emotional, historical, and political meaning associated with "Reich"? On the other hand, much of the information, many of the generalizations, many of the values contained in the English background structure are also contained in the German. Fire burns as much in English as Feuer burns in German; "Hund" translates into "dog" and "Katze" into "cat" virtually without remainder. Hence though there are differences in background structure here, they are, from our point of view, minor ones.

Nor, though the linguistic differences are much greater, are we primarily concerned with the differences between (say) English and Hopi. While "Ding" translates smoothly into "thing," since both background structures contain this important concept, there may be no possible translation into Hopi; if anthropologists and linguists like Whorf are correct (see p. 99), the Hopi background structure lacks this concept.

What, are we concerned with? With the sort of linguistic difference represented by difference between what may be called the languages of science and the languages of art. There are, for instance, important differences between (say) physics, whether written in German or English, and poetry, whether composed in French or in Hopi. These are the sorts of differences we are concerned with—intra-cultural, rather than cross-cultural, differences.

As a start, here are three sentences that illustrate some of these differences—and also some important similarities:

(1) Her hair is black.
(2) His heart is black.
(3) Black, black is the color of my true love's hair.

The first sentence designates the color of somebody's hair. This sentence might well occur in the following kind of context: suppose *A* and *B* are discussing a woman neither of them knows well:

A. Is she the redhead?
B. No; her hair is black.
A. Black?
B. Yes; jet black.
A. Oh, so that's the one.

B is trying to clear up an area of diffuse experience for *A,* namely, the identity of a particular woman. Though "black" is certainly not a very precise term (it designates indifferently any one of a good many tones), it is sufficiently precise for the degree of discrimination required in the present situation, especially since *B* specifies it further as being extremely black—thus permitting *A* to distinguish this woman from another of their acquaintance whose hair is black, but not so very black.

In (2), the designative function is still primary, but it is achieved by a metaphor (specifically, by means of associations built up over a long time between the color black and evil), and this metaphor is emotionally (affectively) charged. An assertion is being made about some man's untrustworthiness—not about a physical characteristic (e.g., hair, or heart), but about a moral, or social, characteristic. And this assertion is made more powerful and emphatic by stating it metaphorically than by merely saying, "He is likely to betray you if he thinks he can get away with it."

In contrast to (1) and (2), (3) is not primarily designative. In (1), *A* and *B* are distinguishing one woman (in "real" life) from another by saying that she has black, instead of red, hair. But in (3) the folksinger is not referring to some particular woman in "real" life—his true love in distinction from some passing fancy—he is not saying, "I once thought I loved a platinum blonde, but now I know I really love a brunette." The woman he loves (as a man, not as a folksinger) may not have black hair at all. He has chosen black for the hair of the woman in the song, not because he wants to designate some woman who happens to have black hair, but because of something he wants to say about love.

What, then, is the feeling about love that is being focused in this line of poetry? Like all language segments, this line occurs in a context that is relevant to what is being communicated. The context here is the singer's regret that his true love has left him. He "mourns and weeps"; if he does not see her again, his "life will quickly fade away." Taking into account this context and the fact that it is sung in a minor key, we can say, I think, that the poet is telling us that love is precarious, impermanent, tragic. Thus (3) is indeed communicating some information (some fact that the speaker believes to be true), but it is communicating information about love, not about the color of some woman's hair.

Now how does this line focus the poet's feeling about love? It is focused by means of a series of associations that "black" has acquired over a long period of time. In the first place—as we have already seen in (2)—black is associated with treachery. There is a suggestion in the line that beauty is no guarantee of loyalty: the woman of the song not only has black hair; she has a black heart; she has deceived her lover. But it is not too far-fetched, I think, to find an even deeper association echoing in this line. For black is not only associated with treachery; it is also associated with death. Beyond saying that love is precarious because of the unfaithfulness of one of the lovers, the poet is reminding us that sooner or later death divides all lovers. Thus, here in (3), as in (2), communication is rooted in metaphor. But in (2) the metaphor is used primarily for designative purposes—the speaker is indicating to us his opinion of the character of some third party. Here in (3) the metaphor is used primarily for expressive purposes—to express, to focus, some affect that the poet has encountered in experience, perhaps in the course of a "real-life" love affair with a platinum blonde.

To the extent that a concern for fact-finding predominates in an individual's drive pattern (whether for purposes of self- or other-communication), language will tend to be literal, prosaic, factual. To the extent that affect predominates, language will tend to be rich, metaphorical, expressive. It is possible to designate an affect (for instance, I might designate the affect the poet was experiencing as "sadness"). But to designate an affect is merely to discriminate it for fact-finding purposes. Thus:

> *Psychoanalyst:* And how are you feeling now?
> *Patient:* Sad.

But (3) realizes the affect instead of merely designating it; it relives the affect for the speaker or for the hearer. I say, *"re*lives" to distinguish the linguistic expression of an affect from the mere explosion of that affect, from the mere release of affect into behavior, as when one cries "Ouch!" on experiencing the painful affect of burning or when one runs about wildly while experiencing an affect of high excitement. To the extent that an affect merely explodes into behavior, there is expression and release of tension, but the expression is not linguistic. To the extent, however, that feeling is not merely released, but is illumined (interpreted, understood, clarified, relived), just to that extent expression is linguistic, because the relationship is not merely causal but symbolic. Expressive language releases feeling; but more than the mere release of feeling is involved. The poet is revealing (at once to himself and to others) not only that he feels but what he feels.

Thus sentence (1) and sentence (3) are performing quite different functions; they are, in effect, sentences in different languages (though both are English sentences), with different grammars, different vocabularies, and different structures. I shall call these two languages, respectively, scientific language and humanistic language.

This is not merely to repeat, in slightly different terms, the sharp dichotomy some people draw between cognitive and non-cognitive language (p. 27). Nor am I falling into the fallacy of ideal types (p. 130). There is no language that is purely (completely) designative, barren of any and all expressive elements; there is no language that is purely expressive. On the contrary, there are non-cognitive, affective elements in even the most seemingly neutral, abstract, and scientific language, and there are cognitive elements in all languages, even the most expressive. Thus, instead of thinking of there being two separate pigeonholes, labeled "cognitive" and "non-cognitive," we should think of their being a linguistic spectrum, or continuum, ranging from highly scientific languages (which nevertheless still include expressive components) at one end, to highly humanistic languages (which still include designative components) at the other end. In the middle of the spectrum is a region, which I shall call "commonsense," in which designative and expressive elements are about equally present.

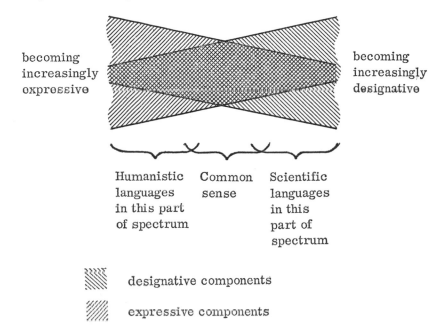

becoming
increasingly
expressive

becoming
increasingly
designative

Humanistic   Common   Scientific
languages   sense   languages
in this part   in this
of spectrum   part of
                        spectrum

designative components

expressive components

For instance, all three of the sentences I have just analyzed function both designatively and expressively, though in different degree. Of the three (1) is the most designative (factual). Nevertheless, there is a slight fringe of feeling around "black" in "Her hair is black"—as compared, say, with "Her hair reflects light of such-and-such a wavelength." I am not saying that *B* should have used the latter sentence; on the contrary, if "black" discriminates adequately for his purposes, it would be pedantic to discriminate more sharply. I am only saying that "black" happens to be, to some extent, also expressive, at the same time that it discriminates. This is more evident when *B* follows up with a further discrimination. Though "jet black" is more specific than "black," it is at the same time also more expressive; it reflects interest, attitude, and affect more strongly than does "Her hair is black," and much more strongly than "very black," or "extremely black" would have done. And the interest that this choice of words reveals is different from the interest that would have been reflected in "coal black," "black as midnight," or "black as the pit." In "jet black" the speaker sees and responds to something hard and brittle about the woman; in "black as the pit" he would have perceived and responded to something different—to something evil or sinister.

On the other hand, there is a designative component in all three sentences, even in (3). For besides expressing an attitude, (3) makes a statement. Something is said—namely that love is precarious, that it passes—even while an attitude toward this fact is expressed, just as in "jet black" an attitude toward the woman's hair, and toward the woman herself, is being expressed even while a fact about the color of the hair is being specified. Further, (2) stands somewhere between (1) and (3). More is said than in (3); or, rather, what is said is said more definitely and more explicitly. And more is expressed than in (1); or rather, what is felt is felt more deeply. It is true that something is felt in the conversation of which (1) is a part, and what is felt is revealed in the selective perception of a similarity between the color of the woman's hair and a mineral. But since in (2) there is selective perception of a similarity between blackness and a facet of a man's character, which is not literally colored at all, it is fair to say that (2) is more strongly charged with affect than is (1).

Thus (1), (2), and (3) do not differ sharply but only in the proportion, the "mix," of designative and expressive elements they contain. A moment ago I said that (1) is a sentence in scientific language and that (3) is a sentence in humanistic language. But I did not mean that (1) is purely designative and (3) purely expressive; I meant only that (1) is relatively more designative than (3), and (3) is relatively more expressive than (1). Thus I draw the line (make a "cut") between designative and expressive somewhere between (1) and (3), in the region of (2), since "black heart" is still metaphoric although on the way toward becoming literal. I shall not quarrel, however, with anyone who wants to make the cut somewhere else. The main point is to recognize that, wherever we choose to make the division between those languages that are primarily scientific (or designative) and those that are primarily humanistic (or expressive), we are dealing throughout with a linguistic continuum. This is indeed the major positive thesis of this book.

In contrast, most philosophers either deny that there is any important difference between scientific and humanistic languages, or else, if they recognize a difference, they regard it as radical—a sharp difference in kind. If either of these positions is accepted, the conflict between the scientific and the humanistic views of life—whose reverberations we examined in chapter i—cannot be satisfactorily resolved.

First, as regards those who deny that there is any difference between the scientific and humanistic languages. These people believe that humanistic language, like scientific language, is primarily designative in function. Hence they suppose that the sciences and the humanities (e.g., religion) are offering us two rival descriptions of the same Reality (upper-case), between which we must choose. There is no doubt, in this competition, which of the rivals usually wins. Since humanistic language is thought to be designative, it is natural to judge it by standards appropriate for designative language. Weighed by these standards, it is written off as "false," while the scientific view is affirmed to be "true." The only way the humanistic view of man can be validated, from this basic stance, is to rely on some special, "higher" criterion—such as faith, authority, the Bible, or revelation; and then the scientific view, in its turn, becomes "false." Neither of these alternatives is very satisfactory.

To those who reason in this way, I say: the sciences and the humanities are different languages with different functions. They ought, therefore, to be evaluated by criteria appropriate for these different functions. I shall call these criteria "preference rules." I call them preference *rules* to indicate that they are normative in character: the preference rules of a given language define what can be said in this language and the conditions under which what can be said can be well said. (For instance, it is possible to say in English, but not to say very adequately, what is well said in German by "Reich" and by "Kaiser." It is not possible to say in Hopi what is well said in English by "thing" and in German by "Ding.") The rules, however, only define what can be well said at any given time. New rules, which make it possible to say something different, something novel, are constantly being introduced into every living language as a result of the creative insights of individual men and women.

I call these criteria *preference* rules to emphasize that there is a plurality of languages, each with its own rules, and that an individual's basic value attitudes determine which of these languages provides him with maximum insight into the nature and character of experience. Since these basic attitudes are largely determined for him by the culture into which he is born, the individual is not free (in the abstract sense) to choose one over the others. The rules reflect preferences not because we consciously opt for one language over others, but because alternative value complexes are imbedded in each of the languages.

There is, for instance, an obvious difference between the preference rules of painting and the preference rules of sculpture. If someone were equally proficient in both arts (i.e., used both of these languages with equal facility) and if this person wanted to clear up some diffuse experience he was having of a sunset or of light reflected on running water or of the texture of silk or satin, he would probably choose the medium (language) of oil paint or watercolor, rather than the medium of stone or bronze. What I am calling the preference rules of sculpture make it difficult to say in sculpture (at least to say well) what one is likely to want to say about surface sheen.

This example is to some extent artificial; it presumes an equal facility in two languages and a greater degree of self-conscious choice than we usually have. But it does bring out some points of importance: (1) The superiority of one language (e.g., painting) over another (sculpture) is a function of the interest of the user (e.g., an artist's interest in surface sheen), rather than of any absolute criterion. (2) The interest shows through (is reflected in) the language used—both in its vocabularly and in its structure. If the artist is primarily interested in surface sheen, this will "stand out" in the finished product, in contrast to those other aspects of running water that might be foci for other artists with other interests; and his "delight" in the surface sheen (if delight is the affect he is experiencing) will be revealed in his treatment of it. (3) Every language is limited by its preference rules (there is no single language in which all that can be said can be well said). (4) The preference rules are not absolute: there is always the possibility of discovering and exploiting some wholly unforeseen potentiality of the medium, so that a truly creative sculptor (a Bernini or a Rodin) might find a way of rendering (i.e., saying) in marble or bronze characteristics of surface sheen which theretofore had been sayable only in watercolor or in oil pigment.

Thus, in reply to those who believe that humanistic language functions designatively (and who usually conclude that it performs this function very poorly) I maintain that the preference rules for scientific and humanistic language are different—sufficiently different for there to be no possibility of conflict, no need to choose between them as alternative descriptions of Reality.

So far, of course, many contemporary linguistic analysts would agree with my analysis. But currently fashionable theories deny my second thesis that the difference is a degree-difference only. Thus most linguistic philosophers today argue that what I call the humanistic languages (art, morals, religion) are not languages at all. There is no contradiction, according to this view, between what science tells us and what the humanities tell us, not because the humanistic view is false, but because, strictly speaking, the humanities do not *tell* us anything; they are merely subjective, expressive, or "emotive."

To these people I reply: The sciences are indeed factual, but not so sheerly factual as you suppose. The humanities are indeed expressive, but not merely expressive; they are also cognitive. Anybody who wants to can certainly denominate as "the world of fact" the reality that we experience in and through the (relatively) designative languages and their characteristic background structures; anybody who wants to can denominate as "world of value" the reality we experience in and through the (relatively) expressive languages. But facts and values are not utterly separate and distinct. Still less are facts purely "objective" and values merely "subjective." On the contrary, all so-called facts are through-and-through colored by values, and all values are through-and-through marked by factuality. Hence, instead of there being two separate worlds, that of science and that of humanism, we can hope to find, within experience, one world, one reality. But the unity thus discoverable is a structural, or functional, unity, not the ontological unity of the traditional philosophy.

Doubtless these two types of (functionally) diverging background structures exist, and to some extent diverge, in all cultures; in every culture some sort of distinction is drawn between what is fact and what is value. In most cultures, however, because of the relatively undeveloped state of the sciences, the factuality of fact has not been sharply perceived; indeed, we may say that in most cultures (including Western culture in classical times and in the Middle Ages) the problem has been to find a place for fact in a world of values, that is, in a world experienced primarily in terms of affects, purposes, and ends. Only in our own culture and in recent times (since the seventeenth century) has scientific method developed to a point where facts are clearly and sharply distinguished as facts. When this happened the whole metaphysical problem shifted: it became the problem of finding a place for values in the world of fact that science reveals (see pp. 273–274). But we are now, finally, in a position to see that both the old problem of validating a world of fact and the new one of establishing the objectivity of values rest on a confusion: the facts that we encounter in experience are a function of a fact-type of background structure; the values we encounter in experience are a function of a value-type background structure. And these two types of background structure are mutually complementary.

This, at least, is the thesis of this chapter. So far I have been merely stating what I hope to establish. I have now to show that the preference rules of scientific and humanistic language (1) differ, yet (2) differ only in degree.

The model of a linguistic spectrum (p. 153) provides a simple one-dimensional system for ordering all actual language—for instance, the particular segment of language that we call a poem, the particular segment that we call a physical or chemical theory, the particular segment that we call a conversation between two friends about the weather. As we move out toward the designative pole of the spectrum, we are moving toward languages that are increasingly "scientific" in the sense that the facts are more and more rigorously and precisely designatable and ascertainable. On the other hand, as we move to the expressive pole of the spectrum, we are moving toward languages in which the parameters are looser and in which affect therefore plays a more and more decisive part.

Roughly in the middle of the spectrum is common sense, the language everybody uses some of the time and that some people use all of the time. Common sense is the language people use for everyday, common-sense purposes—for writing letters to our children, for shopping in the supermarket, for chatting over the back fence, for what Wordsworth called getting and spending. In common sense, expressive and designative elements are inextricably mixed. Because it is such a mixture, neither physicists nor poets (for instance) find common sense very satisfactory—except for commonsense purposes; it is too unspecialized for their scientific or poetic purposes. Hence scientists of all kinds and literary artists of all kinds refine in varying degree the language of common sense. These refinements lead in different directions, since the demands scientists and poets make on language, the areas of diffuse experience on which they are focusing, and so their criticisms of common sense, differ. The results of these specialized developments are, on the one hand, increasingly scientific languages (the various special sciences) and on the other hand increasingly humanistic languages (the various arts). But both of these developments show traces of their origins, since neither is wholly purged of that mixture of elements by which common sense is characterized.

This one-dimensional ordering system can be converted into a two-dimensional system by combining it with the notion, developed in chapter iv, of a variety of functions for language. This yields a space in which it is possible to locate (only very roughly, of course) any particular language segment whatever in terms of (1) the designative/expressive ratio of each language and (2) the functions that are being performed (i.e., the needs that the language is reducing). An example is the Viennese doctors' dictum about hysteria (p. 126). Presumably, this language segment functioned in part as an attempt to alter Freud's behavior (to cause him to abandon his researches), and in part to reduce the doctors' anxiety by "proving" that Freud was either a fool or a knave. But it also functioned, at least to some degree, to satisfy curiosity. For the doctors' anxiety could be allayed only by finding a satisfactory "proof" that hysteria really was a female disease. Accordingly, the language they used presented an explanation, though of course the criteria of what they regarded as a satisfactory explanation were affected by their other, unconscious aims. Or as another example, there is Lord Kelvin's insistence, as he thumped a table for emphasis, "The ether is as real as this table." Though on the surface the sentence is simply an assertion of fact (designative), satisfying curiosity about the ether, it also functioned as an attempt to influence the behavior of bright young physicists whose theories Kelvin felt as a threat to his scientific reputation.

These examples will perhaps serve to show how language segments that serve the same function (say, satisfaction of curiosity) may yet vary widely along the designative/expressive spectrum, depending on the other drives present in the drive complex. A study in some detail of several representative actual languages will show how the designative and expressive components in a language vary in proportion from one language to another, while remaining present in all.

i. *Normative Language*

The following sentences

(1) In bridge the dealer bids first
(2) An apple a day keeps the doctor away
(3) Arsenic is a good poison
(4) Do you want a spanking?
(5) Murder is a capital offense
(6) Blessed are the pure in heart
(7) Do not overlook the inconvenient fact

all lay down norms, either explicitly or implicitly. Norms may be simply stated—it is a matter of fact that such-and-such is a rule, as in (1). Norms may be hinted at; they may be suggested; they may be recommended more or less strongly; they may be authoritatively imposed, with legal sanctions attached. Norms may prescribe patterns of overt behavior, as in (2), or attitudes and ways of feeling (6), or ways of thinking (7).

In the total human economy, normative discourse is indispensable. A certain minimal amount of social cohesion and cooperation is necessary, and without norms such cooperation is impossible. I do not mean that social cohesion is impossible without the verbal communication of norms —the Hymenoptera maintain complex societies without words, and even in human societies much norm-maintaining behavior is non-verbal in character. Still, in human societies much norm-maintaining behavior is necessarily verbal; and a very large part of ordinary verbal discourse is concerned directly or indirectly with the prescription and with the maintenance of norms, that is, it functions normatively, even while perhaps also performing other functions.

For instance, normative language is manipulative in character, since it aims at influencing behavior, including, on occasion, the behavior of the speaker himself as well as that of his audience. Again, to the extent that people feel anxious about how to behave (Do you eat peas with a knife or a fork? How do you address an archbishop? Should I become a conscientious objector?), normative discourse serves an anxiety-reducing function; the prescriptions offered give ego-support for the timid, the uncertain, or the concerned.

To the extent that there is curiosity about what exactly the norms are (apart from anxiety and insecurity), normative language serves a cognitive function, clearing up some diffuse experience of the norms in question. Finally, since what is recommended or prescribed is either the promotion of some good or the avoidance of some evil, normative language inevitably has expressive components. State a norm in the most neutral, matter-of-fact way possible; it is still to some degree both revelatory of the speaker's attitude and a recommendation for action. For instance:

A. What will kill rats?
B. Arsenic is a good poison.

Or:

C. What is a good bank?
D. Well, *I* bank at the First National.

Though Mr. *D* is more guarded than Mr. *B*, he has not managed to avoid proposing (however tentatively) a norm, nor has he escaped revealing an attitude. I said that (1) above—the bridge-playing example—is matter-of-fact; it is, but it is not *merely* matter-of-fact. In any real-life situation in which somebody makes this remark, it is either a reminder to the dealer to go ahead and bid, or it is an instruction to another player to wait until he has bid.

The current heated debate among philosophers over whether ethics is cognitive or non-cognitive overlooks the great extent of the area of the language map occupied by normative discourse. The cognitivists take as typical of normative discourse, language that is relatively far out toward the designative pole of the spectrum—language concerned with stating norms, articulating hierarchies of norms, pointing out means-ends relationships, such as "An apple a day keeps the doctor away." The non-cognitivists go to the other end of the spectrum for their examples; they take as typical of normative discourse language that is relatively highly expressive, such as "Do you want a spanking?"—language that reveals strongly held attitudes and that makes no bones about attempting to influence behavior.

Actually, however, normative language ranges over virtually the whole of the designative/expressive spectrum. What is more, as I have already pointed out, even the most humanistic language contains designative elements and even the most scientific language contains expressive elements. This applies just as much to language that is functioning normatively as it does to language functioning in other ways. Hence the ethical cognitivists and the ethical non-cognitivists are both correct. The cognitivists are simply insisting that there are designative elements even in normative discourse that is highly expressive. For instance, though "Do you want a spanking?" is expressing an affect (disapproval of a child's behavior), it is also saying, "If you go on doing that, I shall spank you." On the other hand, the non-cognitivists are reminding us that even normative language that is highly designative nevertheless contains an expressive component ("Want to be healthy! Do eat an apple!"). Thus each party to this philosophical debate is correct in calling our attention to what he sees. But each ignores what the other sees, because different interests cause the two parties to focus on different regions of the field (cf. pp. 80–81).

ii. *Legal Language*

One extremely important sub-type of normative language is the language of the law. Since legal language is a very clear example of the way in which designative and expressive elements intermingle in all language, I shall examine it in some detail.

The function of legal procedure is to ascertain the facts in certain particular regions of experience: Was this man killed or did he commit suicide? Was it first-degree murder or manslaughter? Is or is not a parking lot a road in the meaning of the act? Are or are not "separate and equal" educational facilities constitutional? I want to show that this primarily scientific and designative language is also, and inevitably, expressive. Later (pp. 175–193) I shall argue that what is true about legal fact-finding is also true of fact-finding in the sciences—that the sciences, too, contain expressive components.

But before considering either legal fact-finding or scientific fact-finding, let us look briefly at some cases of commonsense fact-finding—from which (if my general thesis is correct) legal and scientific fact-finding have developed as more refined types of fact-finding, answering to more specialized needs (see pp. 158–159).

Suppose that a committee is deciding whether to appoint *A* or *B* to a

responsible post. Somebody says that *A* is untrustworthy; somebody
else denies this. If a discussion ensues (as it is likely to), this will be an
instance of what I call fact-finding at the commonsense level—trying,
by more or less commonsense procedures, to ascertain whether *A* is, or
is not, reliable. If *A*'s critic is challenged, he may reply that *A* has had a
lot of traffic tickets for speeding or that he once voted for Norman
Thomas. Does this make *A* untrustworthy? Arguments of this kind
usually go on and on (or rather, round and round) without making any
headway, until a committee member exclaims, "Oh well, if *that's* what
you mean!"—in a tone of voice that implies that some queerness or
impropriety in the other member's usage has hidden his meaning—"But
what an odd way of saying it!" This is why, in such cases, people are
inclined to say that the dispute was "merely verbal." Of course, questions that are derogated as merely verbal are also factual questions
(questions concerning the facts of correct usage), but they can often be
settled by appeal to the dictionary, and the adverb "merely" suggests
that committee members regard questions about the facts of usage as
trivial compared with questions about the facts of the candidate's character. Thus a sharp distinction is often drawn between factual arguments (Is *A* really untrustworthy?) and verbal arguments (Is it correct to call somebody who has had a lot of traffic tickets "untrustworthy"?).

But what about the dispute between Freud and the Viennese doctors
(p. 126)? Was this merely verbal, merely about the facts of usage?
Some people may say so, but this is because they do not share Freud's
and the doctors' special (and opposing) interests in "hysteria" (the word,
not the disease). The doctors felt a proprietary interest in the word,
which, from their point of view, Freud was misusing. And this interest
was linked with their interest in their professional reputations and their
investment in a whole way of looking at disease. On the other hand,
Freud too had an interest in the word; terming male patients "hysterics"
called attention forcefully to a relationship he held to be important in
connection with a different conception of disease.

There is a whole spectrum of cases in which patients are manifesting
a variety of symptoms. Every patient manifests his own particular combination of symptoms, which is not exactly like any other patient's. At
one end of the spectrum are patients whose symptoms are such that
"everybody" (Freud and his opponents) agrees that they are hysterics;

at the other end are patients whom everybody agrees are not hysterics. These are the clear-cut instances. In the middle of the spectrum there is a borderline area, a "vagueness band," of cases that are in dispute. Freud would call these patients "hysterics"; his opponents might call them only "hysteroids"—similar to hysterics but not really hysterics. Freud makes the cut between hysterics and hysteroids at one place; his Viennese opponents make it at another. The locus of each cut is affected, not only by "evidence" (the empirically observable symptoms), but by "interest," including an interest in, a commitment to, a certain theory about the nature of mentality.

Thus, though the dispute between Freud and the Viennese doctors may be verbal, it is not *merely* verbal; the verbal dispute is the surface manifestation (symptom) of a profound difference in interest. Some people may write this off as a "far-fetched" example. It may be extreme, but it differs only in degree from all so-called merely verbal disputes (which, it should be noted, are themselves factual disputes about verbal usage). Indeed, no disputes are purely factual in the sense of being *exclusively* concerned with the facts or with verbal usage. All disputes reflect to some degree the different purposes, or interests, of the disputants.

For the most part, these differences do not show up at the level of common sense, since our (mutual) interest in resolving these disputes is usually greater than our individual interests in our own cuts. For instance, most people agree about what objects are chairs and what are not. But now and again we find someone saying "Bring me that chair," and someone else replying, "That's not a chair, that's a sofa." [1] Here, as with "hysterics," there is a spectrum of instances, not of patients with symptoms but of pieces of furniture of different shapes and design. Everybody will agree that some of these pieces of furniture are chairs; everybody will agree that others are not chairs (they are sofas or stools . . .). But there are borderline cases—how broad does the seat

---

[1] Child psychologists have pointed out that children characteristically go through a very legalistic phase (some amusing examples are given in L. Joseph Stone and Joseph Church, *Childhood and Adolescence* [New York: Random House, 1957], pp. 244–246). A child who is passing through this phase might very well say to his father, "That's not a chair, that's a sofa." I would myself interpret this reply in terms of the distinctions made above. The child does not share the adult-world's community of interest in resolving disputes; *his* primary interest is to avoid the task and to assert his independence.

have to be to be the seat of a sofa? how narrow to be the seat of a chair? Such disputes arise because a term such as "chair" or "sofa"—or "hysteria," for that matter—does not name a set of properties that is repeated exactly in a number of individual instances. Rather, "chair" names a number of similars, and it is an open question, usually, how similar to each other similars have to be for us to feel that they are the "same" (i.e., for us to ignore the differences) and so to be willing to call all of these in-varying-degrees different things by the one name "chair."

When one person calls a particular piece of furniture a "chair" and somebody else calls it a "sofa," we are likely to say their dispute is merely verbal, because nothing much hangs on whether it is a sofa or a chair and because we have agreed-on procedures for stipulating which it "really" is—for example, appealing to mother or father to settle the argument, consulting the dictionary, or asking a furniture dealer or other expert. Usually our common interest in treating the dispute as verbal and so disposing of it is greater than our individual interests in being "right."

But suppose that a new tax bill passed through Congress puts a high tax on sofas and leaves chairs untaxed. This creates new and strong interests in where the line of demarcation is drawn. Whereas, before the tax bill is passed, no one had any great interest in defending his own line, everyone now has an economic interest in where the line is drawn. For instance, A may be a tax collector whose interest is in maximizing the revenue and who therefore tends to defend a line that is drawn high up—one that incorporates a large part of the vagueness band into the category "sofa." B, on the other hand, is a taxpayer, with a contrasting interest in drawing the line low down, so as to exclude as many pieces of furniture as possible from the sofa-category.

Wherever economic (or any other) interests are strong, the rough-and-ready procedures of common sense are probably no longer sufficient. But agreed-on metaprocedures are available for just such cases: the disputants go into court. In this way, typically, we move from commonsense fact-finding to judicial fact-finding. I shall now show that values and interests operate in this arena as well as in commonsense fact-finding, and I shall start with a few typical cases.

(1) Is Spanish champagne "champagne"? There is no question of fact here—the facts have all been stipulated. The wine is Spanish in provenance; it effervesces; it is labeled as champagne. The question is

where to make the cut in the spectrum of effervescing wines—high up so as to include only effervescing wines of French origin, or lower down so as to include effervescing wines of Spanish origin? What is the *relevant* similarity—the fact of effervescence? or the fact of provenance? Since the term "champagne" is an honorific, the Spanish producers of effervescing wines are likely to take effervescence as the relevant similarity; it is to their interest to do so, because it extends the applicability of the term. The French, on the other hand, are likely to take provenance as the relevant factor, since this restricts the term to French wines.

(2) There is a statute providing a penalty for making an "annoying noise" in the street. Under this statute someone has been arrested and fined for using obscene language. Again, the facts are stipulated: it was in the street that the incident occurred; the language was obscene. The issue seems to be merely verbal: Is, or is not, obscene language an annoying noise?

(3) The building code prescribes that certain standards must be met by walls and certain other standards by roofs. Here is a structure that slopes from ground level at the back up to full height at the front. Is it a wall or a roof? If it is a wall it satisfies the code; if it is a roof it must be condemned.

In each of these suits, and of course in the parking-lot suit (pp. 114–115), the problem arises because commonsense procedures for ascertaining the facts of the case (for discriminating some area of diffuse experience) have been broken down. And they have broken down because they do not discriminate finely enough for present purposes; they do not discriminate within the vagueness band, where this problem lies. If no practical consequences were involved, nobody would care (probably nobody would even notice) that existing discrimination processes are inadequate in this area. But practical issues *are* involved, and this is why the disputants go into court. Further, there is something to be said on both sides; otherwise one of the parties would think it not worth his while to contest the issue. In the obscene-language case, for instance, obscene language is like a noise in being made by a voice; it is unlike a noise in that it consists of distinct words. In the building-code case the sloping structure is wall-like in that one end rests on the ground; it is roof-like in that it provides cover. The question is, which similarity is the greater? Somebody, ultimately, has to say. Judicial procedure identifies the ultimate declarer and sees to it that, so far as possible, he is "disinterested."

Does this mean that judicial fact-finding is not interested? Not at all. The cuts made by the police and by the defendant in the obscene-language case are likely to be interested, and interested in an obvious way. No one would deny, I suppose, that the speaker and the police have different interests nor that these differences in interest affect where they make the cut between what is language and what is mere noise. It is precisely because we know that interests color perceptions that the metaprocedures call for putting the issue before an "impartial tribunal," which (presumably) will make the cut at the "correct" point.

Now the court can be disinterested in the sense that it does not share either the special interests of the police in making the cut high up or the special interest of defendant in making the cut low down. But it is not disinterested in the sense of having no interest at all in terms of which it decides where the cut "ought" to be made. Good judges decide their cases on the basis of the public interest, but different judges will perceive the public interest differently. A judge who places a high value on freedom of speech (who believes the public interest is best served by minimal restraints on free speech) will be likely to perceive obscene language as dissimilar to an annoying noise; a judge who places a high value on public decency and public morals will be likely to perceive obscene language as similar to an annoying noise.

The facts, juridically speaking, are whatever the ultimate appellate court declares them to be; what the ultimate appellate court declares them to be is in part a function of the judges' version of the public interest. Different judges have different versions of the public interest. Therefore, if one particular interest happens to predominate in the court, it will be a legal fact that obscene language is an annoying noise; if another interest happens to predominate, it may be a legal fact that obscene language is not an annoying noise.

The courts are as much interested as is common sense in reducing the area in which interest of one kind of another is the determining fact. Wherever they can, therefore, courts agree on standard metaprocedures, since each such procedure, so far as it is generally accepted, reduces a large number of disputes to factual ones. For instance, it is a standard procedure in the U.S. Supreme Court to try to ascertain the intent of Congress. This rule enables the Court to decide a number of cases on factual grounds—for instance, the judges now look for factual evidence of Congressional intent, as revealed in hearings or in the debate when the legislation was being voted.

But it is usually possible to find divergent statements of intent in the debates in Congress, and there is no rule or procedure (this is the present point) that will unambiguously discriminate among all these statements. With respect to the various statements of Congressional intent, there will remain a borderline area, a vagueness band, of doubtful cases, which a whole hierarchy of metaprocedures may reduce but which it cannot entirely eliminate. At any time a case may come before the Court which falls in this area. Here, if no interest were at work, there could be no decision. For here, decision does not rest merely on the perception of some fact that the lower courts, or the police, or the defendant's lawyers have overlooked. All the facts have been stipulated or agreed on by the metaprocedures. The determining factor here is therefore some interest that leads the judges to perceive this, rather than that, as the "true" intent of Congress.

At this point someone may say: "This is all very well where appellate courts have to decide where to make the cut with regard to the applicability or non-applicability of a law to a set of similar cases. But it does not apply to cases in which a court has simply to decide a question of fact, such as whether *A* stole the silver candlesticks belonging to *B*, which have been found in *A*'s room, or whether *D* fired the shot that killed *E*. Such questions are purely factual."

But how is the legal fact that *D* did indeed kill *E* established? It is established by a series of agreed-on procedures—examining witnesses under well-established rules regarding the admissibility of evidence, submitting the evidence to the decision of "twelve good men and true," and reviewing the case in the appellate courts. Only after all these procedures is it a legal fact that *D* killed *E*.

Also, there are degrees of factuality. That the candlesticks were found in *A*'s room is more firmly factual than that A carried them there; they may have been hidden there, unknown to *A,* by *C.* That the shot that killed *E* was fired by *D*'s revolver is more firmly factual than that *D* fired it; that *D* fired it is more factual than that he fired it with intent to kill *E*. In the determination of the final fact that *D* killed *E,* there are many choice points, where interests affect the outcome. *D* swears that he was far away in another city when E was shot; F supports him. On the other hand, G testifies that he saw D leaving the scene of the shooting hurriedly. That D swears what he swears is a fact (a hard fact, if you like); what F and G testify are two more hard facts. But every juror has to decide whether to believe D and F or to believe G. When it comes to assessing the reliability of a witness, especially a witness whose testimony is itself at the borderline of reliability, all sorts of imponderables enter. For instance, jurors in the Hiss case who were passionately concerned about the menace of communism might more readily believe Chambers' story of the pumpkin papers than jurors who felt this danger less strongly. In the same way, other interests—from a strong interest in a scrupulous, evenhanded justice to an intense dislike of the prosecutor's appearance—may affect in a decisive way any one of the many sub-facts on which the factuality of the final fact of D's guilt rests.

Again, a moment ago I spoke of "well-established rules regarding the admissibility of evidence." But the rules are not all that well-established. They vary from court to court. Lord Jowett believed, for instance, that if Hiss had been tried in a court governed by English procedures, he could not have been convicted. In any event, procedural rules are subject to review by appellate courts, which, once again, have to make the cuts somewhere in a set of closely similar similars. In this way, too, choices and interests enter into the final legal fact that is the verdict— not necessarily through choices made in *this* trial, but through choices made in earlier trials, which have established the precedents and procedures that determine what the jurors are permitted to hear in this trial and how they hear it.

The factuality of the fact that D killed E is thus far from "pure"; hidden in it are innumerable, if unnoticed, choices, each of which reflects an interest. But a fact like the fact that D killed E is relatively much harder than many of the facts with which courts deal. Suppose, for instance, that, instead of denying that D shot E, D's lawyer claims that D is insane. Here, though it would doubtless be allowed that the facts are more difficult to ascertain, it might be maintained that "Was D insane?" is exactly the same sort of question as "Did D fire the revolver?" The former simply breaks down into two straightforward factual questions. First we ascertain how the term "insanity" is used (in law; not in ordinary discourse), and this is a factual question: we consult the law code instead of Webster. We then ascertain (another factual question) whether D's mental state is or is not characterized by the properties that "insanity" designates.

This does not seem to me an adequate account of the difference between the two questions. It is true that the facts of D's sanity are more difficult to establish than the facts regarding who fired the shot. But the important point is why the former question is more difficult to answer. It is not just that some procedures are simple (measuring the height of a bookcase) and some are rather more elaborate (measuring the height of a mountain). It is not merely that D's hand is easily checked for powder marks, while his state of mind is not so open for inspection. All of this is true. But it is also true that the courts and codes are not in agreement regarding the marks of insanity (i.e., the legal definition); indeed, current definitions are constantly being modified in the light of new moral insights and new clinical information. So a man who is legally insane this year might not have been legally insane had he been tried ten years ago.

But quite apart from changing definitions of insanity, expert witnesses are by no means always in agreement about whether such-and-such a particular definition of insanity is or is not exemplified in the accused. The experts called to testify as to D's sanity may reach different conclusions merely because one of them is careless and the other is careful in applying procedures that they both agree on, as two men measuring the height of a bookcase or a mountain may arrive at different figures because one is careless and one is not. But in the case of D's insanity it is more likely that different conclusions reflect, somewhere along the line, a difference regarding procedure. Or, even if they agree regarding the use of a certain test, they may weigh this test differently in assessing D's sanity. They may both give D a Rorschach; they may even agree on the interpretation of it. But one psychiatrist may set a higher value, the other a lower value, on the Rorschach test as a diagnostic tool, as compared with (say) the TAT.

Thus, even more than in the case of the factuality of D's having fired the revolver, the factuality of D's insanity (if he is finally adjudged insane) is a composite of innumerable choices and interests—the varying interests of the appellate judges who have to decide whether to make the cut in the definition of insanity high up, in the interests of humaneness, or lower down, in the interest of deterring murder; the varying interests

of the psychiatrists in rival theories of mental illness, in alternative interpretations of *D*'s rages, or in different assessments of the Rorschach protocols; the varying interests of the jurors who listen to the expert witnesses.

Hence it is indeed correct to say that the question, "Was *D* insane?" is
just like the question "Did *D* fire the revolver?" It is correct, however,
not because the former reduces to a purely factual question like the latter,
only a bit more difficult to answer, but because the factuality of *both* is
built up out of decisions and choices (interests). Of course, the two questions do differ in degree of factuality: that *D* fired the revolver is a (relatively) hard fact; that *D* is insane is a (relatively) soft fact. To say that
D's insanity is a relatively soft fact is to say that there is less agreement
regarding the procedures by which the insanity of *D* was established.
There are doubtless extensive areas of agreement (reflecting agreed-on
procedures) with respect to many of the facts on which the factuality of
D's insanity rests. That *D* was given a Rorschach test and that these are
the protocols of that test may be stipulated by both parties. They are relatively hard facts, just as *F*'s and *G*'s testimony are relatively hard facts.
But just as the reliability of *F* and *G* are relatively soft facts, so the interpretation of the Rorschach is a relatively soft fact (and it remains a
relatively soft fact, even if the two psychiatrists called as witnesses happen
themselves to agree, for there is by no means *general* agreement regarding
the reliability of Rorschachs).

Thus the factuality of *D*'s insanity and the factuality of *D*'s having
fired the revolver both depend on the factuality of other facts, which are
themselves in varying degrees hard and soft. If *D*'s insanity is a relatively
softer fact than the fact of *D*'s having fired the revolver, this is because
the choices that underlie the fact of *D*'s insanity occur at more critical
and more decisive points.

In view of this analysis, I recommend abandoning talk of there being
two completely different sorts of judicial disputes—factual disputes and
non-factual ones—and replacing it with talk of a continuum of legal
cases, depending on the degree of factuality possessed by the various facts
on which the verdict in each case rests. In every case there will be some
relatively hard facts, for if there were not some agreed-on, stabilized procedures which yield relatively hard facts, there would be no way to reach
a decision. But in every case there will be some relatively soft facts, which
are determined in part by interests.

Every legal decision which establishes some fact (e.g., the fact of *D*'s insanity) is a composite, the terminal result of decisions that reflect the interests of innumerable people—the jurymen, the attorneys who have to decide what questions to put to the witnesses and how to put them, the judge who has to decide which questions to allow and which to disallow. Further, every legal decision is the outcome not merely of decisions made during this trial; it is the result of decisions made in earlier trials carried over into this trial as precedents and procedures. There is a vast bulk of unseen substructure affecting the outcome of this case through all the procedures, rules, and precedents which have issued from prior decisions. Thus the verdict in every case—for example, the established fact of *D*'s insanity—rests on a complex of facts and of decisions; and these facts in their turn rest on complexes of still other facts and of earlier decisions, reaching back to remotest antiquity.

For instance, in the parking-lot case, after the appellate court made its decision, it became a fact that a parking lot is not a road. In subsequent cases, accordingly, the only question will be "factual": "Did the collision occur in the parking lot, as the defendant claims, or on a road, as the police allege?" This is a factual question just because agreed-on, easily applied procedures for answering it exist. But the factuality of this question rests on and, as it were, contains the decision of the appellate court, a decision that reflects that court's conception of the public interest.

Thus in the parking-lot case the appellate court established a new legal fact, namely, that parking lots are not roads; and this will remain a fact unless and until some other court, on some later occasion, guided by some different conception of the public interest, reverses the decision. For courts may not only declare new facts into existence; they may declare old facts out of existence. In the parking-lot case, the ownership of the lot was not at issue and would have been stipulated by both parties; had it become an issue, there happen to exist well-established procedures for verifying title. But it is certainly possible to conceive of circumstances in which these standard procedures might break down when applied in a borderline area, just as the standard routine for establishing whether something is or is not a public road broke down in the borderline area of parking lots. If this were to happen, the previously standard procedures for verifying titles might be challenged and carried to an appellate court. There are certainly conceivable circumstances in which these procedures might be overturned, and with them a whole set of facts about the ownership of land would be swept away.

Accordingly, although a line can always be drawn between the part of a case that consists merely in ascertaining the facts by standard procedures and the part that depends on decisions reflecting interests, this line varies from case to case, depending on circumstances, on context, and even on time. For what was factual at one time may become non-factual at another, and what was non-factual may become factual. Thus legal factuality is constantly changing. Usually the changes are gradual and undramatic—so gradual and so undramatic that laymen do not notice them and lawyers can often persuade themselves that the law, which they actually make, is "eternal." Occasionally, however, the change is abrupt and also momentous in its effect, as in the 1954 desegregation case, when one whole set of facts was declared out of existence, and another whole set of facts, so extensive that we have only just begun to discover them, was declared into existence.

To summarize: a legal fact is relative to the procedures by which it is ascertained and established; as these procedures change, legal facts themselves change. Further, the factuality of a legal fact (whether relatively hard or relatively soft) depends on the degree of general acceptance of the procedures by which it is ascertained, and procedures that are widely, or even universally, accepted at one time may be rejected at other times. It follows that there are no "sheer," "pure," "bare," or "brute" legal facts. All legal facts depend in varying degree on decisions that reflect interests. In some instances, the element of decision may be relatively direct, immediate, and obvious—as when the appellate court decides that a parking lot is not a road. In other instances, the element of decision is indirect and remote, and buried in the past, but no less influential—it may appear only in the effect that the opportunity to cross-examine witnesses has on the outcome of the case. Cross-examination is now such a standard procedure that we are likely to take it for granted, but there was a time, in the remote past, when decisions, taken by people whose names have long been forgotten, established this procedure.

It is for this reason—because in the path to every verdict that establishes a legal fact there have been many choice points where interests determine the route—that I recommend thinking about legal facts as forming a continuum. And if now, even after this exposition, you still prefer to think about there being a sharp dichotomy between factual and non-factual elements in legal disputes, we would be confronted with the familiar issue about where, or whether, to make a cut. Just as there was a question about where to make the cut between things that are roads and things that are not roads, and about where to make the cut between things that are roofs and things that are walls, so there may now be a question about where to make the cut between disputes that are factual and disputes that are non-factual. And just as different people will make the cut between roads and non-roads at points that reflect their differing conceptions of the public interest, so different people will doubtless make the cut between factual and non-factual questions at points that reflect differing metaphysical interests.

In philosophy there are no appellate courts, or formal metaprocedures, for settling disputes about where the cut between facts and non-facts should be made.[2] Accordingly, I can only repeat that to talk, as I do, about a continuum of legal factuality, enables me to call attention to what I take to be an important fact about facts, namely, that even the most factual of facts are rooted in interests, in choices, in affects, in values. The language we usually use to talk about facts tends to obscure this fact about facts.

I want to use language that calls attention to the fact that even when we seem merely to be ascertaining the facts of the case, we are selecting those facts in which for some reason we take an interest, and specifying them by means of procedures that have been selected because they enable us to satisfy some other interest (e.g., due process). As procedures become standardized, the language in which we communicate (to ourselves and to others) the results obtained by using them becomes more neutral, more matter-of-fact, more technical. By this time we have left the choice point in which the use of this procedure was decided so far behind that we have probably forgotten that its use was ever an open question, and that there were once options and alternatives with respect to it. Hence we may take a particular fact to be "harder" than it really is. For this reason it is important to remind ourselves of those forgotten choice points, of those hidden interests. Therefore I use language ("hard facts," "soft facts," "continuum of legal factuality") that is deliberately paradoxical,

---

[2] At least in this country. In the Soviet Union, it seems, philosophical and scientific disputes are thought to be too important to be left to adjudication by public opinion.

even perverse, in the hope that it will direct attention to aspects of the field that are often overlooked. My language for talking about language thus reflects an interest—as all language does.

iii. *Science*

Though some people talk about the law as a science, others are inclined to call it an art. This difference of opinion suggests (what our analysis confirms) that the language of law lies close to the middle of the linguistic spectrum—in the same region as common sense and also history— about which there is also often debate as to whether it is "really" an art or a science.

For this reason, some people may be willing to grant everything I have said about the softness of some legal facts. They will readily admit that legal fact-finding procedures include expressive elements (affects, interests). But they will add that this is precisely what distinguishes juridical procedures from scientific method: instead of relying on objective laboratory tests, the law relies on the opinions of biased juries, prejudiced judges, and district attorneys with an ax to grind. Scientific fact-finding, these people will argue, does not contain any expressive elements at all.

This is why, throughout the last section, I was careful always to talk about "legal facts," instead of "facts" *simpliciter*. I wanted to mark the possible difference between legal facts and scientific facts. Let us now see whether this qualification was necessary. Certainly no one would claim that legal fact-finding procedures are as scientific as the methodologies employed in physics (or chemistry, or biology). But the question is whether the facts as ascertained by scientific procedures differ in kind or only in degree from the facts as ascertained by juridical procedures.

I shall follow the plan of the last section and first show how and why scientific fact-finding develops out of common sense as a specialized language. Common sense, as I have said, is concerned with getting and spending, with the requirements of ordinary, everyday life. For its purposes (to satisfy its interests), common sense needs marks, perceptual cues, by which to distinguish objects it wants from objects it does not want. For instance, for Emily Post purposes, common sense wants to distinguish between knives and forks; the most obvious perceptual cue (prongs; no prongs) is enough. That common sense is not interested in further discrimination is evidenced by the fact that few people, even after they have eaten their way through a whole dinner always selecting the right implement, are able to describe the pattern of the silverware. Such an interest, where it exists, takes us beyond common sense to a deeper level of discrimination, and it is reflected in a semitechnical vocabulary about "hallmarks," "pistol handles," or "rat tails." If the only interests present were those of common sense, they could be satisfied at commonsense levels of discrimination. A technical vocabulary comes into existence only because, since common sense lacks an interest in the elements now being discriminated, there are no commonsense terms to name them. Or, to take a much more primitive level of common sense: in the interest of satisfying hunger, early man needed marks to distinguish edible berries from poisonous berries. Suppose a savage who usually eats red berries happens to eat some green berries and shortly experiences severe stomach cramps. He may establish a linkage between the (unusual) greenness of the berries and the (unusual) pains in his stomach. If so, there is now a generalization (probably not yet verbalized) in his background structure: "Green berries bad, red berries O.K." This may serve for a long time, but if, on some occasion, he has stomach cramps after eating red berries, the old generalization is no longer adequate; new perceptual cues must now be identified. Perhaps, after a time, the generalization "Light red berries good; all others bad" may emerge.

Science begins at some point in this process of finding more adequate perceptual cues, just as legal procedures begin in an attempt to find a more satisfactory way of settling disputes than bashing people over the head. For instance, trial by fire, trial by water, or trial by arms are better procedures than blood feud, because they terminate disputes by establishing the (legal) fact of who is the guilty party. And these procedures are in time superseded by more refined procedures such as trial by jury. So with scientific procedures: Success in getting and spending requires that we know what goes with what (e.g., that a light red color goes with being eatable, that a dark red color goes with being poisonous). As a first approximation, therefore, science may be defined as the attempt to ascertain, more and more precisely, what goes with what, that is, to discriminate unambiguous perceptual cues in the interests of better (more effective) practice. A scientific law, from this point of view, is simply a belief about what goes with what. Laws exist at an operative level (guiding behavior and choice) long before they are explicitly formulated. Thus "Light red berries are edible" is indeed a law of edible berries. Such a law is just below the stage at which we would be inclined to say that science has clearly differentiated itself from common sense. "Fire burns," "Friction causes heat," "Water won't run up hill" can be formulated by simple observation without any *specific* method. But science itself is in part merely the refinement and systematization of such rudimentary laws. I say "in part" because, as I shall show, other interests than an interest in more effective practice are involved in the sciences. However, before touching on these other interests, let us continue for a moment to study the effect that an interest in practice has on the formation of scientific laws.

First as regards refinement: In the empirical generalizations just cited, the "whats" at both ends of the observed sequences are vague and ill-defined: how light is "light red"? It will not solve the problem to introduce names for shades of red between "red" and "light red"—for example, "cerise" and "old rose"—for (1) different people will call the "same" shade by different names, and (2) the vagueness with respect to the point at which "red" became "light red" is repeated regarding the point at which "light red" becomes "cerise" and the point at which "cerise" becomes "old rose." Thus the mark of edible berries remains indeterminate.

Hence, ever since the advantages of measurement were first discovered, there has been a tendency, wherever possible, to replace a term such as "red" with an expression such as "any vibration between such-and-such a frequency and such-and-such another frequency"—where, it will be noted, narrowing the range of tolerated frequencies enables us to be just as precise as we want, or need, to be.

This is one of the refinements that science makes in common sense, and as a result of this particular refinement, the old "what-goes-with-what" (cause-effect) formula becomes a functional relationship in which one quantity varies with changes in another quantity, in some regular and measurable way. Accordingly, one of the marks that distinguishes highly designative languages from languages that are less markedly designative is a mathematical vocabulary. As we move out along the spectrum from common sense toward languages that are increasingly designative, we find a tendency to drop out the names of qualities, all of which have expressive potentialities (fast, very fast, fast as hell), and to translate them into quantities (e.g., 50 mph), which are not only exact but also expressively neutral. Though commonsense terms may not infrequently be retained in the vocabulary ("gravity," "attraction"), they acquire precise meanings (the acceleration due to gravity is specified as 32 feet per second per second). Thus the presence in the drive complex of a strong interest in precision will be reflected in the over-all character of the language used.

Secondly, there is an interest in systematization. At the level of empirical generalization we have no more than an assortment of loosely formulated "laws." Systematization occurs when we discover that some of these laws can be stated as instances of others. Thus, it may be possible to subsume a law of edible berries, a law of edible fruits, and still another law of edible meats under a single law of edible foods. Francis Bacon was one of the first thinkers to point out the power inherent in such high-order generalizations. But Bacon mistakenly believed that the common mark that would simplify the problem of (say) food selection was an empirical property—what he called a "nature," for example, color, shape, or heat. He did not see, as we can now see, that the common mark is usually an "intervening variable."

I will explain this notion by reference to what engineers call a "black box." We see inputs entering the box and outputs issuing from the box, and we make an empirical generalization—some particular input, we find, goes with some particular output. But what is happening inside the box, by virtue of which the observed input gets transformed into the observed output? Since we cannot open the box, we cannot say; but we *can* construct hypotheses (derived by analogy with processes we have observed elsewhere) of the following form: "If such-and-such a process were occurring in the box, that would account for what I observe." Thus an *intervening* variable is any variable, introduced for explanatory purposes, between the independent variable on the input side and the dependent variable on the output side.

Now it is often possible to explain the input/output relations of a large number of quite different black boxes by means of the same intervening variable or variables. In such empirically diverse processes as the rusting of iron, the oxidation of blood, the burning of wood, and the photosynthesis of plants the inputs and the outputs, at least at the level of ordinary observation, are very different. The rust on metal exposed to the weather does not look at all like the coal burning in the fireplace. But it is possible to give an account of all of these input/output relationships (and, of course, of many more) in terms of the same intervening variable—the gain and the loss of oxygen atoms by various chemical compounds.

Great advances in explanatory power occur whenever the same inter-vening variable can be used in a large number of different kinds of black boxes. But this is usually possible only if we move away from the level of directly observable, commonsense objects and properties (red and green berries) to the level of what are sometimes called scientific objects, that is, objects such as atoms, electrons, and positrons, which are not directly observable by the naked eye. We would probably not get very far with a law of edible foods if we stayed at the Baconian level of commonsense properties (for it might turn out that, while red berries are edible and green berries poisonous, green vegetables are edible and red ones poison-ous). But suppose we introduce intervening variables such as "protein," "amino acid," and "polypeptide chain." Certainly these do not automat-ically give us a law of edible foods, but at least they are immense unifiers, enabling us to talk in identical terms not only about all eatables but about all organic materials. Proteins, however, are not directly observable, as red and green are directly observable (i.e., proteins are not part of the commonsense world).

Thus, the presence in the drive pattern of a strong interest in systema-tization will be reflected in the language used—the language will come to have characteristics that enable this drive to be satisfied. I am not speaking here merely of the introduction of a technical or semitechnical vocabulary. For, in the first place, the use of a technical vocabulary may indicate only the presence in the drive pattern of something like the courtier drive—an attempt by the students in the softer sciences to imitate the harder sciences. In this event, outsiders are likely to characterize the technical vocabulary as "jargon." And in the second place, the existence of a tech-nical vocabulary is an indication only of the presence of some interest other than the ordinary interest of common sense in getting and spending, not necessarily an interest in systematization (p. 176). What shows the presence of an interest in systematization is the appearance in the tech-nical vocabulary of the names of scientific objects, that is, objects that are not directly observable. Pistol handles, hallmarks, ormulu mounts, and cabriole legs are directly observable once we acquire an interest in antique silver or furniture, but atoms, electrons, and positrons are not directly observable even when we do acquire an interest in them. For this reason they are sometimes called "constructs." Thus one of the marks of an in-terest in systematization is the appearance in the language of constructs, which come into the language not because people happen to observe them and need names to talk about them (as we happen to observe pistol handles and want a name to designate them) but because they prove useful to explain other, observable occurrences and events, such as a green light in the end of a partially evacuated glass tube.

Perhaps someone will ask about the ontological status of scientific objects or constructs. The answer I would give should be evident after the discussions in chapter iii: they have exactly the same sort of status as any other (e.g., directly observable) objects. They are foregrounds as interpreted by standard backgrounds. The only difference is that the standard background that yields a scientific object is not the background of common sense, but the specialized background structure of one or another of the sciences. If scientific objects seem to have a special, and puzzling, ontological status, this is because (1) the background structures in question are specialized, and (2) they come into operation only on special occasions.

When the name of a scientific object (e.g., "electron") first appears in a scientific language, the object so named is almost always regarded as a construct. This is because everybody is aware of its novelty and its tentativeness. Interpretation by means of the background structure containing this new generalization is not smooth; there is hesitation: we are doubtful whether the concept works. Gradually, however, if the concept does work, the generalization becomes both more stabilized in the background structure and also more widely disseminated. This is especially true if the concept turns out to work in other, and originally unforeseen, regions. As a result, the object tends to become more real, less of a "mere" construct. We no longer say: "See that green light in the vacuum tube? That may be caused by electrons." Instead, we say, "Look at that stream of electrons in the tube."

In a word, as a result of successful use, what was once background structure gets incorporated in foreground. The process does not differ from the process by which what was first a stick and subsequently a stick used as a pointer, eventually becomes a pointer (pp. 79–80). Thus if someone says, "But we can now see electrons; once we believed they were merely hypothetical; now we know that they are established facts"—if someone says this, I reply: You see (in a perfectly acceptable sense of "see") your cat now, even though all of the cat except his tail is out of sight (in a perfectly acceptable sense of "sight") under the sofa. If you see your cat and I see only a white blob beside the sofa, that is because your background structure (B_a) contains a number of memories and commonsense generalizations that my background structure lacks, which enable you to make a smooth interpretation where I hesitate. But in time I, too, may come to see a cat where now I see only a white blob. So, if you now see electrons where you once saw only faint lines on a photographic plate, this is because you are now making a smooth interpretation by means of a background structure (B_s) containing a number of highly specialized generalizations and concepts, which are proving more and more helpful in systematizing larger and larger regions of experience. So if someone now declares, not necessarily thumping the table as he does so, "Electrons are real," a part of what is meant is that the electron is an enormously useful explanatory concept; but affect is also communicated and realized in the sentence. To this extent, "Electrons are real" is an expressive sentence: it expresses an interest in, a confidence in, electrons.

It is possible to distinguish one scientific language from another in terms of the different types of scientific objects they employ. In general, as we move out toward the designative pole of the linguistic spectrum, the scientific objects in the vocabulary become more numerous and more abstract. In the language of history, for instance, there are almost no scientific objects and indeed very few technical terms—history is almost at the level of common sense. In sociology there are many technical terms (e.g., "social mobility upward") but few scientific objects. In psychology there are perhaps more scientific objects (e.g., Oedipus complex), but both the explanatory power and the extent of the explanatory domain of these objects are debatable.

When we pass from the social sciences to the physical sciences, we find a high degree of translatability from one language to another. The various physical sciences can be arranged in a rough order, or series of levels; though each language has its own scientific objects, the scientific objects of a language at a lower (i.e., less general) level are usually translatable into scientific objects at a higher (i.e., more general) level.

Here is an example: I will begin with an "obvious" generalization—one that can be made at the level of common sense, say, that the knee jerks when it is tapped. "Knee" and "jerk" are both fairly vague terms, but the "law" that relates them may suffice for commonsense purposes: when you tap somewhere below the knee, the lower leg jerks. At the next level (perhaps the level of medical practice and diagnosis) there is a further and more exact specification, beyond the resources of common sense, of the exact area that is tapped. But we are still at the level of empirically observable inputs and outputs (taps and jerks). If we now describe this sequence, as we can, in terms of "receptors," "effectors," and "nerve paths," we will have introduced some scientific objects between the input (tap) and the output (jerk); and these scientific objects are both more abstract and more general than "knee-jerk." Moreover, not only the knee-jerk, but all sorts of other behavior, voluntary and involuntary, can be explained in terms of the interaction of these scientific objects. But it is possible to move to a still more abstract and systematic level; we can take any of the scientific objects at this level (say, nerve path) and analyze it in terms of other scientific objects (say, "potassium ions," "permeable membrane"). And the scientific objects at this level are still more general, since they explain not only nerve impulses but a vast number of other and quite different types of occurrences. This capacity for translation to successively more abstract levels of scientific objects is an extremely important characteristic of the advanced scientific languages.

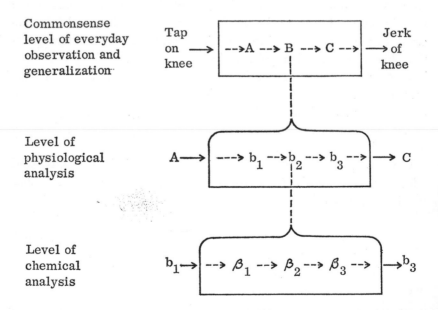

So far in this discussion I have emphasized the way in which an interest in more efficient practice is responsible for the differentiation of scientific language out of common sense. It is obvious that both the precision resulting from quantification and mensuration and the systematization introduced by such scientific objects as atoms are useful; to this extent these features of the various scientific languages can be explained by an interest in more efficient practice. But when quantification and systematization are carried, as they often are, far beyond any foreseeable practical use, there must be some other interest at work, as some other interest accounts for the rats' learning more about the maze than they need to find the food box at the end. This added interest is an interest in explanation. We want to *understand,* as well as to control, the world about us.

But understanding is an interest that varies greatly as regards the rigor and refinement required of an adequate explanation, and these variations, once again, are reflected in the characteristic differences between the scientific languages and the language of common sense. At the level of common sense very crude explanations appear quite satisfying. An authoritative tone of voice, a charismatic personality, a headline in heavy black type, a white jacket and a stethoscope are often enough—especially when the explanation thus embellished serves not only to allay curiosity but to satisfy some other drive, such as hostility to Jews or Communists, dislike of high taxes, or fear of cancer.

Repetition is also an important element in explanation at the level of common sense: "What I tell you three times is true." The reason is that we tend to be puzzled, not about what is habitual and usual, but about what is unusual; not about the familiar, but about the odd. Suppose we find the dowager duchess lying on the floor in a pool of blood. We are puzzled; we want to know why she is lying there—after all, this is not the usual posture of duchesses. Then someone says, "She was murdered by her butler; he is an embezzler and a bigamist, and she found him out." We are satisfied, for we are accustomed to criminals who take desperate measures to try to protect their guilty secrets.

Or a child who encounters for the first time one of those automatic devices fitted into the surface of the street which trigger a change in a traffic signal, may be puzzled because he is accustomed to traffic signals that work by a timing device. "How does that work?" he asks. Answer: "You know the light switches on the wall at home? You press the switch and the light in the ceiling goes on. Well, this is exactly like that, except that the switch is in the street and is pressed by the car as it passes." "Oh, I see," says the child, perfectly satisfied.

You may say that the child ought not to have been satisfied, and you may be right. But that is another question. The point is that he *was* satisfied, and that common sense, too, is often satisfied by just such explanations. Ever since Hume's day, philosophers have debated whether a scientific explanation does any more than this, and if so, what. When we turn to the actual procedures of scientists for the answer to this question, we are likely to be disappointed, for manifold and various are the criteria that scientists employ. However, this should not surprise us. People, including scientists, are content whenever the answer offered them, or that occurs to them, satisfies current requirements. But these requirements change through time, both in the history of the race and in the life of the individual. To say this is simply to say that men learn by their mistakes and are constantly revising their criteria so as to improve their chances of not being disappointed later on by explanations they now accept. For instance, until we have reason to believe otherwise, it is reasonable to accept what we are told; but how soon, alas! we have reasons to believe otherwise. When informants contradict each other or when they promise us something subsequently falsified by the event, we must, on some basis or other, distinguish between trustworthy and untrustworthy informants. If our initial criteria for selecting reliable informants are a pleasant smile and an agreeable manner, the chances are that we shall sooner or later want to revise these criteria. It is thus that the process of criticizing and refining criteria of explanation begins; once begun, the process seems endless.

At some point in this process of refinement we pass beyond common-sense, to scientific, levels of explanation, but though we now enter a region of more formal and more rigorous inquiry, we still find that conceptions of rigor vary greatly. For instance, some social scientists put a major emphasis on formal elegance, others on empirical relevance. Some want the social sciences to be as much like physics as possible; others regard this as a dangerous ideal. It may be necessary, in the social sciences, to choose between human significance and precise prediction, since precision is usually possible only by restricting the behavior studied to essentially "artificial" situations. Hence, if the social scientist wishes to study real-life situations in all their complexity, he must be willing, to some extent, to sacrifice rigor. There is thus a choice point between the criterion of real-life relevance and the criterion of quantification. Where any individual student of society makes the cut depends on what his major interest is. Suppose the object of study is small-group behavior. If the former interest is predominant, a sociologist may go to live on intimate terms with a gang in a Boston slum; if the latter interest predominates, he may take his "subjects" into the laboratory and measure changes in the time required to exchange information as the shape of the communication net varies.

Thus, as I predicted, a survey of the practice of scientists does not resolve the philosophical debate over the distinction between explanation and "mere" description. But the survey at least shows why such a survey is inconclusive, for it turns out that the whole debate is only a dispute about whether, and where, to make a cut in a continuum of similars. It is a question of which similarities and which differences the disputing philosophers think are important. Those who lump explanation and description together (i.e., those who minimize the differences) believe that what is important is the contrast between empirical and teleological approaches. Accordingly, philosophers who adopt this stance are likely to remind us that "even so-called explanations really explain nothing." By saying this they wish to call our attention to the fact that modern scientific explanations do not give us a purposive why. The force of the "even" is to remind us that in *this* respect (which they regard as the important respect) explanations are exactly like descriptions. On the other hand, philosophers who are impressed by the possibility, especially in physics and the other advanced sciences, of axiomatization and deduction will emphasize the inter-family difference between explanation and description. They will talk about description as being "mere" description in order to bring out the difference (which they regard as all-important) between the simple formulation of a correlation and the ability to derive this from a more general principle.

To put this another way: philosophers who are thinking in broad, historical terms are likely to be impressed by the extent to which, since the sixteenth century, the old explanatory schema, which was dominated by the search for ends, has been replaced by one that ignores ends. These philosophers will therefore tend to minimize the differences between explanation and description. On the other hand, philosophers who concentrate on more recent developments probably take the change-over from a purposive schema for granted. They are more impressed by current differences between more advanced sciences, like physics and chemistry, and less advanced sciences, like sociology or botany. These philosophers will therefore emphasize the differences between explanation, which is possible in the former, and description, to which the latter are largely limited.

Thus this dispute springs from a differential evaluation of the various foci in the field. As with so many philosophical debates, the two parties are attending to different foci and are mistaken only insofar as each rejects what the other sees. Is explanation merely a matter of becoming habituated to occurrences? Answer: Yes and No. Yes, to the extent that reference to an established, familiar regularity is the central feature of explanation. No, to the extent that most people nowadays demand more of an explanation than merely a high degree of correlation. Indeed, most scientists confronted with a high degree of correlation between two variables would be puzzled, not satisfied. Why should there be this correlation? Obviously, to the extent that a regularity makes scientists curious, regularity cannot be the sole criterion of satisfaction. But this does not mean that the regularity view is mistaken in what it asserts; it merely means that additional requirements have been built into many scientists' criteria for satisfaction.

In view of all these differences—scientific, philosophical, and common-sensical—and the varying interests they reveal, it would seem that the only *general* definition of explanation (and/or description) that is possible is that it is what allays curiosity. It is where a curious mind rests.

This is not to deny the normative character of norms and criteria of explanation; it is not to say that every explanation is just as good as every other explanation. It is rather to say that norms arise in experience and are modified by experience. An example is the way we learn (i.e., come personally to experience) the unsatisfactoriness of "momentary" satisfactions and of "private" satisfactions. We live in a context of memories of our own past experiences and of observations of other men. In this context our curiosities are sharpened, our criteria for "what satisfies" are refined. Over time, it comes about that men are no longer satisfied by a simple pragmatic test (Do those berries give me a stomach cramp?). They demand symmetry, simplicity, elegance, and inclusiveness of their explanations. Instead of being satisfied by any explanation, however messy, that permits them to control the environment, they may set themselves as an ideal a fully axiomatized theory. They are not content with explanations that describe *how* things happen; they want to be able to deduce the exact occurrence (time, place, character) from general laws and, ultimately, from one very general set of laws. They aim perhaps at a "unified field theory." This would be systematization indeed! Though some—perhaps all—of these criteria of explanation are justified to a large extent on pragmatic grounds, for many minds they become primary ends. In this way, interests that are metaphysical, esthetic, and even religious enter into the formation of scientific objects.

A good way to study this influence is to see the way different metaphors or models dominate, or even control at decisive points, the explanations that different scientists put forward. There is, for instance, the story about the German chemist Kekulé. During the period when he was working intensively on the structure of the benzene molecule, he happened to return home late one night on a tram. As he sat dozing, he had a vivid dream of snakes biting each other's tails and so forming a ring. He awoke and realized that this shape would solve his problem. The result was the concept of the benzene ring, a closed ring of six carbon atoms with hydrogen atoms attached. This metaphor (or model) brought into focus a similarity between things that are otherwise very different. Indeed, the benzene molecule differs in so many respects from snakes biting each other's tails that you could, if you liked, construct a very difficult riddle or conundrum: How is the benzene molecule like a bunch of snakes biting each other's tails? But despite all the differences, they *are* alike in at least one respect—both form a closed ring. And in this particular context, this particular similarity made all the difference. The metaphor formed the basis for a hypothesis that worked.

It may be said that we need to distinguish between (1) the psychological source of a particular hypothesis, and (2) the hypothesis itself. Of course, the psychological roots of a hypothesis—the genius, the good luck, or the obscure psychological set that caused the metaphor to pop into Kekulé's mind—are no part of the hypothesis. A hypothesis is not validated or invalidated by examining the circumstances in which it occurs to a scientist, but by empirical verification procedures. But the point is that there are marginal cases where more than one hypothesis may be reconcilable with all the available facts. When this happens, some other interest determines which hypothesis is preferred and which, ultimately, becomes a "law of nature." It is certainly not inconceivable, for instance, that some other (even several other) patterns of arrangement of the carbon and hydrogen atoms could be postulated for the benzene molecule which would fit all of the available facts. Given a different pattern of interests and affects, one of these might have occurred to Kekulé or to some other chemist.

This may seem speculative. But the history of science is full of instances of such influences. Thus both the Ptolemaic and the Copernican hypotheses were reconcilable with all known facts (observations of planetary motions); if the latter was preferred (and not everybody by any means *did* prefer it), this was because it was simpler and more "elegant." Here are interests quite different from either an interest in more efficient practice or an interest in conformity with the facts.

Or there is the dispute between Newton and Huygens over the nature of light—Newton holding it to be corpuscular and Huygens denying this. Why did they differ? Of course two physicists might differ if one had access to relevant information that the other lacked, as two psychiatrists might differ about *D*'s sanity if one had seen his paranoid rages and the other had not. But Huygens did not know some fact unknown to Newton which was "obviously" incompatible with the corpuscular hypothesis. Newton knew, for instance, and repeated, Grimaldi's observation of the phenomenon of diffraction, which seemed to Huygens to be incompatible with the corpuscular theory and to support an undulatory theory. But in Newton's view the colored bands inside and outside the shadow were caused by an "inflexion" of the rays as they passed near the edge of the object casting the shadow.[3] The issue was how much weight to give to this particular piece of evidence. Newton gave Grimaldi's evidence less weight than Huygens did—he was satisfied by an interpretation of it that failed to satisfy Huygens—because he weighed very heavily certain other evidence, such as the evidence of rectilinear propagation, which seemed to him incompatible with an undulatory theory—though Huygens, for his part, had produced a construction which seemed to him to reconcile rectilinear propagation with his undulatory theory.

It is possible, I think, to explain why evidence that satisfied Huygens that light is undulatory did not satisfy Newton. They weighed the evidence differently at such critical points as the interpretation of Grimaldi's experiment because they had different basic, underlying models of what

---

[3] There is a useful account in A. Wolf, *A History of Science, Technology and Philosophy in the 16th and 17th Centuries* (London: Allen and Unwin, 1950), pp. 254–271.

the universe is like. Newton's model was corpuscular; Huygens' was wave.

Such very basic models (or metaphors, or pictures) of what the universe is like seem to exist in most minds. Usually it is difficult to account for the predominating role that a particular model comes to have—why, for instance, a corpuscular model at certain periods, rather than wave? and then a wave model at other times? In Newton's case, however, the enormous success of the gravitational hypothesis, which presupposes a corpuscular model, with distinct and encapsulated masses interacting at a distance, would make the corpuscular model seem to him "natural" also for light, and so satisfy a deep desire for symmetry, generality, and simplicity in the world picture.

Even more evident is the influence of such basic, underlying models in the thinking of metaphysicians and of the early natural scientists (before the development of experimental methods). Democritus' vision of the universe as consisting of a rain of hard, indestructible atoms in empty space clearly reflects a preference, like Newton's, for a corpuscular model. So does Hume's conception of "loose and separate" impressions, and so does his favorite metaphor of a billiard game. All three men show an interest in externality, in sharp distinctions, in "atomicity." Such basic preferences—biases, if one likes—cause one model to be preferred over another and influence the formation of theory—metaphysical or physical— at decisive points. In Democritus' case (and in Hume's) the model could have a more preponderant influence than in Newton's, since there was available to Newton much more, and more precise, evidence than was available to Democritus, and any theory that would be acceptable to Newton had to conform to this evidence. Still, at the margin, conformity to the evidence is itself a flexible requirement. Grimaldi's evidence was sufficiently loose to permit varying interpretations by Newton and Huygens.

Thus there is certainly a difference, but only a difference in degree, between legal facts and scientific facts. An appellate court's decision is of course limited by the hard facts before it—the effervescing wine was produced in Spain and nowhere else; the car was on a parking lot, not in a meadow; the language was clearly obscene. But, since some of the facts before the court are soft, the judges' conception of the public interest affects the point at which the court makes the cut between what is "champagne" and what is not; between what is a road and what is not; between what is a noise and what is not. Similarly, some of the evidence before a physicist at any time is hard; his theory has to conform to it. But at some points the evidence will be relatively soft, though probably none of it will be as soft as many of the facts with which judges and juries customarily deal. At these points interests other than the drive to conform to the fact—interests such as a preference for this or that underlying model—may exercise a determining influence on the formation of theory.

It is irrelevant to reply that Newton was subsequently shown to be wrong, and that we now "know the facts about light." Perhaps we do; certainly there is now a vast reservoir of hard facts about these and other matters which constitute the resistances (the check-points, the anchor points) to which theories and hypotheses must conform. But if there are hard facts, there are always other, relatively soft facts. In every science, at any given time, there are settled areas, more or less extensive regions of accumulated fact, which nobody now questions, and where current theories and current conceptions are being deployed in the expansion and stabilization of knowledge. This corresponds to the way in which, guided by the great mass of established precedents, the lower courts deal with large numbers of cases in an almost routine way. But in every science there are also frontier regions where, as yet, some of the facts are not firm, where, perhaps, even methods are not yet entirely agreed-on, and where, therefore, the evidence is so nearly in balance that any one of several hypotheses may fit pretty well. (How well is "pretty well"? How well is "well enough"?—here is another point at which interest may be a determining factor.)

At present, learning theory is such a frontier in psychology. There are many quite different and opposed theories of learning—Tolman's, Guthrie's, Skinner's, Lewin's, Hull's, for instance. These theories do not differ because the different theorists have access to different facts; they differ because, though all the theorists have access to the same facts about rates of learning and forgetting, about reinforcement and so on, they weigh these facts differently. Commenting on this situation, one distinguished observer has said: "All the theorists accept all of the facts. . . . Hence the differences between two theorists are primarily differences in interpretation. Both theories may fit the facts reasonably well, but the proponent of each theory believes his view to be the more fruitful. . . . An appeal to the facts as a way of choosing between theories is a very complex process, not nearly as decisive in practice as we might expect it to be." [4]

Unless one supposes that everything that can possibly be known will someday be known, there will always be frontier districts in the sciences (though the frontiers will doubtless shift from time to time), where the facts are relatively loose. There is always the possibility of a new synthesis that will shake loose the old accumulated facts in a settled area. This process, which is roughly analogous to the way a major constitutional case may overturn a great variety of established legal facts, has occurred many times: Ventris' decipherment of linear B, the discovery of X-rays, the Van Allen belts, Freud's and Breuer's successful treatment of Anna O., Leakey's find of the Kanam mandible in East Africa, Galileo's observation of the stars that moved, and Köhler's work with the chimpanzee Sultan are all examples of discoveries at the frontier which caused shifts, large or small, in what were supposedly hard facts. The more novel and radical the changes at the frontiers, the more likely it is that interests other than an interest in conforming to the facts are playing a role. In every massive new physical synthesis, such as Newton's or Einstein's, there is an element analogous to poetic, religious, or metaphysical vision.

This account of the languages of science does not "undermine" the sciences. The factuality of fact is not destroyed by admitting that every fact, including every scientific fact, is relative to a background structure which reflects, among other things, a complex of affects and interests. Because of the nature of these interests, scientific facts are more stable, more reliable, than any other facts (for instance, legal facts or common-sense facts). If anyone feels that this undermines science, this is because he insists on thinking of facts as out there, utterly apart from us. But to be utterly apart from us would be to be utterly unknowable by us. When some belief (say, about the structure of the atom) which we have held to be true changes (e.g., as a result of the discovery of X-rays), people may be disposed to say, not "What was once a fact is no longer a fact," but "What I thought was a fact is not one." They may want to reserve the term "fact" for what can't change. But is there any fact that *can't* change?

---

[4] Ernest R. Hilgard, *Theories of Learning* (New York: Appleton-Century-Crofts, 1956), p. 9.

Not, it would seem, unless there are facts that are not relative to background structure.

But perhaps we are merely disagreeing ("a verbal dispute") over the circumstances in which it is appropriate to use terms like "cannot," "impossible," and "certain." How certain does one have to be in order for it to be appropriate to say that such-and-such a fact can't change? If this is what the disagreement is about, though it is verbal it is not merely verbal: here again, differences of interest play a determining role (see pp. 163–165). If you maintain that my position undermines the sciences and I maintain that it does not, this may possibly be because of a factual difference between us (you may know some fact about the sciences that I do not know; there may be some fact about my view which I have not succeeded in communicating to you). But it is more likely to result from a difference in interest. You may have a very strong interest, for instance, in achieving certainty and absolute truth, and you may hope that the sciences are going to give you the certainty that you crave. But the absolute truth of science is an interest—not a scientific fact. I happen to believe that it is, on the whole, a harmful interest. This may be where we differ, not at all with respect to the actual and operative status of the sciences.

To put this slightly differently: though some of the things I have said may sound as if I belong to the school of thought, fashionable in some humanistic quarters, that wants to "destroy the pretensions of science," this is not so. What I do criticize are the pretensions of some philosophers, many laymen, and perhaps some scientists that science can provide us with the absolute truth about things. Few scientists, I think, actually make this claim, but the nonscientific, lay public often does. Thus I emphasize the conditioned character of scientific knowledge, not to condemn science, but because most people praise it for the wrong reasons. In the mass media, science is treated partly as magic and partly as cure-all. It has become a gimmick invoked to sell soap and cigarettes ("best by scientific test"), to decide the kind of career we ought to follow, and to resolve all the problems of foreign policy. For purely extrinsic reasons (e.g., because of its great technological by-products), it is regarded as being the ultimate court of appeal.

There is a tendency, then, on the part of the public to venerate "facts," especially those facts that science discovers. To counteract this tendency, I have tried to show that *all* facts, including the facts disclosed by scientific inquiry, are the products of interpretative processes in which foregrounds are structured by backgrounds. What distinguishes scientific facts from others, is the kind of background structure involved in the interpretative process, and this in its turn depends on the purposes that the sciences serve.

This is why I have throughout spoken of the "languages" of science, for within the general field of scientific language, there are different sublanguages. Though, as I have pointed out, translation from one of these languages to another is often possible, it is far from perfect. What unifies the sciences is less a body of achieved knowledge than it is an attitude of mind, a purpose, and a general procedure. Because the preference rules of all the scientific languages are dominated by a common, strongly designative purpose, they all emphasize externality, neutrality, separateness, and order. The ideal for all of them, as yet very imperfectly attained in some, is a world of simple recurrent entities, each of which is clearly demarcated from every other and which combine into more complex structures in regular ways.

To the extent that people derogate as "subjective" any experience that fails to measure up to the criteria appropriate for scientific purposes, they are simply revealing where their primary interests happen to lie—in order, precision, and regularity of pattern, and in the control and manipulation of the environment that science makes possible. Since these values are deeply rooted in our culture, since the whole shape and tonality of life today depends on them, it is not surprising that we all take science seriously.

But we can take science seriously without claiming that it is, or could be, unconditioned. Since it is impossible to eradicate the interpretative, affective elements that operate in the formation of scientific theory, it is a grave mistake to persuade ourselves that they are not there. Scientists and laymen alike should recognize and acknowledge their presence, that is, accept with humility the fundamentally conditioned, "human," character of scientific inquiry and scientific truth.

iv. *Literature*

In the preceding section I examined the nature and the preference rules of what I call scientific language—language tending toward the designative pole of the linguistic spectrum. My main problem there was to overcome the common tendency to think of science as purely designative and coldly factual, the revelation of the world as it "really" is. Now I turn to what I call humanistic language—language that lies toward the other pole of the spectrum. My problem in this section will just be the opposite: I have to show that humanistic language (e.g., poetry) is cognitive. The difference between scientific language and humanistic language is not a difference in kind; it is a difference in the proportion of designative and expressive components.

I shall begin once more with common sense. I have already pointed out why the specialized languages of science develop out of common sense—because our interest in more effective practice and our interest in more rigorous explanation require a linguistic precision that common sense lacks. Literature develops out of common sense for a parallel reason—because of an interest in expression which common sense cannot satisfy. Common sense *is* expressive: this is just the trouble with it from the point of view of science. If red berries are edible, a strong positive affect becomes associated with red, just so far as red becomes a perceptual cue for eating. Hence the generalization "Red berries good" is inevitably expressive as well as designative, and is expressive just because it is designative. Thus from the point of view of science "red" is not only a vague term (and perhaps an insufficiently precise perceptual cue); it also lacks "neutrality." But from the point of view of literature common sense is equally unsatisfactory: (1) Words at the commonsense level have too many linkages; they may be swamped with inconsistent affects. Not only are edible berries red; roses are red, sunsets are red, blood is red, angry faces are red, traffic signals are red. (2) Some of these linkages are private and idiosyncratic: you may like red hair because your mother had red hair; I may dislike it because I used to be paddled by a redheaded bully. (3) Linkages that are not idiosyncratic tend to suffer from an opposite failure: they lose expressive power by becoming banalities and clichés.

Accordingly, poetry and the other humanistic languages begin where scientific language begins—in an area of diffuse experience that is demanding clarification, and where the interest in understanding is greater than can be satisfied at the level of common sense. But beyond this, the interests diverge: in scientific language the interest is primarily in becoming clear about what is "out there," for the sake of more effective practice; in the humanistic languages the interest is primarily in becoming clear about some affect. An affect is nudging us; we want to find out exactly what it is we are experiencing. This state of mind is described amusingly, but very well, by V. Nabokov (that is, he has found the right words for clarifying the diffuse experience of being about to start to work):

Perhaps, if I had a new fountain pen instead of this wreck, or a fresh bouquet of, say, twenty beautifully sharpened pencils in a slim vase, and a ream of ivory smooth paper . . . , I might start writing the unknown thing I want to write; unknown, except for a vague shoe-shaped outline, the infusorial quiver of which I feel in my restless bones, a feeling of *shchekotiki* (as we used to say in our childhood), half-tingle, half-tickle, when you are trying to remember something or understand something or find something, and probably your bladder is full, and your nerves are on edge, but the combination is on the whole not unpleasant (if not protracted) and produces a minor orgasm or *"petit éternuement intérieur"* when at last you find the picture-puzzle piece which exactly fits the gap.[5]

Literature in one of its aspects is the process of rendering, of communicating (self- and other-communication), some powerful but obscurely felt affect. This process by which some "vague, shoe-shaped" affect is condensed into the concrete end-product, the work of art, has been well described by Miss May Sarton in her account[6] of the composition of one of her poems:

The occasion was my being given a Guggenheim Fellowship and for the first time in some years able to foresee an open space; . . . with this great news of imminent freedom in my pocket, I went for a walk. It happened that I came to one of the small ponds along The Fenway in Boston and stood for some moments watching the ducks swim about, watched, and suddenly experienced one of those "moments of vision" of which I spoke earlier. It is hard to define just what this moment contained; the work sheets we shall look at will gradually define it. At any rate I was seized by some intimation about time and what it is, and some weeks later the idea teased me into sitting down to try to capture it.

The first sheet is very much crossed-out. . . . I mentioned that I did not begin to write the poem until some weeks after watching the ducks, and in the interval I had evidently forgotten the original key to the experience. The early work sheets are really hunting expeditions in pursuit of an image.

[5] V. Nabokov, *Bend Sinister* (London: Weidenfeld and Nicolson, 1960), p. 140.

[6] "The Writing of a Poem, an Address by May Sarton" (Claremont, Calif.: Scripps College [1957]), pp. 11–12, 13, 14, 15–16. "On Being Given Time" has been published in Miss Sarton's *In Time Like Air* (New York: Rinehart, 1958) and in her *Cloud, Stone, Sun, Vine* (New York: Norton, 1961).

After a number of tries, Miss Sarton "came out with what looked like a poem." It was titled "Journey Toward Time," but it did not satisfy her: "I sensed . . . that what I was doing was writing *about* the subject; I was playing with words, instead of translating the experience." So she put the poem aside, and went back, several days later, to her old work sheets. There she found "the kind of image I was looking for, the image that made the thing happen instead of just talking about it":

> The ripple behind the duck as it swims
> The release after music.

Given this clue, which, it will be seen, took her back to the actual context in which her "moment of vision" had occurred, the poem now began to develop in stanza form. But three or four more years were to pass before she produced what she felt was the "final" version:

On Being Given Time

Sometimes it seems to be the inmost land
All children still inhabit when alone.
They play the game of morning without end,
And only lunch can bring them, startled, home
Bearing in triumph a small speckled stone.

Yet even for them, too much dispersal scatters;
What complex form the simplest game may hold!
And all we know of time that really matters
We've learned from moving clouds and waters
Where we see form and motion lightly meld.

Not the fixed rigid object, clock or mind,
But the long ripple that opens out beyond
The duck as he swims down the tranquil pond,
Or when a wandering falling leaf may find
And follow the formal downpath of the wind.

It is, perhaps, our most complex creation,
A lovely skill we spend a lifetime learning,
Something between the world of pure sensation
And the world of pure thought, a new relation,
As if we held in balance the globe turning.

Even a year's not long, yet moments are.
This moment, yours and mine, and always given,

When the leaf falls, the ripple opens far,
And we go where all animals and children are,
The world is open. Love can breathe again.

A poem is thus the pursuit of precision beyond the capacities of common sense. But it is the attempt to render some affect precisely, not to designate some fact precisely. For this reason, the preference rules by which poetry, painting, and the other arts achieve precision are very different from the preference rules of the scientific languages. Nevertheless many people (presumably because of a one-sided emphasis on designative language in the schools) evaluate works of art by quite inappropriate, designative, criteria: "Why I never saw a sunset like that!" or "That doesn't look like a tree!" The best way to understand how literature functions in the total human economy is to compare the preference rules of humanistic language with those of the more scientific languages. Here are some examples:

(1) That color is a dirty red.
(2) Smith is a dirty red!
(3) But where the ship's huge shadow lay
    The charméd water burnt alway
    A still and awful red.

And:

(4) His heart is black.
(5) For I have sworn thee fair, and thought thee bright,
    Who are as black as hell, as dark as night.

"That color is a dirty red" is primarily a designative sentence (at the commonsense level). "Dirty" functions to give a further specification of the color, as "light," "pitch," and "Prussian" do in "light green," "pitch black," and "Prussian blue." A dirty red is a particular and identifiable tone of red, and "dirty" names a discriminatable property which blue, green, and orange, as well as red, may have. But "dirty" is also loaded with affect. Either the speaker is experiencing an affect or else he is using language manipulatively to influence our attitude, and so our behavior, toward this color. (For instance, he may be a salesman who is trying to get us to buy a more expensive paint.)

There are other terms available in the standard vocabulary, besides "dirty," for specifying this particular tone. As is the case in all displacement to symbolism, which of these available terms a speaker actually uses reveals his operative drive pattern. For instance:

> Ugh! Dirty!
> That color is a dingy red.
> That color is a dullish red.

These sentences reflect progressively less negative affect. "Ugh! Dirty!" is very strongly negative. But it is not merely an ejaculation of disgust; it is a small discovery—the discovery of a similarity between the affect this tone arouses and the affect that being dirty arouses. The feeling of disgust is condensed for the speaker in his exclamation (is given local habitation and a name). This is a discovery, of course, that any number of people may make for themselves; the successful condensation of the affect for the speaker and for others explains why "dirty" has gradually emerged as a standard term to designate this tone.

On the other hand, if a speaker says "That color is a dullish red" we might conclude that he feels little affect himself and indeed may even be trying to designate the color without arousing affect in us, that is, without manipulating our behavior toward it, since "dullish" is probably the least negatively expressive term available in the ordinary vocabulary for designating this particular tone. In this event the speaker would have been straining, within the limitations of a commonsense vocabulary, toward a greater degree of designative precision. Thus "dullish red" would be moving in the direction already reached by "Prussian blue." For, whatever private, idiosyncratic linkages you or I may have with Prussia or Prussians, to call a color "Prussian blue" is now merely to designate it. Nobody, not even somebody who disliked this color and who also disliked Prussians intensely, would be likely to focus his affect by exclaiming with contempt, "Why that's a Prussian blue!" as somebody who disliked an opinion you expressed might exclaim, "Why that's a Prussian attitude toward life!" Unlike "dirty" in "dirty red," "Prussian" in "Prussian blue" is now virtually a literal adjective.

Sentence (2), "Smith is a dirty red," utilizes the same emotive-conative linkage as (1). The first person who called somebody a "dirty Communist" made a discovery—the discovery of a relevant similarity between the loathing communism aroused in him and his dislike of dirt; and calling communism "dirty" condensed this affect for him. But now, as a result of frequency of use, the "dirty" of "dirty Communist," like the "dirty" of "dirty red," has started on the road toward becoming a literal adjective. But where "dirty red," when applied to a color, specifies the color within a fairly narrow range of possible tones, "dirty red" leaves Smith's political opinions virtually unspecified. Smith may be in favor of overthrowing the Constitution by force and violence; he may merely advocate recognizing Communist China. We cannot tell.

Since "Smith is a dirty red" is too vague even for common sense, it must perform some other function in the economy of the speaker. The sentence is certainly manipulative; whether intentionally or not, it tends to cause hearers to respond unfavorably toward Smith. Some people might say that the sentence is primarily expressive: that it expresses the speaker's dislike of Smith and, indirectly, of communism. For my part I would call the sentence emotive or ejaculatory (compare "Ouch!" when one puts a finger on a hot stove, or running around when one is excited and tense [p. 148]). I reserve the term "expressive" for a sentence that is functioning to clear up and focus some affect, that is, one that is functioning cognitively. I would not deny that "Smith is a dirty red" may be to some slight degree expressive, but it is unlikely that the speaker is chiefly concerned to focus and clarify his affect toward Smith (as "Ugh! Dirty!" focused his affect toward some shade of red). It is more likely that the speaker wishes to hide both from himself and others his dislike and fear of Smith, rather than to clarify his feeling. "Smith is a dirty red" not only diverts attention from the speaker's feeling toward Smith; it also reduces the pent-up aggression and hostility he feels. If he cannot strike Smith, at least he can call him bad names. In a word, "Smith is a dirty red" may be some passion's spontaneous overflow into speech; but there is no recollection in tranquillity. There is no conscious determined effort to focus the affect; the drive to clarify it, so far as it exists at all, is easily satisfied with a vague and indeterminate cliché. And this is also true of "That color is a dirty red," to the extent that it is expressive in addition to being designative.

Now, to pass on to Coleridge's lines, the "red" in (3) designates the color of the water, as "red" designates the color in (1). And "still and awful" further specify the color, as "dirty" further specifies the color in (1). But "still and awful" are not names of particular tones of red, as "dirty" and "Prussian" can be said to be the names of particular tones. In (1) the color is called "red" because that is the color it is; the speaker is talking about a particular color and is trying to characterize that color, in addition to expressing whatever affect he may be experiencing. In (3) the color is characterized as "red" because Coleridge believed that what he wanted to express at this point could be best expressed by a red that was "still and awful." In (3), then, "red" functions expressively.

But what affect does the "red" of (3) focus? We can answer only by considering the context, for here "red" is not an isolated adjective, but a part of a passage in which the Ancient Mariner is describing his situation after all the crew have died. He feels their accusatory stare; he tries to pray; he sweats in the tropic heat; the sea is full of animal life; finally the sun sets, and the moon rises. In its light the sea is white, but the shadow cast by the ship is red.

So much for a rough prose translation of the context in which "red" occurs. Now, of course, what I have translated as "accusatory stare" is "the curse in a dead man's eye" in the original, and "full of animal life" is

> And a thousand thousand slimy things
> Lived on; and so did I.

Similarly, the ship's shadow was "huge," and it "lay" (not "was cast")— "lay" is heavier, more palpable, more substantial, and so comports with "huge," rather than with (say) "extensive." Then there is the contrast between the pale whiteness outside the shadow and the vivid brightness inside the shadow; in this context, it is the linkages of "red" with what is dangerous and sinister that are focused, rather than its linkages with courage (e.g., *via* blood) or with beauty (e.g., *via* sunsets and roses). Finally the selected linkages are reinforced by the fact that the water "burnt" and by "still and awful." Thus in this context, along with "curse" and "slimy," "red" functions to contribute to the expression of terror, strangeness, and despair.

Next, as regards (4) and (5): both of these rest on the associative link between treachery and the color black. Why, then, is (5) so much more powerfully and precisely expressive than (4)? In the first place, though "black-hearted" may once have been genuinely expressive, it has now almost become a literal adjective. When we read "black-hearted," we no longer discover with a shock of surprise an illuminating similarity between malignancy of character and the color black; we merely understand the writer to be stating matter-of-factly that somebody is not to be trusted. Anyone who is content to describe somebody else's villainy as "black-hearted" is not penetrating very deeply into the complexities of that person's character. He is just about as interested as the man who looks long enough at the silverware on the table to distinguish knives from forks, but not carefully enough to take in the design and the pattern: in both situations curiosity is only superficial and so is easily satisfied.

In contrast, Shakespeare's lines (5) jolt us by an abrupt, almost violent, contrast: the double comparison, fair/black, bright/dark, echoes one of the deepest and most pervasive of all human symbols, the linkage of good with light and of evil with dark. Hence, instead of petering out in a prosaic literalness, these lines reverberate with a truly massive and sustained affect. Finally, the rhyming of "bright" with "night" rounds off and completes thought and affect simultaneously. In the same way,

(6) It is cool here under these green trees,

which is prosaically designative and at the same time manipulative (an invitation to the hearer to join the speaker), contrasts with

(7) Annihilating all that's made
    To a green thought in a green shade,

which is minimally designative and manipulative, and highly expressive. Marvell looked sharply enough to see not merely that the trees were green, but that sunlight filtered through leaves is green; then he passed beyond this observation to the startling and paradoxical "green thought." But his purpose was not merely to be paradoxical: Taken with the very strong "annihilating" in the first line, there is a concentration on the felt greenness of the experience to the exclusion of everything else.

These are some examples, then, of the way in which poetry, a typically humanistic language, refines common sense. As a final example, we may contrast what science and poetry, respectively, do with commonsense terms such as "water." At the commonsense level, "water" designates the colorless liquid that falls from the sky in rain, that bubbles up from the earth in springs, that surrounds us in the oceans, that is used for drinking, washing, and so forth. Science characterizes "water" in the same *kinds* of ways, though more precisely; thus, "water" is the liquid that freezes at 0° Centigrade, that boils at 100° Centigrade at sea level, that is used as the standard for measuring the specific gravity of other materials, and so on. But since there are many colorless liquids that look like water (e.g., alcohol, sap in trees) which do not have just these scientific properties, and since the term "water" has a number of extraneous emotive connotations, "H_2O" is typically substituted for "water" in the scientific languages.

Though the term "water" of common sense is retained in the humanistic languages, it is not used in a commonsense way. Suppose that there is something in the poet's foreground (some "vague, shoe-shaped" affect) demanding clarification. Perhaps it is a sense of the transitoriness—the impermanence—of fame or character. He may then write

(1) Here lies one whose name was writ in water

or

(2) Unstable as water thou shalt not excel.

In these sentences "water" is not functioning as it does in "May I have a glass of water?" In this request "water" is loosely designative, but sufficiently so for the commonsense purpose of quenching one's thirst. In (1), however, "water" is functioned expressively to focus the particular affect —a feeling about transitoriness—that was in Keats's foreground, nudging him. And so, also, for (2) and its author, the writer of Genesis. This requires a high order of precision, but a precision very different from the precision of science. Scientific precision requires selection of just those cues (perceptual or otherwise) that designate water and no other liquid. Expressive precision requires selection of just those associated linkages (e.g., the linkage of water with impermanence) which focus the affect now demanding clarification, and no other affect. If other linkages intrude, expressive force is weakened and perhaps destroyed. Such an intrusion occurs, I think, in a passage already cited in another connection (p. 19). In *The Horse's Mouth* Joyce Cary wrote that one of the characters wanted "things to come and lick his feet. But they can't—they can't lick. They can only fall about like a lot of loose rocks in a runaway train." Now "fall about," "loose rocks," and "runaway" all support the notion of irrational, unplanned meaninglessness. But "train" does not. Trains travel on tracks; they go in some particular direction. So far as "train" arouses these linkages for the reader, the affect Cary is aiming for is diluted.

Now, water certainly seems impermanent as compared with (say) marble or brass. On the other hand, since the times of the Greeks it has also been regarded as one of the four basic elements of things; this gives it a linkage with permanence, which has to be suppressed when the impermanence of water is being used to focus the affect the poet feels as he contemplates the transitoriness of fame.

Here are two somewhat more complex examples of a poetic use of the term "water":

(3)   and makes it indistinct
As water is in water.

(4) Not all the water in the rough rude sea
Can wash the balm off from an anointed king,

In (3) there is not merely a linkage with impermanence; there is also a linkage with dissolution. When we write in water, the writing at least remains intact until it fades away, but when we pour water into water, it disappears as we pour, without retaining even for a moment a distinguishable shape or character of its own. This linkage, together with the suggestion of a fading echo, which the repetition ("water . . . water") evokes, is thus much more powerfully expressive than "writ in water" or "unstable as water."

In (4) also, several separate linkages of "water" mutually reinforce one another. There are links with washing and with anointing, as well as with impermanence: the holy water used in the coronation of a king is contrasted with ordinary water; all the water in the ocean ("rough, rude" suggests not only the turbulent seas but the unruly mob swarming about the king's person) cannot eradicate the tiny drop of water that symbolizes Richard's right to rule. Here the poet exploits, by deliberately contradicting, the water/impermanent metaphor, as it occurs in (3).

Again, after Macbeth's terrible

(5) Will all great Neptune's ocean wash this blood
Clean from my hand? No, this my hand will rather
The multitudinous seas incarnadine
Making the green one red

we have Lady Macbeth's

(6) A little water clears us of this deed—

as flat and pedestrian as "Her hair is black," and for this very reason pointing up Lady Macbeth's effort to calm and strengthen her husband.

Water is not only physically cleansing, as in (5); it is also sacramental, as in (4). To say that water is sacramental is to say that some physical act in which water is used (dipping in holy water, baptism, ritual cleansing) long ago became a *non-verbal* symbol which clarifies and focuses the affect in question. As a result, the *verbal* symbol "water" has a double linkage, both literally and metaphorically, to purification. This linkage to purification is so deeply rooted that it may echo in a context where it is not at all primary:

(7) Water, water, every where,
Nor any drop to drink.

Taken at one level, the Ancient Mariner is expressing his physical thirst. The lines are certainly expressive at this level—partly through the ironic contrast between the presence of a great body of salt water and the total absence of potable water, partly through the sort of repetition and inversion that is effectively used in

Black, black is the color of my true love's hair.

But there is surely a strong, if submerged, reliance on the purification linkage: though the Mariner is surrounded by a beneficent, because divinely created, world, forgiveness and purification are withheld from him: he longs to repent and cannot. Thus, whereas the preference rules of scientific language require that "water" uniquely and unambiguously designates H_2O, the preference rules of humanistic language exploit multiple linkages: the poem gains expressive power by using "water" to mean at one and the same time, both something that relieves thirst and something that purifies. I believe some echo of this second linkage unconsciously echoes in the mind of even the most literal reader, increasing his sympathy with the Mariner's plight.

In the following lines from *The Waste Land* Eliot exploits the double linkage of water with physical thirst and with spiritual purification even more dramatically:

(8) Here is no water but only rock
Rock and no water and the sandy road
The road winding above among the mountains
Which are mountains of rock without water
If there were water we should stop and drink
Amongst the rock one cannot stop or think
Sweat is dry and feet are in the sand
If there were only water amongst the rock.[7]

The affect of thirst is built up by images of rock, desert, sand, and

[7] *Complete Poems and Plays* (New York: Harcourt, Brace, 1960), V, ll. 331–338.

drought, and by the way in which the lines themselves hammer away at us. In this context water is at once thirst-relieving, physically refreshing, and spiritually purifying (e.g., in the rite of baptism), and these connotations mutually reinforce one another. Moreover, in addition to the natural, or physical, associations, there are literary linkages as well—for instance, to the Bible and to the Book of Common Prayer: "My soul thirsteth for thee, my flesh also longeth for thee: in a barren and dry land where no water is," and "Must we fetch you water out of this rock?"

Every prior poetic use of a term becomes a part of the total reservoir of meaning available for subsequent exploitation by some other poet; every new usage changes, however slightly, the meanings available for future use. However, any particular linkage, if subjected to repeated use, either becomes literally designative or loses its effectiveness because it degenerates into a cliché. This, I should say, has now happened to "writ in water."

Sometimes an artist is so afraid of banality, so concerned to be novel, that he relies on idiosyncratic associations (e.g., his private association of red hair with injustice, because as a child he was beaten by a redhaired bully). Sometimes, of course, it isn't just fear of banality; the affect the artist is struggling to focus may be so deeply buried or so personal that he may be able to find no linkages to a common fund of associations. In either of these cases he will seem eccentric unless or until similar linkages occur in the experience of readers. And a sufficiently great artist can, as it were, make them occur for his readers. That is, the linkages he has forged operate very much as scientific hypotheses operate in other areas of experience—collecting, condensing, and organizing what would otherwise be inchoate, or even subliminal, feelings.

Expressive power, in a word, depends on tapping the great reservoirs of feeling accumulated over centuries. The mark of creative imagination in the arts is the capacity to condense feeling into ever new and fruitful metaphors, which have expressive power because they evoke old echoes in new contexts. Thus the problem of the artist is to work within a body of shared associative links—both inherited ones and those constantly emerging in the culture—but to do so without falling into routine or banality.

It is just the same with the scientific languages. Even major innovators do not completely break with the past. Every scientific discovery (corresponding to every new poetic insight) occurs within a context of the familiar; for example, Galileo continued to interpret certain of the pinpoints as "planets"; Einstein continued to interpret motion at relatively low velocities as Newtonian. On the other hand, unless there is *some* (however slight) reorganization of the familiar, there is no scientific advance. We can define "advance" in terms of the degree and the extent of the reorganization that occurs. So, in the humanistic languages there will be different degrees of newness in a "new" literary or artistic style. In both the sciences and the arts there are major innovators (e.g., Galileo, Michelangelo) who radically reorganize their respective fields, so that, as a result, we get a profoundly different perception of reality; and there are lesser innovators who work within the patterns of reorganization set by the major innovators.

This act of discovery, of reorganization, is like seeing the point of a joke or seeing the solution of an anagram. In all these cases, coming to see the connection involves a restructuring of experience: what was a meaningless welter, a hodgepodge, now makes sense—NECCIES suddenly becomes SCIENCE. In poetry, by contrast, seeing the similarity enables the poet to focus with precision an otherwise elusive affect. In most respects islands and thrones are so different that one could easily conceive of there being a conundrum—"When is an island a throne?"—with the answer turning on some trivial play on words. But there happens to be one, not at all trivial, similarity between islands and thrones, the discovery of which enabled Shakespeare to express his loyalty and patriotism, his pride in being an Englishman and a subject of the Queen:

This royal throne of kings, this scepter'd isle.

Here, then, as with Kekulé (pp. 187–188), we have a metaphor—a similarity is perceived between things otherwise very different. The similarity that Kekulé perceived resulted in the achievement of designative precision regarding the shape of the benzene molecule. Shakespeare's metaphor, on the other hand, resulted in the precise focusing of an affect (patriotism, loyalty). In both instances, however, the new insight—one designative, one expressive—was formulated in a new symbol; and in both the new symbol was constructed out of standard available symbolism.

"Benzene" and "ring" are in the standard, commonsense vocabulary, but they had never been related in this way. So are "throne" and "island" —and "Taj Mahal," for that matter—in the standard vocabulary. But in the standard vocabulary an island is no more a throne than a hat is the

Taj Mahal. Observing that the way I feel about this hat is similar to the way I feel about the Taj ("too grand by far") parallels my observation that the way I feel about this English island is similar to the way I feel about the English throne. The result in both cases—in all cases—is a new symbol that expresses the novel insight. For the poet (and also for the reader) it is an act of discovery: a discovery of the elusive, the haunting, the faintly familiar: "So *that* is what I have been feeling without fully understanding it!" we say. A welter of feeling has been distilled into clarity.

Unfortunately, just as the very success of some new scientific insight eventually destroys its value—after first meeting with resistance, it catches on and finally becomes a new dogmatism that obstructs new insights until it is dislodged in its turn; so with a novel poetic insight. Almost always, at first, it meets with resistance; it seems bizarre and outlandish to those whose perceptions are set in the older mold. Gradually, however, men find that the new symbolism opens up new ranges of experience. It directs their attention to aspects of their experience, to affects, they had not before been aware of. Dante's *dolce stil nuovo* is an example. So are the *Lyrical Ballads*. The latter opened up a range of feelings about nature that have since become a permanent possibility for men, but which, before Wordsworth and Coleridge found verbal symbols to condense these feelings, men had hardly been aware of.

So far I have been emphasizing how the humanistic languages (e.g., poetry) focus and clarify the affective elements present in a diffuse form in common sense. But I also said that none of the humanistic languages—not even the most expressive—is ever purely expressive; they all also function cognitively. For instance:

> She should have died hereafter;
> There would have been a time for such a word.
> To-morrow, and to-morrow, and to-morrow,
> Creeps in this petty pace from day to day,
> To the last syllable of recorded time;
> And all our yesterdays have lighted fools
> The way to dusty death. Out, out, brief candle!
> Life's but a walking shadow, a poor player
> Who struts and frets his hour upon the stage,
> And then is heard no more; it is a tale
> Told by an idiot, full of sound and fury,
> Signifying nothing.

What is being communicated? To translate in the baldest prose, it is the affect Macbeth experienced on being informed of his wife's death. All the images focus, through a variety of linkages, on the meaninglessness and futility of life. There is a linkage to time and then a linkage to light: time is not going anywhere; light illumines nothing. Light and time come together in "brief candle": the image of a momentary light flickering in the midst of a universal night. These are followed by other images of meaninglessness: the play that hangs together so poorly that a role could be omitted without making any difference; the incompetent actor; the noisy babbling of the madman. So, instead of the irruption of an irrelevant linkage, as in the Cary passage, we have reinforcement through a variety of linkages all directed to the same affect.

In these ways, then, a feeling—the poet's (or, if you prefer, Macbeth's) response to the fact of death—is being focused with precision. (Once again, this is not the designative precision of science but the expressive precision of humanistic language.) Because of this precision and clarity, we may for the first time understand something we have ourselves obscurely felt; and there is a release of tension as a result of getting a welter of our own impressions well-ordered. This is the mark of cognition: the reduction of curiosity that occurs when a puzzle is solved—why are those fixed stars moving? Because they aren't fixed; they are moons. What is it that I have been feeling? That life is flickering, dim, and short; in fact, a brief candle.

But there is more than just the clearing-up of a puzzle about the nature of an elusive feeling. And, in any case, we ourselves may never have felt the frustration and despair that Macbeth experienced. Perhaps our own response to the omnipresent fact of death is the assured faith expressed in the Book of Common Prayer. But, all the same, Macbeth's response is a *possible* response; it is one of the array of responses that men may make. As such, it sets our own, very different response in a context of alternatives. We *understand* (the cognitive factor) our own response better now, for seeing contrasting possibilities. Thus art does for us what travel is supposed to do (a banal comparison, this; a cliché). It "broadens" us; it makes our experience more meaningful by giving it a new dimension, by setting it in a context of possibles.

Here is another example:

> Whenas in silks my Julia goes,
> Then, then (methinks) how sweetly flows
> The liquefaction of her clothes.

For Herrick himself and for the reader the important thing about these lines is doubtless the way the image focuses a diffuse feeling about Julia—as the images in Macbeth's speech focus the very different diffuse affect that Macbeth was experiencing. No one, however, can deny that at the same time these lines call attention to a quality of silk that we might otherwise, being less observant than Herrick, never notice: that under certain circumstances and in certain lights silk seems to flow. The poet has seen a similarity between water and cloth, which are otherwise very different. By calling our attention to it he has added to our total sum of knowledge. That we may enjoy it, that it may focus an affect for us, is, from the present point of view, another matter.

Thus, in addition to the enlargement of experience that results from the focusing of an affect too obscure or too powerful or too complex to be readily understood, a work of art always has a second cognitive function in that it directs attention to some aspect of the world of fact. Sometimes of course this function is incidental, and sometimes the facts themselves are trivial. In the following lines, for instance, George Herbert tells us something about orange trees:

> Oh that I were an orange tree,
>   That busy plant!
> Then should I ever laden be,
>   And never want
> Some fruit for Him that dressed me.

Of course, we hardly need a poet to inform us that orange trees bear fruit; we may not even need a poet to tell us that, because flower, green fruit, and mature oranges are found on these trees at the same time, they appear continuously productive and therefore "busy." Indeed, Herbert directs our attention to this property of orange trees only because he sees a parallel between it and a solemn offering which enables him to focus the affect he is experiencing. Nevertheless, in the course of focusing this affect he does call our attention to an item of information about orange trees which we may have forgotten or never known.

Again, it may be thought (though I would not myself agree) that the fact about light filtering through foliage to which Marvell directs our attention, is quite trivial. Still, even though trivial, it *is* a fact—language does not cease to be informational merely because we are uninterested in, or happen already to know, the fact it brings to our attention.

To take another example: one of the climatic scenes in *The Portrait of a Lady* turns on the social convention that a gentleman does not remain seated while a lady is standing. When Isabel walks into a room and finds her husband and her best friend in this position, she at once realizes that their relations are far more intimate than she had believed them to be. Not everyone by any means is as sensitive to gesture and to social ritual as James was; not everyone, certainly, wants to be. Nevertheless, all of us, even not particularly sensitive people, are to some extent influenced by them, and most of us are more influenced than we are aware. By presenting us with characters who are unusually sensitive to such usages— even hypersensitive—James directs our attention to facts about ourselves and about the role of gesture and ritual which we might otherwise quite overlook. His novels bring these facts to attention as surely, indeed in some respects more surely, than a treatise on sociology might.

Thus a good many of the facts on which the power of expressive language rests are not exactly commonsense facts, even though they may not be scientific facts either. Poets and novelists are often singularly perceptive and sensitive observers. These observations enter their poems and novels; without them, there would be no poems and novels—at least, not *these* poems and novels. The Barchester novels, for instance, contain quite penetrating expositions of episcopal and archdeaconal realpolitik, which are as factual (for all that they are fictitious) as the writings of many historians and political scientists. The struggles of the Archdeacon, Mr. Slope, and Mrs. Proudie for control of the diocese illumine the political process, as a good treatise on presidential, or international, politics might—just as the tactics employed in *The Masters* to win the headship of a tiny, fictitious Cambridge college throw a good deal of light on strategies of actual, and much larger, political bodies. So, to pass on to novels of very different quality and different esthetic purpose, *A Passage to India* can be read today with profit by anyone who wants to understand the foreign policy of the subcontinent; and the conversations in *Ulysses* between Stephen and Haines, the visiting Oxford undergraduate, and between Stephen and Mr. Deasy, the schoolmaster, are illuminating as regards Anglo-Irish relations and The Trouble.

Nor do novelists merely direct our attention to particular facts, important or trivial, which we might otherwise overlook. In these examples we have already passed from the mere notation of fact to the presentation of psychological, sociological, or historical hypotheses—for instance, a hypothesis about the causes of The Trouble. A novelist may of course formulate such a hypothesis explicitly, either in his own person or in declarations that he puts in the mouth of one of his characters. But he need not do so. Indeed, characteristically, a novelistic hypothesis is not so much formulated as displayed—it is displayed or exemplified in the interactions of the characters. It is clear, for instance, that Joyce had formed a hypothesis about the deleterious effect of the Irish Catholic Church on Irish life and politics—a hypothesis displayed, for instance, in the bitter quarrel that broke up the Dedaluses' Christmas party in *The Portrait of the Artist as a Young Man* and in Father Conmee's walk through Dublin in *Ulysses*.

Doubtless this hypothesis functioned (in part) non-cognitively for Joyce. He hated the Church, and it relieved his feelings to suggest that it had had a harmful effect on Ireland. But Joyce was also puzzled about the causes of the relatively low economical and cultural level of Ireland; and the various hypotheses contained in the novels are attempts to satisfy this curiosity by exhibiting the effects of Britain's colonial policy and of the obscurantism of the Irish Church.

A novelistic hypothesis may be only incidental to the main purpose of the novel, or it may be central. Many of James's novels, for instance, turn on the relations between Americans traveling or living in Europe—Milly Theale, Maggie Verner, Lawrence Strether, Isabel Archer—and more experienced, upper-class Europeans, whose backgrounds and values are very different from those of the Americans. The interactions of James's characters deploy a hypothesis about the acculturation process, which does not differ in kind from one an anthropologist might frame about what happens to young and vigorous cultures when they come into contact with old and decadent ones. The novels do not verify this hypothesis, they exemplify it. Though exemplification is admittedly quite a different process from verification, James's novelistic hypothesis would actually be capable of about the same degree of verification as any formal anthropological hypothesis, since in both cases much the same sort of evidence would be required.

The exposition of a hypothesis is perhaps more congenial to a novel than to a poem, since in the novel the hypothesis can be displayed in terms of the interactions of the characters. But it is also possible in more epigrammatic form within the limits of even a very short poem. For instance, what we may call the Jamesian acculturation hypothesis is stated very compactly in one of Eliot's early poems, "Burbank with a Baedeker: Bleistein with a Cigar."

In the first stanza of this poem Burbank, an American, arrives in Venice, meets and falls for an Italian, the Princess Volupine. The next two stanzas leave Burbank and Venice altogether and contain instead allusions to Antony and Cleopatra and to Antony's defeat at Actium, for which Cleopatra was responsible:

> the God Hercules
> Had left him, that had loved him well.

Taken together, these three stanzas formulate very succinctly the sociohistorical hypothesis that there is a parallel between American-European interactions, on the one hand, and Roman-Egyptian interactions on the other hand. That this is deliberate, and indeed one of the "points" Eliot intends to make in the poem, is shown by a quotation, in the epigraph, of a phrase from *The Aspern Papers,* one of James's numerous novels concerned with the problems of acculturation.

So far, I have drawn my examples from novels set in real places or in obvious amalgams of real places (e.g., Barchester is a blending of Salisbury, Wells, and other cathedral towns). But everything I have said applies equally to novels remote from definite, concrete factuality; for instance, Kafka's *The Trial.* By the standards of science, even by the standards of common sense, there is a hopeless vagueness here, and readers who approach Kafka with these standards in mind will be baffled and irritated. Who is Joseph K? Who indeed? We are never told. In what city, in what country, do the events described occur? No answer. How long ago? There is no possibility of telling. What does the novel "mean"? Are we to understand it as a story of the workings of a huge amoral and totalitarian bureaucracy or as a morally sensitive man's efforts to account for his oppressive feeling of sin and guilt? Are we meant to take the events recorded as actual or as a dream encountered in some nightmarish sleep?

But this uncertainty that results from the multitude of *possible* (alternative) meanings is, I should say, precisely the author's point and the source of the novel's power. The author has seen, and wants us to see, similarities which we did not before know existed (conundrum principle: shock and resolution). For instance, there is the similarity between waking ("real") life and dream ("mere" imagination). The conundrum principle operates even though, in the novel, the similarities between the dissimilars are developed slowly and in detail, rather than, as in verse, abruptly and epigrammatically—"brief candle"; "royal throne."

And again, in the novel as in verse, the recognition of the similarity of dissimilars results in an expansion of self-knowledge: under certain circumstances I might behave like Joseph K. I too may become aware of a sin that is terribly real to me for all of its being inexplicable by the standards of conventional morality; I too may find myself immeshed in meaningless procedures from which I am unable to extricate myself; I too may find my guilt everywhere assumed, and myself even acting as if I were guilty, though all the while believing myself innocent.

Finally, whether or not it was intended as a political study, *The Trial* throws light on life and society—say, the Soviet purges in the mid-30's, even though it was written years before these trials occurred. That is, just as a scientific discovery reorganizes our background structures, with the result that the perceptual field makes more sense than it did before (we see moons instead of fixed stars); so this novel reorganizes the background structures with which we perceive certain aspects of totalitarian policy: we understand the Soviet trials better than we did before.

I can summarize what I have thus far said by describing scientific language as an "either/or" language and the humanistic language of poetry and the novel as a "both/and" language. Each starts from common sense and develops in its own way to accomplish its own end. In science the goal is, ideally, a completely unambiguous, one-to-one correspondence between a term and the class of entities designated by that term. The business of science is to study the interrelations among variables; and its underlying presupposition, obviously, is that there *are* variables, that is, that there exist such isolatable, discrete, recurring, self-identical units, or entities. The function of scientific definitions is to enable us to distinguish any one of these discrete classes from any other. As long as we use a term such as "green," we do not have a discrete class. There will be tones that everybody will allow to be members of the class; there will be tones that everybody will agree to exclude from the class (the not-green tones); but there will be other tones which some people

will include and some people will exclude. How are we to proceed? Shall
we count heads and settle on the majority opinion? Shall we ask Dr.
Gallup to conduct a poll? No; we substitute "vibration of such-and-such
a frequency" for "green." Now we know where we are. All tones without exception will *either* fall into the class *or* be excluded from it. Of
course, achieving a one/one correspondence between the term and some
class of entities is just the starting point; it is then the business of science
to formulate generalizations regarding the interactions between this and
other sets of entities. But this is why I call the language of science an
either/or language.

An example will make clear why I call humanistic language a both/
and language. One of the pigs in *Animal Farm* is called "Napoleon." In
the fable "Napoleon" designates this pig and no other pig on the farm,
but Orwell surely intends us to think also of Stalin and Caesar and
Franco and Bonaparte. . . . The events of the fable are presented in such
a way as to suggest these and other parallels. Now in an historical work
or a biography, "Napoleon" names one person and no other person: the
man who was born on Corsica, who came to power in the *coup d'état* of
the 18th Brumaire, who was crowned emperor, who died on St. Helena.
In order to distinguish this Napoleon from other Napoleons (e.g., his
nephew, Louis Napoleon), the historian unambiguously designates him
Napoleon I. The kind of double, triple, or quadruple reference that
"Napoleon" has in *Animal Farm* would be intolerable in an historical
treatise; on the other hand, the specificity of designation essential for the
latter would exclude the expressive and suggestive power obtained by the
use of "Napoleon" in *Animal Farm*. But *Animal Farm* aims in its own
way at generality, just as the sciences do: the parallels I have just referred
to between Napoleon the pig, Caesar, Franco, Stalin, Napoleon I, and
Louis Napoleon constitute a hypothesis about the rise and fall of tyrants.

As a second example of the both/and character of humanistic language,
here is a poem by Edward Weismiller called "College Town":

> How gravely all this goes. The street lights burst,
> At six o'clock, into their guarded flame;
> All corners, it is clear, are not the same:
>
> It matters where you turn
>
> To someone. . . .
>   Matters, of course, to you.

> Go gravely home, and kiss your wife, and weigh
> How best to be a father; say
> *Do you like school: What did you learn?*
>
> And nod, and nod. . . .
>   Somewhere in dark fields,
> Far from the level headlights of the cars,
> Someone stumbles, looks up: Oh stars, stars
> No matter where you turn. . . .[8]

Is the speaker nodding in agreement with what his child tells him? or in absentmindedness? or in drowsiness as he falls asleep? Who can say? Judged by the criteria of science or of common sense, the line is outrageously ambiguous. But its poetic effectiveness derives precisely from this ambiguity: from the reader's discovery that all of these noddings have a common quality which characterizes the dull, routinized, and pedestrian life of the speaker.

Thus one of the functions of the humanistic languages is to keep dissimilarities together, instead of separating them: life (which the scientist is intent on analyzing into unambiguously designatable entities such as proteins, carbohydrates, and fats) is both a candle *and* a poor player *and* a tale told by an idiot—all at once. This is why I call humanistic language a both/and language; and this is why, from the point of view of science, poetry is incorrigibly, hopelessly vague. But poetry is only vague by the standards of science. As I have tried to show, it has its own precision, and its own preference rules for achieving this precision.

v. *The Linguistic Continuum*

I have now given some examples of representative languages along the linguistic spectrum that I introduced earlier in this chapter (pp. 152–154). I shall next show that the locus of any particular language on this spectrum can be defined in terms of our concept of check-point, or resistance (pp. 86–91). A check-point, it will be recalled, is any fact to which a statement has to conform at the risk of being "false"—for instance, the observed movement of the stars was a resistance on which the old astronomy broke. (Check-points may of course resist policy as well as theory, but that is another story.) Further, when I was discussing scientific and legal facts, I pointed out that check-points differ in degree of

---

[8] *Harper's Magazine,* March, 1957, p. 80.

firmness. A check-point is relatively loose or soft, if it is capable of interpretation in several ways, that is, if two or more alternative theories conform to it equally well, or can be perceived as conforming equally well.

The extent to which expressive elements can enter a particular language is an inverse function of the firmness of the check-points. In the sciences, as we saw, the loose check-points of common sense (shoes, ships, trees) are replaced by much harder check-points (electrons, protons). Where the check-points are relatively firm (as in physics) the influence of affect is correspondingly slight. But even in physics there are frontier areas where check-points are relatively loose and, where, for instance, images that reflect unconscious cosmological preferences (e.g., Huygen's preference for continuity, Newton's preference for discontinuity) influence the shape of what scientists conclude are the "facts of the case."

When we move from physics (and chemistry and biology) to psychology and sociology, we move into areas where the check-points are much looser, but still not so loose as in common sense (compare "drive"—as defined by Clark Hull—with "electron" on the one hand, and with "chair" on the other). In the social sciences, in a word, since the check-points are looser than in physics, there is a greater opportunity for the affects and attitudes in our background structures to shape the "reality" we encounter. Examples of such influence are, for instance, the contrast between a behavioristic and a psychoanalytic interpretation of such a phenomenon (check-point) as stuttering. Such differences, like the differences in learning theory already referred to (p. 190), reflect different interests—for instance a high value attributed to rigor, which results in isolating each element in a learning situation for separate study, as contrasted with a high value put on an organic approach that treats learning as an on-going process in the personality as a whole.

In historical inquiry, the check-points are still looser (here we are virtually at the level of common sense). Accordingly, the influence of affect is even greater. Here, indeed, in addition to the various underlying cosmological preferences that operate in the physical and social sciences (e.g., monism/pluralism, etc.), we find political bias (e.g., the "Whig interpretation of history"; varying interpretations of Lincoln's decision to reinforce Sumter) and religious bias (e.g., Jesuit and Protestant interpretations of Luther's personality). Nevertheless, there are many histori-

cal check-points that have been established by generally accepted procedures, such as the use of archives and documents, and these limit the
influence of bias. For instance, there are documents showing that during
April, 1861, Lincoln talked to certain people and took certain actions
with regard to Sumter. It is possible for a Southern historian to interpret
these acts as a maneuver to put the blame for the conflict on the South,
where a Northern historian sees them as no more than the natural hesitation of a new president confronted with an appalling decision. Still,
the documentary evidence limits the extent to which it is plausible to
portray Lincoln either as a successful Machiavellian or as a hesitant
Hamlet.

Finally, still moving along the linguistic continuum, we come to the
humanistic languages, among them those, such as poetry, that are
highly expressive. Even here, however, there are check-points that limit
the free, unrestricted expression of affect. A trivial example is the line
already discussed:

> Black, black is the color of my true love's hair.

Certainly a poet who wishes to clarify his sense of the inevitable fragility
of love does not have to focus on a woman's hair; nor, if he happens to
do so, is he restricted to the actual color of his beloved's hair. Still, he
has to focus on *something:* otherwise nothing is clarified or communicated (self- or other-communication). And whatever object he focuses
on has a nature of its own which operates as a resistance, or check-point.
For instance, if it is hair that he happens to focus on, then there is a
range of colors he can work with, and there is also a range of excluded
colors. The poet could not have written

> Puce, puce is the color of my true love's hair

except as a joke or for comic effect, as W. S. Gilbert included

> The lady who dyes a chemical yellow
> Or stains her grey hair puce

among those for whom the punishment should fit the crime.

Not only is there no puce-colored hair in nature. It happens that the
color puce is not connected by any associative linkages with death, as
black is. Hence, though dresses are sometimes puce-colored, and though

> Puce, puce is the color of my true love's dress

is therefore not absurd, this line would not clarify the poet's sense of the precariousness of love. Not only the nature of hair but the actual associative linkages of hair and of black are check-points for the poet.

The need to conform to check-points, even if only in this minimal way, means that literature is, and inevitably remains, informational. Moreover, as we pass from lyric poetry to reflective poetry, the check-points become firmer and more restrictive. For instance, in *Paradise Lost* Milton's purpose was to justify the ways of God to man. He could do this only by accepting, and working within, certain check-points consisting in Christian doctrines of original sin, of divine omnipotence, and of human free will. Doubtless Milton had his own doctrinal interpretations, but these personal interpretations were themselves limited by other and still harder check-points, such as documentary evidence in the Bible and in the writings of the Church Fathers. Hence for all these reasons the range of free expression in *Paradise Lost* is much more restricted, the requirement of conformity to the relevant facts is much more severe.

Even where explication is not one of the writer's prime purposes, conformity to factuality can nonetheless be a major requirement. Henry James was primarily interested in moral questions—in the "close connection of bliss and bane, of the things that help with the things that hurt," as he said in one of his *Prefaces*. Nevertheless inner character—"somebody's right and ease and the other somebody's pain and wrong"—can only be displayed in some social context or other. And the novelist's narrative must take this context, whatever it happens to be, into account and conform to its factuality. Hence the manners, customs, dress, and social ideals of the English and American upper classes constitute important check-points for him (p. 210). This is true even of the novel or play that unfolds in a dream context—*The Trial* or "Nighttown" in *Ulysses*. The author is committed, by the very fact of its being a dream, to conforming to the facts of dream experience.

The same requirement of conformity to check-points holds for a non-verbal language such as painting. The painter always has a subject, and this subject is a check-point to which the painting must conform, just as the data of observation constitute the check-points to which a physical theory must conform. Of course there are enormous differences between the loose check-points of painting and the firm, determinate check-points of physics. Even within the field of painting, check-points differ a great deal in the restrictions they impose. If a painter has been commissioned to paint a portrait, the check-points are relatively firm—the painting must be a good likeness. Often, again, the painter's subject is specified by tradition or by history. It does not matter that these check-points may be quite fictitious (e.g., the amours of Venus and Mars). Even so, the subject exercises a restraint on the painter in the sense that he will be judged by his fidelity to whatever facts happen to be relevant to this subject. Nor are the relevant facts merely iconographical detail (Mars was a warrior, Venus was a beautiful woman; Christ died on a Latin, not a Greek, cross). Every particular subject entails certain psychological facts as well; these also are resistances, check-points, that limit the painter's freedom of expression—exactly in the sense that underestimation of the size of a dime limits the psychologist's freedom to formulate a simple, linear law of increasing distortion of coin-size (see p. 47).

At the humanistic end of the linguistic continuum, then, expressive components predominate because in the languages at this end (e.g., poetry, painting) the check-points are relatively loose. It is for this reason, of course, that the world of the poet is sometimes called a realm of imagination and is contrasted with the facts that science discloses. ("Imagination" may be either an honorific term or a pejorative one: to assign the poet to the realm of imagination may be either to exalt him or to relegate him to obscurity and insignificance, depending on the underlying values of the speaker.)

But even in poetry and painting all is not imagination. Indeed, in these areas there is something that corresponds closely to the testing of a scientific hypothesis by appeal to observation (i.e., to approved scientific check-points). For instance, someone may say of a painting of a tree that it is "not true to life" and mean simply that it does not look like a photograph of a tree. But here as elsewhere there are differences in the degree of sophistication with which men define their various criteria, including the criterion of "fidelity to life." Though every poet's hero, and every poet's villain, is his own, an imaginative construction, we readers test this construction against our own understanding of the good and evil in human nature. Only a devil, not a man, would act in this way, we may say. Yet, at the same time that such an imaginative construction is tested by its fidelity to present knowledge of human nature, it may also extend this knowledge and reshape it. Thus a particular poetic villain (Iago, for instance) may force us to reorganize the basic background structures by which we cognize villainy. Villainy, since

Shakespeare, is different from what it was before, because his conception of Iago has been assimilated (to some degree) into the common culture, that is, has become part of a new check-point.

In two respects, then, a poetic construct is like a scientific theory—both in that it is tested against present knowledge and also in that it may expand present knowledge. A poetic construct, like a scientific theory, survives testing if it "makes sense" in terms of what we already know, or think we know, about the area of nature with which it deals. It extends that knowledge if it helps us make better sense of this area than we made without it. One poetic construct replaces another poetic construct, as one scientific theory replaces another scientific theory, if, and so far as, we are enabled by means of it to make better sense of the relevant area of experience with the new construct than we could with the old one.

"Making sense" is a vague expression; but the expression is rightly vague, for the conditions under which things make sense are complex and variable. Certainly, even in scientific theory, esthetic conditions enter in (e.g., elegance, simplicity). Thus the heliocentric hypothesis made better sense to the early modern astronomers than the geocentric hypothesis because they valued simplicity highly. Fewer epicycles and less complicated paths were criteria of truth for them only because simplicity and mathematical elegance were meta-criteria. On the other hand, even in poetic constructions there are, as I have just shown, non-expressive, or "factual," conditions: we test Iago by the villains we have known, perhaps by the villainy we feel within ourselves. It follows, then, that though there are great differences between the humanities and the sciences, these are differences in degree, rather than radical differences in kind. There are great differences, for instance, between Shakespeare's freedom in the construction of his Iago and Galileo's freedom in the construction of his astronomical theory. Certainly Shakespeare was much less confined by "facts" than was Galileo. But it is easy to exaggerate the difference; it is easy to suppose that while Shakespeare was moving with complete freedom in a realm of imagination and responsive only to certain inner needs that demanded expression, Galileo was the cold, emotionless scientist, submissive only to the "stubborn and irreducible facts."

It is a comment on our society that it will probably be easier to convince people of the factual aspect of artistic creativity than of the imaginative and creative aspect of scientific theorizing. Thus, after a little thought, most people may be willing to admit that Shakespeare was not completely free to create any sort of Iago he wanted; he had, people will see, to make Iago "believable." But they may insist that science is very different. The whole business of science, it will be said, is to "explain" the facts, and you explain the facts when you discover a law that formulates a regular relation between them, such that, when such-and-such events have occurred, you can predict the occurrence of such-and-such others. But what *are* the facts that are to be explained by science? One such fact (up to January, 1610) was that all the stars, except the seven planets, are fixed in a sphere that turns about the earth; and scientific theory stood or fell, depending on whether or not it fitted with this fact. After January, 1610, the facts were different, and they were different because the observed data (the pinpoints of light) were interpreted by a new set of background generalizations. Thus, if in the short run facts test theory, in the long run theory tests facts.

Both in the sciences and in the humanities (it is important to see) this contrast between short- and long-run occurs. At any given time, we find ourselves in a world that is independent of us. This is so because at any given time most of the members of a culture are interpreting their experience in terms of background structures that are in many respects similar. The practical importance of these similarities causes us to concentrate our attention on them (on the least-common-multiple aspects of the various background structures) and to ignore the individuating characteristics that actually differentiate every man's background structures from every other man's. As a result, at any given time it seems to us that we are exploring an independently existing "reality" out there. We forget, or fail to realize, that other men at other times and in different cultures have encountered vastly different realities that seemed as independent to them as our reality does to us, and for exactly the same reasons.

So far, I am speaking of ordinary minds: at any given time all minds save those of the highest creative power accept the check-points that their culture offers them and work within these check-points—that is, use them as the basis for explanation and expression. In the humanities these check-points include not only what is believed true, at that time, about the color of hair or the nature of villainy, but also the current conventions of diction and of style: at any given time it seems "natural" to us to express ourselves in certain standard patterns of imagery, of metaphor, and so forth. In the sciences the resistances are the "facts" as known at that time (e.g., fixed stars in the sixteenth century, gaseous nebulae in the nineteenth).

Both in the humanities and in the sciences, genius does not passively accept all the check-points that the culture offers it; it reshapes them by a more or less radical reconstruction of the underlying background structures. Hence the difference between short-run and long-run may also be described as the difference between the ordinary mind and the genius.

Again, both in the sciences and in the arts, genius involves the imaginative perception of a new connection (Kekulé and the benzene ring; Shakespeare and the island that is a throne).

Finally, both in the sciences and in the arts, this reconstruction, however radical it may be, is never *total.* Even the genius works within a context, and the test of the success of his reconstruction is the improved understanding (in scientific reconstruction) and the improved expression (in esthetic reconstruction) of this larger context that it makes possible.

Thus the sciences and the humanities are to be conceived, according to the conceptual scheme proposed, as forming a continuum, ranging from sciences such as physics, to sciences such as sociology, to history and common sense, to literature and the arts. All of these various languages are at once explanatory *and* expressive processes. Something is *expressed* in the sciences (e.g., a preference for discontinuities and for particle models in Newton's theory of light, in contrast to Huygens'), but expression is generally subordinated to explanation. Something is *explained* in the arts (e.g., in *Macbeth,* what ambition will do to a man), but explanation is generally subordinated to expression.

Or, to put this differently, and in terms of the process by which backgrounds organize foregrounds: the world we experience in the sciences is as much a construction as the world we experience in the arts, but it is a different sort of construction because the interpretative backgrounds we employ in the two sorts of process are different. However, the two sorts of backgrounds are not radically different in kind: *all* backgrounds contain generalizations of varying degrees of explicitness; in *all* backgrounds, affects are imbedded. The place a particular cognitive process occupies on the continuum is determined by (1) the character of the check-points, and (2) the freedom for affect to influence the product of the interpretative process.

Accordingly, to say—some people do—that the world that science discloses is "more real" than the world of art and of literature, is simply to reveal a preference for the sorts of values—externality, discreteness, order, simplicity, hierarchy, for instance, and the practical and technological consequences that depend on them—that are attainable in this linguistic medium. To say, as others do, that the world of the arts is more real is simply to express a preference for the different values realizable in this medium. A man who tries to live exclusively in one of these "realities" (it does not matter which one), and who accomplishes this difficult feat only by downgrading the other or closing his mind to it, is simply depriving himself of ranges of experience which he might otherwise enjoy. As soon as we understand the reciprocal relation that exists between language and reality, we will see that the sciences cannot possibly contradict the humanities. Indeed, far from contradicting, they supplement one another.

VI THE ETHICAL LIFE

IN THIS CHAPTER and the next I shall continue to apply the notion of a linguistic continuum to the supposed conflict between the scientific and the humanistic conceptions of life. And I shall begin with some ethical issues, for it is here—in the contrast between man as a free moral agent making responsible choices and man as a machine (or, if not a machine, a collection of protein molecules, amino acids, and polypeptide chains)—that the two views seem to come into sharp opposition (see pp. 10–12).

In this connection it is important to distinguish between what I shall call policy problems and the problems of metaphysical ethics. This parallels the distinction between science, on the one hand, and epistemology (or theory of knowledge) on the other. The sciences ask questions of the form "What is that?—Why is it behaving as it is?" Epistemology asks second-order questions, such as "What do we mean when we ask, 'What is that?'" It is concerned, in a word, with the sort of problem we have been considering in earlier chapters—with questions about the nature and status of those facts whose interactions the sciences investigate; it is concerned with questions that arise in the course of trying to answer factual questions, but which are not themselves factual questions and so are not the subject matter of any of the special sciences.

In a similar way, what I call metaphysical ethics is concerned with second-order questions that may arise in the course of resolving policy problems. For instance, are there moral laws? and, if so, how do we know them? Is there a supreme good and what is it? Is the will free, and if it is not, how can we hold people responsible for what they do? In contrast to such large-scale questions, there are what I call policy questions. A policy problem is the problem of deciding what to do whenever we don't know what to do next: for instance, when a rat is confronted with two indistinguishable cards and so no longer knows which way to jump. Policy problems may be matters of personal morals, as when a man has to decide whether to keep a promise that he has made, or matters of public policy, as when a Highway Commission has to decide on the route for a new freeway. Policy problems may be relatively trivial, as when we have to choose between roast beef and roast lamb on a table d'hôte menu; or relatively serious, as when (in *By Love Possessed*) Arthur Winner has to decide between his loyalty to his partner, who is involved in a large embezzlement, and his duty to expose the crime.

Usually philosophers have not drawn this distinction, as I have, between questions of policy and questions of metaphysical ethics. For the most part they have chosen to concentrate on the distinction between relatively trivial policy problems (such as whether to order roast beef or roast lamb) and relatively grave policy problems (such as whether to protect one's partner or do one's duty as a citizen). Philosophers have tended to regard the former sort of problem as too inconsequential for them to bother their heads about, and the latter sort as too serious for anyone but philosophers—who are supposed by philosophers to have special talents for dealing with them. Further, instead of seeing that what I have called the problems of metaphysical ethics are not policy problems at all, they have lumped them together with grave policy problems as the special domain of philosophical inquiry.

To summarize what I shall argue in detail in this chapter, I believe, first, that the difference between trivial and important policy problems is only a difference in degree—it is a trivial difference, not an important one. The same sorts of strategies are appropriate for the one sort as the other, and these strategies are not especially "philosophical" at all. In earlier times, when little was known about economics, sociology, and psychology, a philosopher's proposals for solving complex policy questions were as relevant as those of the next man. But with the development of the policy sciences, the formulation of high-level policy for resolving particularly difficult choice-situations has largely passed to other hands. In saying this, however, I don't mean that philosophy has nothing to do with policy problems. On the contrary, I believe that the concepts I have introduced in earlier chapters can illumine the nature of policy problems in general, and so have a significant bearing, even though only indirectly, on policy formation, both at the individual and at the public level.

Second, I believe that the distinction between the sort of question that is a policy problem (whether trivial or important) and the sort of question that I have called a problem of metaphysical ethics is important, not trivial. It is fundamental because, as soon as we realize that questions about the moral law and the supreme good are of a different order from policy questions, the way is open for dealing with them effectively. Since these problems of metaphysical ethics have been debated for centuries without a consensus being reached, many people have concluded that further preoccupation with them is a waste of time. This inference seems to me mistaken. Questions that men and women return to again and again, over the centuries, and despite the seeming sterility of all discussion, are by definition serious issues, highly relevant to our human condition. Here again, the concepts introduced in earlier chapters will show why these questions are important and also why their solution has so long eluded us.

So much for preliminaries. I shall first discuss the nature of policy problems and show that many mistaken assumptions cluster around this notion. Since the questions of metaphysical ethics typically arise out of the anxieties and frustrations to which these mistaken assumptions give rise, I shall then go on to deal in turn with some of the major questions of metaphysical ethics and show that, once these are rightly understood, the ethical view of man does not in the least conflict with the scientific view of him.

i. *Policy Problems*

The main thing to see about policy problems is that they do not differ in kind from cognitive problems. Both are discrimination problems that arise when there is failure to fit between a present foreground and the background structure by means of which we are trying to interpret it. In both cognitive and policy problems, failure to fit may be more or less prolonged, more or less serious. For instance, in policy problems, it may involve merely a relatively routine search among a limited number of standard available strategies ("Shall I part my hair behind? Do I dare to eat a peach?") or it may require a radical reorganization of background structure to find a novel strategy for dealing with a new situation (e.g., the possibility of so-called "Doomsday Machines" which could destroy the whole world creates a situation in which none of the standard available military strategies is appropriate).

Again, though we notice the interpretative process only in cases of failure to fit, there is interpretation (smooth) in all action, just as in all perception and cognition. Except for automatic reactions to stimuli (e.g., the knee-jerk), there has been learning. As a result, even in very simple behavior, we are for the most part not reacting to stimuli but responding to a situation. That is to say, items have been laid down in the background structure which affect the responses we make. Background structures contain not merely neutral generalizations but generalized instructions, and often (especially in the commonsense parts of background structures) the same item is at once a generalization and an instruction. For instance, "An apple a day keeps the doctor away" is both a generalization (at the commonsense level) about the relation between two variables, apple intake and health, and also an instruction to eat lots of apples.

This is why the end-products of interpretative processes are not neutral, purely cognitive meanings, but also action meanings. For instance, we do not merely interpret the red color patch we see ahead of us above the street as a traffic light; we also interpret it as a stop signal. Or we begin an afternoon's walk, look up at the sky, and note a black cloud. Black cloud means "rain coming" (cognitive meaning), but it also means "Better go back and get your umbrella" (action meaning). Long before a particular face and form mean "mother" for the baby, they mean "Get ready; food coming," or "Cuddle coming," or "Dry coming." "Mother," as meaning "female parent," is a late arrival; and "mother" never loses the cluster of action meanings it originally had, even though, as the baby grows into a boy and man, it stops getting ready to cuddle or to have its diapers changed whenever it sees that particular face and form.

It is, of course, because of all the affects associated with the action meanings of words that words have expressive potentiality; this is why, from the start, fact and value are intertwined in experience.

But what, then, is the difference between a cognitive problem and a policy problem? If someone is primarily curious and the diffuseness of the field is blocking some identification he wants to make (Is the thing in the path a snake or a stick?), I call the problem cognitive. If the diffuseness of the field is blocking some action (shall we advance or retreat?), I call it a policy, or practical, problem. Thus there is nothing about a problem that makes it intrinsically cognitive or intrinsically practical. The same problem can be cognitive for one person (the ophiologist) and practical for another (a timid soul who fears snakes), or a problem may change from being primarily cognitive to being primarily practical (or vice versa) while we are engaged in trying to solve it.

This is why I said that cognitive and policy problems do not differ in kind. Even in problems that people are likely to think of as "purely" contemplative, there is a policy aspect. For as soon as we clear up the cognitive puzzle, we always act on our findings in some way, if only to write down the answer we have reached or report it to somebody else. On the other hand, there is a cognitive aspect to every practical, or policy, problem, since we lack the resources (e.g., adequate perceptual cues) to decide which of several possible policies is the right one.

Given the same degree of diffuseness in the field, policy problems are often more difficult to solve than cognitive problems. In the first place, problem-solvers are likely to be more emotionally involved in their policy problems than in their cognitive problems. In the second place, despite great advances in recent years, psychology, sociology, and the other behavioral sciences are far behind astronomy, physics, and chemistry. As a consequence, much of the information that is essential for reaching sound decisions is simply lacking—what, for instance, is the relation between prejudice and overcrowded housing? between vitamin deficiency and a tendency to respiratory infection? between a particular pattern of family relationship and a disposition to schizophrenia?

Since enthusiasts sometimes claim more for the policy sciences than they have yet achieved, it is sound for humanistically inclined critics to point out the danger of relying too much on them in their present state. But it is quite unsound to attack them as necessarily inhumane or prejudicial of morals. Such attacks are often motivated by a fear of change, by a preference for the vague (but comfortingly familiar) generalizations of common sense in contrast to the more rigorous (but often novel) generalizations obtained by the application of scientific intelligence to the study of behavior. And even when the motive is not intellectual obscuratism, we have to ask, What exactly do those people mean who say, "But science is not enough"?

Perhaps they mean that science as an abstract *vis cognoscens* is not enough. If so, they are correct. A mind without interests of any kind certainly could not make decisions, since decision involves choosing among interests. But to use the expression "science is not enough" in this way is misleading. For as I have already pointed out, the very notion of an abstract, "pure" curiosity drive is a figment of the philosophical imagination (pp. 135–138). Even in the sciences, even in dealing with cognitive problems, the intellect is always interested; and to say that it is interested is to say that it is concerned with values.

However, what some people want to say is not merely that there must be a concern with values, but that there must be a commitment to a certain set of values. This puts the cart before the horse. For among the jobs of intellect is precisely the job of determining which values, under which circumstances, are those worth committing ourselves to. What is required to make this determination is a quality or character of mind that I shall call acuity, or sensitivity to the multiple, diverse, and often incompatible values that cluster about alternative courses of action; sensitivity both to the values that may be realized by adopting some particular policy and to those that are inevitably foregone by the adoption of that policy. For the most fundamental fact in any choice situation is precisely the hard fact of choice—if something is gained, something else is always lost. The various values realizable by any course of action are like the visual and auditory cues that guide problem-solving when we are confronted with an ambiguous field. The keener our appreciation of the various potential achievements attainable by means of various alternative policies and the finer our weighing of their relative significance, the sounder our ultimate decision will be.

I have already discussed the difficulty of discerning perceptual cues, especially when there is a failure to fit between the perceptual cue and the standard background. For instance, there was the problem of discerning the difference between the grays of two cards in front of the jumping stand, and there was the problem of discerning the difference between a star that doesn't move and the movement of one that cannot move. It is quite acceptable to distinguish between physical acuity and moral acuity—that is, between a sensitivity to visual or auditory nuances (e.g., pinpoints of light that move slightly from one night to the next) and a sensitivity to value nuances, such as the difference between mine and thine or the difference between what is my duty and what is to my interest. But it is easy to exaggerate this difference. There are no "bare" facts whose differences are perceived by an exclusively physical acuity, nor any "bare" values whose differences are perceived by a wholly distinct moral acuity. As we discern any distinction (factual) we respond to it either positively or negatively. Every discerned distinction, that is to say, is at least to some degree affectively toned; on the other hand, every affect occurs in a context of facts that are its causes and its effects. Hence "physical acuity" has a moral aspect—the satisfactions (or dissatisfactions, as the case may be) experienced in connection with the physical nuances discerned in the field; and "moral" acuity has a physical aspect (the factual relationships obtaining among the events that constitute the various strategies available to us).

Affect without adequate information concerning the relevant factual context is sentimentality: for instance, a concentration on the undoubted value of human life so exclusive that it overlooks the adverse affective consequences of a dogmatic pacifism. On the other hand, information without affect is barbarism. This is why a computer (unless it could be programmed both to feel affects and also to become increasingly sensitive to them through further experience) would not be a good decision-maker. It might make "sound," but at the same time barbaric, decisions. It would lack what we may call wisdom, a quality that is quite compatible (alas!) with fallibility.

At this point someone may say: "But what you are calling 'moral acuity' is nothing other than what most people call 'conscience.' You gain nothing by abandoning a perfectly familiar term except disguising the fact that you are not saying anything new." I agree that I am talking about what other people call "conscience" and that in this sense I am not saying anything new. Here again, as so often, what looked at the start like a deep metaphysical dispute about what is true—this time about what more is needed beyond science—turns out to be only a dispute about how best to describe what everybody agrees is true. However, I believe that "acuity" calls attention to aspects of the field which "conscience" fudges; and in this sense I *am* saying something new, or at any rate something overlooked by people who talk the language of conscience.

Specifically, "conscience" suggests that sensitivity to values is a special sort of power, if not supernatural at least non-natural in some vague way. People who prefer this term are likely to regard conscience as sacrosanct and immune to criticism or analysis. I prefer the term "acuity" because it does not have these connotations; it suggests what it seems to me important to emphasize—that the capacity for discerning value differences is fallible and corrigible, that is, it can be improved by practice. Everyone agrees that this is true of visual or auditory acuity. Some people are born with a greater capacity for distinguishing auditory nuances than other people. If someone is born tone-deaf, he is hardly likely to develop into a sensitive and skilled musician; nevertheless, within the range of acuity determined by inheritance, the kinds of training, the kinds of experience, and the kinds of incentive a child encounters determine whether or not he develops a high degree of auditory acuity. All of this seems to me to apply equally to conscience: there are people with too tough consciences, who are too insensitive to value differences; there are also people who are too sensitive, at least to certain ranges of value. As we come to know more about the variables that bear on this aspect of personality, much can be done both to raise the general level of moral acuity and also to relieve the morbidly sensitive, or too tender, conscience.

I can reformulate all of this in terms of the concepts of foreground, background, and interpretative process. What is required for sound decision-making is backgrounds that are sufficiently complex and highly structured to order the field well, but at the same time sufficiently flexible to permit us to experience any nuances of difference and of novelty that may occur in the field, whether these nuances be primarily facts (visual or auditory differences) or primarily values (e.g., difference between mine and thine). There is certainly a difference between a factual difference and a value difference, but the difference between these differences is less important than the similarities; and less important, also, than the difference between a background flexible enough to distinguish differences (whether factual or valuational) and a background so rigid as to blind us to these differences.

And what I said about the role of language in cognitive problem-solving (p. 123) applies equally in the field of policy decision: language is both a help and a hindrance. Without language, background structures could never become highly structured. Specifically, without a language in which to fix the values we aim at attaining, long-range planning would be wholly impossible. We would live from moment to moment, our acts cued off by present pleasures and pains. On the other hand, language is always tending to fix values too firmly, too rigidly, too abstractly. Thus a man may say that he wants to be healthy, wealthy, and wise (or, for that matter, that he wants to be truthful, virtuous, and dutiful); and he may regard these as self-identical "ends" that he has wanted all his life and that he shares with other men. Of course, he recognizes that his ideas of how to become healthy may change as he acquires new information about calories and cholesterol; but, because he continues to use the same old words, he may not see that his idea of what it *means* to be healthy changes as well. Similarly, one's conception of virtue alters as the attainment of any particular level opens up new possibilities that one had not been virtuous enough to conceive at an earlier stage. One of the main uses of literature and poetry is precisely to help in this process of expansion. In the last chapter I emphasized the cognitive function of the humanistic languages. But they also have the immensely important practical function of breaking down the rigid abstractions and oversimplifications of common sense, calling our attention to changes in our value systems which we have overlooked, and forcing us to scrutinize more closely the rich diversity of the valuational field in which we must make our choices.

In a word, the goods men aim at, as well as the character of the reality they find "out there," are functionally related to the degree of organization of the backgrounds they use to solve their problems. We start life with a few simple conceptual categories and with strong, but relatively inchoate, dispositions to act and to appraise. As children, we see things in strong colors, as whites and blacks, sheep and goats; our sorrows and our joys are unmixed, unclouded by reflection; and, since we live in the present, they are untouched by memory or anticipation. Some people seem hardly to get beyond this level; they continue all their lives to rely on background structures that limit the problem-solver to an all-or-none effect. As a result, decision-making may come to be conceived, as the Utilitarians conceived it, as consisting in totaling up the various "units" of satisfaction obtainable after so-and-so many neutral acts ("means") are performed.

On the other hand, we may gradually develop more subtly articulated background structures. Partly by trial and error, partly by the application of scientific knowledge, partly by a process of self-examination in which the humanistic languages play their part, we may learn to appreciate nuances, to find interconnections, to see that the actual always stands in a context of possibles which affect its character as actual. In such circumstances, decision is more difficult than when it follows the all-or-none pattern; indeed, *simple* solutions now become impossible, since satisfactory solutions, even of the simplest policy problems, are now seen to involve continuations and reconciliations, rather than complete inclusions or complete exclusions. Awareness of the complexity of even the easiest ethical problems is what is sometimes called the tragic sense of life, but tragedy in this sense is not incompatible with joy.

These are, so far, only very broad generalizations. Therefore I shall give some examples that illustrate them and that hopefully carry us farther. I will start with a problem that is socially trivial, though it may be of some importance to the person concerned and to his friends—a man who has to decide what wines to lay down in his cellar. No one would deny that there are differences among wines; some are poor, some good, some excellent. There are nuances both of fact (e.g., the provenance of the wine) and of value (the qualities appreciated and enjoyed). To the uneducated drinker, every bottle tastes the same: it is all "red ink"; he might as well be drinking a *vin ordinaire,* instead of a Romanée-Conti. The connoisseur not only distinguishes claret from burgundy, and one burgundy from another; he distinguishes the vintage of one year from that of another, and the produce of one vineyard from that of its neighbor. How is a good wine taster made? The answer is, by tasting. Certainly not simply by reading books about wines or by reaffirming the valuations his grandfather made. For old wines deteriorate and great new wines are laid down. And in any event, there is all the difference in the world between mouthing somebody else's assessment, even if it be still applicable, and an assessment that is made in the mouth of the taster himself.

Sensitivity to nuances of difference between wines certainly depends to some extent on initial differences (organic) in tongue and taste buds.

But to a large extent it depends on experience—on a critical exploration of the field. As the wine taster comes to know more and more wines, he acquires a complex, highly articulated background structure. And, ideally at least, the concepts in this background structure function not merely as static pigeonholes but as active hypotheses. As a result, each level of sensitivity achieved becomes the basis for a further refinement of sensitivity. Thus, ideally, the connoisseur carries about with him a cognitive map that is constantly growing more detailed and more highly organized.

And this cognitive map is at the same time an appreciative map. Differences are not merely noted by the connoisseur; they are appreciated. "Bouquet" and "body," for instance, are the names of nuances that the connoisseur at once discerns and enjoys. This is why "sensitivity" is a good term to use in this connection: it denotes the discernment of differences not ordinarily detected; but it denotes more than a mere neutral taking note of them: it connotes a stance toward, a weighing of, the differences discerned. The wine taster's enjoyment of wine is thus richer and deeper (his satisfactions are more satisfactory) than those of the inexperienced drinker who "misses" the body and bouquet of a fine burgundy. But also—alas!—if the connoisseur is deprived of access to good wine, his deprivation is greater. This is the risk that sensitivity always runs: chance of greater disappointment always accompanies opportunity for greater satisfaction.

This wine-tasting example points up how increases in sensitivity (in the double sense of discerning and of appreciating) grow out of experience—providing, of coure, that the drinker's attitude toward his experience is flexible, explorative, and experimental. But the prominence of connoisseurship in this example may suggest small elites who have the leisure to cultivate their palates. Further, since the enjoyment of wine is a socially useless pursuit, the example may suggest that I am advocating a passive and selfish sensuality—at best, a sophisticated and refined hedonism.

Here, therefore, is another example—a Highway Commission deciding the route of a new freeway. If their decision is made on the basis of engineering criteria alone (e.g., maximum rate of permissible curvature; maximum gradient), the route is relatively easy to fix. There are standard procedures for evaluating alternative routes in these terms and for reaching fairly definite answers. If the decision is made on the basis of political criteria (who will squawk loudest if the freeway goes through his property? who has the most influence?), the solution, though more difficult to obtain, is still in principle fairly simple. On the other hand, it is more difficult to get agreement on the value of unimpeded open spaces or on the beauty of a range of hills, and still more difficult to decide how much to weigh such considerations against, say, economy.

The Commission should certainly pay attention to engineering criteria; nor ought it ignore political criteria, since, given the world as it is, it is often necessary to make concessions if one wants to accomplish anything at all. But surely it ought also to take account of less easily measured social and esthetic factors. I shall call a Highway Commission "just" if it aims at some sort of overall balancing of gains and losses. But we want from it even more than justice; we want "wisdom" as well: we want the members not merely to have the honesty to balance the gains and losses that they themselves happen to see; we want them to have the capacity to see and to take account of all the kinds of values and interests involved, including those the average citizen doesn't now see but which, in the years to come, he will wish he had seen now. Political wisdom and the sensitivity of connoisseurship do not differ in kind; they differ only in difficulty, because of the greater range and variety of the values affected by alternative policies open to the Highway Commissioners, and because of the greater seriousness of a decision that affects large numbers of people. But political wisdom is like connoisseurship in that it too requires the cultivation or education of congenital capacities— for the discernment and appreciation of nuances that less sensitive individuals might overlook.

Thus "sensitivity," as I am using this term, should not be construed merely as a passive enjoyment; on the contrary, it issues in action— action that is effective precisely because it is responsive to nuances discerned in the field. Nor should it be construed as a merely selfish hedonism; it involves appreciating and weighing not only one's own personal satisfactions but also the satisfactions of others.

This brings us to egoism vs. altruism, which has traditionally been regarded as one of the main problems of ethical theory. Most philosophers have concluded, first, that people ought to be altruistic, and second, that, left to their own devices, they won't be. But philosophers have seldom agreed on the arguments in favor of altruism, and their inconclusive debates seem in large measure to result from an over-rigid dichotomizing of a kind we have so often encountered in our discussions of epistemological confusions. It is impossible to be either as much of an egoist or as much of an altruist as the philosophical debaters of this issue presuppose. For life does not divide neatly into such simple all-or-none options. It is tempting, for instance, to call a baby the complete egoist, and to say that the only good he conceives is his own. But this is inaccurate; babies do not make a distinction between self and others, and nobody should be called selfish who does not see that there are interests other than his own. Perhaps people mean that any adult who behaved as a baby does would be a complete egoist. But would—could—any adult behave in this way? If an adult's conception of now and here were as narrow as a baby's, we should think him not only an egoist but a madman. For, as we grow up, we find our lives involved, inevitably and irretrievably, in the lives of others. Increasingly, the now and the here turn out to be continuous with the later and the over there. Indeed, the more we come to know about the complex of interactions in which we live, the more extensive we find this mutual involvement of self and others to be. Thus, to a large extent, the conflict between altruism and egoism results from a simple failure to perceive the facts—a failure that results in its turn from interpretation of the foreground by means of a background structure containing faulty metaphysical notions.

To conceive the self as an enclosed, encapsulated atom glaring across an ethical gulf at other, similarly self-enclosed units is to fall victim to the same epidermis fallacy that has led people to suppose that the self stares across an ontological chasm at the objects it perceives (pp. 96–97). In experience—in distinction from some particular metaphysical theory—the self reaches as far as its grasp. It *is* wherever and whenever its "concerns" extend. We often say, speaking loosely, that a woman sacrifices herself for her children, a man for his family, a college president for his institution. But what we mean is that, for us, with our very different interests, to act as they do would be a sacrifice. Given *their* interests, it may not be sacrifice at all. The president may be so deeply involved in the prospects of his college that his own ego is expanded in and by its successes. Does this mean, then, that the seemingly altruistic college president is actually selfish? Possibly, but not necessarily.

It would be selfish, for instance, if he devoted himself so completely to the college as to neglect his wife and children, whose well-being he ought also, certainly, to consider. Thus, paradoxically, conduct that from outside looks highly altruistic may, on a closer look, turn out to be selfish.

How much ought the president sacrifice his family for the college? Surely the only possible answer is, it depends on the circumstances—on the needs of the college, which may vary from time to time; on the needs of his family which will also vary, depending on the age of his children, the health of his wife, and numerous other considerations. Accordingly, apart from saying that each specific case has to be dealt with on its merits, I can only emphasize that appropriate policies are more likely to be reached by those who approach decision-making with flexibility and intelligence and with sensitivity to all the values involved, including their own satisfactions as well as the satisfactions of other people.

Just as there are too-tender and too-tough consciences, there are those who are too altruistic (not sufficiently sensitive to their own satisfactions) and others who are not sufficiently altruistic (not sufficiently sensitive to the satisfaction of others). Indeed, these failures in sensitivity and perception are closely connected, since one of the chief objects of the scrutiny of conscience is precisely the self-other relationship. Usually, and perhaps rightly, people are concerned lest they—or, at least, lest others —be too selfish. But it is arguable that at least as much harm is done in the world by excessive altruism as by excessive selfishness. Large and grandiose ideals seem to fascinate some minds. Such people may expend great efforts on projects that, however noble, are impracticable, while they neglect more modest but also more realizable goods nearer home, such as the well-being of family and friends. The test in any particular circumstance (and *every* decision-situation is particular) is surely what satisfactions are achievable in *those* circumstances. There are circumstances in which it is better, and therefore more moral, to aim at "selfish" goods (i.e., those with a limited range of effect) than to aim at "altruistic" ones (i.e., those with a wider range of effect), since, in these circumstances, the former are realizable and the latter are not.

So far I have been discussing problems that, though difficult enough, are nevertheless relatively small-scale—that is, problems that arise within a larger context of well-established procedures, routines, institutions, and norms. Highway Commissions, for instance, operate within a normative framework explicitly established by legislative action, reaffirmed, if necessary, by judicial review, and sustained by, and reflecting, widely accepted values of the society in which the freeways are to be built (e.g., a prevalent aspiration for faster transportation and fewer motor accidents).

But at times large parts of this institutional and normative context, whose existence makes specific decisions relatively easy, come into question. Established institutions no longer work; established norms no longer function normatively. Such a major policy breakdown exactly parallels the kind of major cognitive breakdown described in earlier chapters. The collapse of the Roman republic in the first century B.C. is an example. A social system, a set of institutions, that had worked well in earlier times, when Rome was a small city-state exercising its imperium only in nearby areas, became increasingly inefficient as the imperium expanded to all of Italy and overseas. From the perspective of 2,000 years many signs of incipient collapse are visible, even as early as the second century. There were ineffective attempts at reform (e.g., the Gracchi); there were, as always, opportunists, like Cataline, ready to take advantage of public confusion and discontent; there were, of course, those like Cicero who could think of nothing more effective than a return to the good old days. Only Caesar seems to have seen that a profound reorganization was necessary, and it is not clear that he himself was clear about the form it should take. It was therefore left for Augustus to work out the reorganization that was to prove sufficiently resilient to survive, at least in its major outlines, the changing vicissitudes of centuries.

Such major policy breakdowns usually develop slowly. As small environmental changes occur, minor adjustments are continually made, corresponding to the ad hoc hypotheses by means of which the fit between some major scientific model and the experiential field is maintained. But gradually there is an increase in strain on the whole institutional system, corresponding to the increasing strain on a cognitive system as an established theory becomes more and more complex and awkward. Then, sooner or later, the old institutional framework, burdened with all its accumulated adjustments, no longer elicits an appropriate response: a crisis has occurred and a drastic restructuring becomes necessary. Statesmanship of the highest order is then called for.

What the truly creative statesman produces is a new life style. At his best, he articulates the as yet only inarticulate (obscurely felt) aspirations of the masses for a better way of life. In part, this articulation is verbal; like the poet, the statesman finds a way of giving local habitation and a name to diffuse feeling. And, incidentally, this verbal formulation is often as paradoxical and metaphorical as the poet's: the novelty of the aspirations he is articulating require him to use language in odd ways. An example is Stoic talk about a "universal city." As it stands, this is a simple contradiction, and must have seemed absurd to many literal-minded Romans—as absurd as Galileo's talk, later on, about fixed stars that moved (p. 120). But in a society dominated by a particular background structure, so that only small-scale political organizations seemed natural, how was someone to talk about his faintly perceived notion of a single, world-wide society? Because the idea was new, there was no language in which to communicate it. The contradiction and paradox of "universal city" called attention dramatically to the novelty of a political organization in which all men were citizens, a community in which there were no resident aliens. It thus provided a focus for aspirations that were beginning to stir in the Roman world. But no statesman merely articulates such aspirations verbally; to be a statesman he must manage to condense them into new institutional and social structures—for instance, into a constitution that actually extends the rights of citizenship more widely.

It would be a mistake to suppose that this process is ever completed. The values that exist in a society at any given time are not all capable of equally articulate and precise formulation (again I am thinking not merely of verbal formulation but also of institutional formulation). For, as the institutions of any society are brought into alignment with the relatively articulate inspirations of that society, new aspirations become visible on the horizon, or rather, clearer articulations of latent aspirations emerge. In the arena of value there exists the same dynamic relation between structure and content that exists in the arena of cognition. Structures (theories in the field of cognition; policies in the field of value) are always outdating and outmoding themselves by presenting us with new contents that do not fit. This is why political wisdom does not consist, as Plato supposed, in first perceiving clearly and distinctly the ideal and then finding appropriate means to realize it. This is why it consists rather in working gradually and tentatively, by stages which themselves clarify an ideal always only dimly felt.

Thus in politics, as in art and in morals, there is a constant tendency toward collapse into cliché. What I have said regarding the over-abstraction and rigidity of much talk about personal morals (p. 232) applies equally to formulations of political ends. Take the case of American democracy. It is not enough endlessly to repeat the verbal, legislative, and institutional formulas of the Founding Fathers. Times change, just as wines change. A program for purchasing and laying down wine which had been drafted in the eighteenth century and was appropriate at that time would be largely irrelevant today. Similarly, institutions that implemented liberty and equality in an eighteenth-century agrarian society do not necessarily implement liberty and equality in a twentieth-century urban and industrial society. Nor is it merely a question of adopting different policies in changing circumstances in order to promote the "same" end. The end itself changes—except verbally. As advances toward democracy and equality are made, our notion of these ideals expands to include black people as well as white people, and economic opportunity as well as political rights.

Again, background structures organized on the principle of the national, sovereign territorial state may have worked pretty well in the eighteenth and even in the nineteenth centuries. But in the mid-twentieth century, in the close-coupled economies that exist today and in an era of increasingly rapid communication, we confront an environment in which this way of organizing the political field has broken down and in which, in consequence, a massive reorganization has become imperative. I cannot see what form this reorganization should take; for *that,* political wisdom of the highest order is needed. But it seems probable that we are living in a period not unlike the first century B.C., in that the small-scale political units that operated effectively in earlier times are becoming increasingly incompetent for directing large-scale, integrated societies. That there will eventually be some more centralized direction of human affairs seems inevitable—unless we blow ourselves to pieces trying to keep the peace by means of the old forms. The real question is how this centralized direction will come into existence. Two world wars have already been fought on this issue. So far, attempts to impose centralized solutions of a totalitarian kind have been defeated, but the nation-states that emerged victorious, though debilitated, from these struggles have not had the vision to conceive of reform except on the basis of outmoded models—alliances and groupings, large and small, of nation-states. Terms such as "League of Nations" and "United Nations" reflect a conservative and conventional approach, as compared with the novel insight reflected in the Stoics' "universal city."

All this adds up to the fact that nobody can ever be sure that he has made the "right" decision, whether in matters of private morals or of public policy. It is not merely a matter of lacking the relevant information, as we so often do. When, as at present, there is a major failure to fit between the existing normative structures and the social environment, the very meaning of "right" becomes questionable. The situation here is just the same as with cognitive strategies at major turning points (pp. 87–90): we can never be sure in advance whether it would have been better to launch a radical reconstruction or to cling to the old, continue to make minor adjustments, and fight rearguard actions. Nor can we be sure in advance whether a given reconstruction is going to turn out to be retrograde or progressive. We can only tell by watching the new institutions —and the new criteria by which we judge them—as these develop through time.

Of course, people hardly need a philosopher to tell them that decision-making is difficult, or that, even with the best will in the world, they may make tragic blunders. But there is all the difference in the world between merely experiencing the uncertainty of decision-making, and understanding why decision-making must, by its very nature, be uncertain. Those who do not understand that policy formation always involves the structuring of changing foregrounds by means of variable backgrounds—those who do not recognize that every such structure involves a change, however slight, in the foreground to be structured on some subsequent occasion—are likely to set too high standards for their solutions to policy problems. They are likely to be discontent with any solutions that are not so final and definitive as those eternal truths which they believe themselves to have latched onto in the field of cognition. Awareness of the actual uncertainty of the decision-process, coupled with the mistaken belief that it could—and should—terminate in certainty, greatly increases the frustration, the disappointment, and the anxiety people feel.

I have already pointed out that curiosity may collapse into cognitive anxiety and that this may result in withdrawal or in other defensive operations, such as refusing to look through Galileo's telescope or rejecting Freud's theories out of hand. But when the problem is not so much cognitive as behavioral, a desperate desire to be assured regarding the right policy may be superimposed on the cognitive anxiety. This applies especially, of course, when great issues depend on the decision (e.g., peace or war).

Belief in absolute moral laws is a refuge which many people adopt in these circumstances—this belief works well as a defensive strategy against excessive anxiety over decision-making, if it is coupled, as it usually is, with the further belief that we know what these command. For moral laws have a convenient all-or-none character. Because they allow for no exceptions, they simplify the decision-process enormously. Indeed, they transform it. Our problem is no longer the essentially ethical, or cognitive, one of figuring out what we ought to do, that is, what is best in these circumstances; for the moral law purports to supply a simple, ready-made answer to that question. Our problem is simply the psychological one of bringing ourselves, by an act of will, to do what our moral law tells us we ought. Thus, if we can persuade ourselves that the moral law decrees that taking human life is unconditionally wrong, we thereby relieve ourselves from the agony of committing ourselves to some policy (say, our country's decision to go to war) that may turn out to be hideously mistaken. To become a conscientious objector, automatically and on general principles, without considering the context in which war has broken out, who the enemy is and what the alternatives are, is not to make a decision; it is an escape from decision-making. Usually—not always, of course—this belief in absolute moral laws is reinforced by the conviction that these laws are divine, God-given.

To be convinced of the importance of decision-making is socially useful; it saves us from a tendency to be cavalier, careless, or cynical about the conclusions we reach; it saves us from making snap, off-the-cuff judgments. It serves much the same function in the area of private decision-making that the ceremonials and ritual of the law courts serve in the arena of public contracts. Accordingly, so far as a belief in God-given, absolute moral laws supports this conviction, the belief is socially useful. It seems to me likely, however, that on balance this belief is deleterious. For if the world we live in is complex and changing, as it certainly seems to be, and if the environment in which we act is relevant to ethical decision and wise choice, as it certainly seems to be, then the only hope for moral behavior is to develop a sensitivity to nuances, a flexibility and capacity to adjust to differences. If the world is complex, then the most likely way to bungle morally, to bring down trouble on ourselves and on others, is to oversimplify, to categorize, to persuade ourselves that we can operate ethically by adhering to a few rigid formulas. Further, and paradoxically, the belief in absolute moral laws, which initially functions to relieve anxiety regarding possibly mistaken choices, may in the long run generate new and even deeper anxieties, connected, not with mistaken decisions, but with a failure of will—the failure to live up to the exalted ideal that the God-given rule sets before us.

Of course, the fact, if it is a fact, that a belief in absolute moral laws has such-and-such deleterious effects on policy has no bearing on the question whether or not there are moral laws. Questions about the consequences of a belief are straightforward empirical questions. In contrast, questions about the nature and status of moral laws raise metaphysical and epistemological issues which take us away from policy problems into what I have called the domain of metaphysical ethics.

ii. *Problems of Metaphysical Ethics*

It should surprise no reader of the earlier chapters on epistemological puzzles to learn that I propose to approach these questions linguistically. That is, instead of asking: "Are there moral laws? Is there a *summum bonum?* Is the will free?" I shall ask: "What do people mean by asserting the existence of moral laws, of a *summum bonum,* of a free will? How does such talk function for them?" I shall show that these and similar sentences function expressively as well as designatively and that when their expressive function is taken into account, the puzzles that have so greatly perplexed traditional ethics largely disappear.

First, then, as regards so-called moral laws. In choice situations we almost always feel some anxiety about whether we are making the best decision possible in the circumstances. Part of this anxiety may result from the difficulty we have in deciding how much, if any, our own interests should weigh in the calculation; and unfortunately our own interests are often directly, and always at least indirectly, involved. Where they are deeply involved as well, it is extremely difficult not to treat ourselves as a special case. It is quite possible, of course, for a man to recognize that general rules such as reporting crimes, keeping contracts, and telling the truth are very useful, and that wholesale violations of them would cause a social collapse. Yet, as we cannot fail to recognize, it is the wholesaleness of the violations that matters; one violation here or there obviously isn't going to bring down the social fabric. Hence the disposition everyone feels to make an exception of himself. On the other hand, we see that if *everybody* reasoned in this way, the general rule would collapse.

In a choice situation we thus feel a variety of affects: one of these affects may be worry lest we give ourselves (or our friends and relations) the benefit of the doubt, and then there may be worry, too, lest in trying to avoid this mistake, we lean too far in the opposite direction. If we verbalize this sentiment to ourselves, it may well take the linguistic form of, "It is my duty to. . . ." And then, against temptations to make an exception just this once (temptations which we may feel internally or which may be verbalized to us by others), we may reply, "But duties are absolutely binding," or "Duty is the voice of God," or in a similar vein. I suggest that sentences containing such expressions are less ways of asserting some fact than they are ways of focusing an affect. Specifically, they focus, they make clear to ourselves and to others, the importance we attach to not making exceptions in our own interest. That is to say, though these look like sentences in a relatively scientific language (i.e., on the designative side of the linguistic spectrum), they are sentences in a relatively humanistic language (i.e., on the opposite side of the spectrum).

Here are two snatches of dialogue to contrast. First:

A. Why do you take such good care of those cheap old cuff links?
B. Because my dear mother gave them to me just before she died.

and second:

C. Why do you take such good care of your tiresome old mother?
D. Because God commands it.

Though the second of this pair of exchanges looks much like the first, I believe that it functions very differently. In the first dialogue both *A* and *B* recognize that *B* is experiencing a strong affect (he "prizes" the cuff links). *A* wants to know the cause of this affect, and *B* tells him. I shall call language of this kind "provenance talk." Much provenance talk is primarily designative, as for instance in

E. Where did you buy that book?
F. At the bookstore on the corner.

But provenance talk may be affective as well as designative; and it will be powerfully affective if (as in *B*'s case) we happen to have strong feelings about the cause or source. For this reason, provenance talk becomes, in the course of time, a good expressive vehicle. For instance, *B* may not have realized, until *A*'s inquiry, that he displayed an unusual regard for those cheap cuff links, still less, why he did so. Hence *A*'s question may jolt him into a discovery about himself (a focusing of affect): "Why, my mother gave them to me! That's why!" In this event, "Mother gave them to me" does not merely designate the provenance of the cuff links; it also, and at the same time, focuses, an affect for *B*.

But once provenance talk has become an expressive vehicle in some such way as this, people may now use it for the purpose of clarifying some affect, in circumstances where provenance is no longer at issue and even where questions about provenance are not appropriate. I think that this has happened in the second dialogue. *D*'s mother is querulous and demanding; he may feel a strong desire to get away from her and to be able to live his own life. If so, he probably feels under strain: duty and interest, as he understands them, pull him in different directions. In this case, "God commands it" expresses his fear that he may sooner or later weigh his own interests too heavily, just as "Black, black is the color of my true love's hair" expresses the poet's sorrowful recognition of love's impermanence.

If *C* and *D* understand "voice of God" language to be functioning in this expressive way, use of it does no harm; on the contrary, much is gained by its greater vigor and power: *D*'s determination to continue looking after his mother may be reinforced. But unfortunately, because *D*'s language has the look of provenance-type talk, both he and *C* may suppose that the sentence is functioning designatively. That is, instead of understanding it to be articulating a particularly strong (and socially useful) affect, they may believe that *D* is asserting that somebody called "God" commanded him to look after mother, as *B* is asserting that somebody called "Mother" commanded him to look after the cuff links. The trouble with taking the sentence to be functioning designatively, instead of primarily expressively, is that it then seems proper to ask whether *D* is correct in thinking that God issued this command, just as *A* can properly ask whether *B* is speaking truly when he says that his mother gave him the cuff links.

In a word, the belief that "absolute" or "God-given" are functioning designatively is unfortunate, because a designative sentence is either (literally) true or else (literally) false. Some people today, if faced with this choice, may doubtless cling to the belief that "God-given" is literally true, but most people are likely to conclude that it is downright false. The latter may then wholly miss the affect which, had they but taken the sentence expressively, would have been brought into focus. And this may have a deleterious effect on their policy decisions: they may now fail to take account of the pervasive human tendency to make exceptions of ourselves and our friends.

To summarize: Here, as so often, the dispute is not about the facts but about the best language in which to talk about the facts. Thus I am not denying the existence of moral laws, even though it may sound as if this is what I am doing. I am not questioning the existence (or the importance) of what people are trying to call to our attention when they talk about moral laws. I am simply pointing out that use of "moral laws" language to call attention to this area of the field may be very misleading. The trouble is that "law" almost inevitably suggests something eternal and immutable. But the principles that guide our conduct are, at best, tentative—subject to endless qualification as our circumstances change, subject to continual modification as our knowledge and experience improve. I deprecate any disposition to make such tentative principles even more sacrosanct, more immune to criticism and correction, by calling them "God-given." We can understand and appreciate what people are expressing when they make these assertions (viz., their sense of their responsibility to decide rightly, without making exceptions in their own favor). But the language they use sounds designative, and to take it literally only makes the application of intelligence to policy, difficult enough under the best of circumstances, still more difficult.

If talk about moral laws is abandoned as a result of this kind of analysis, people are likely to fall back on The Good as an absolute standard. This notion of there being a *summum bonum,* or highest good, arises in the following way. Some decisions merely involve a choice between two or more means to the same end (we want to lose weight; we have to decide which of two diets to follow). Sometimes, however, decisions involve a choice between two goods (e.g., telling the truth and helping a friend to stay out of trouble). How, supposing we have abandoned the notion of a moral law that tells us categorically, "Never tell a lie," do we choose between two such different goods? The answer is, we choose between them in the light of some greater, or higher good. If there are not to arise situations in which we might confront two incommensurate goods (and this would be irrational, according to philosophers), it follows that there must be a *summum bonum,* the criterion in the light of which all choices are ultimately made.

Since I am going to expose this notion of an ultimate criterion to the same analysis I made of moral laws, I may as well first deal with what some people will think is an overwhelming objection to my position. Whenever anyone questions the existence of moral absolutes there is likely to be an immediate shocked reply: "But to deny absolutes is vicious relativism!" Now, an ethical theory might fairly be called vicious (though I should myself call it "naïve," rather than "vicious") if it were to maintain that the only satisfactions worth considering are those of the self beneath the skin, and that, of these, only those satisfactions are worth considering at any particular time that are here, now at that particular time. However, such a view is not relativistic; it is a form of extreme dogmatism and absolutism. I am certainly not committed to *this* form of absolutism if I deny there is an absolute criterion, a *summum bonum.* But how, I may be challenged, can anyone who denies an absolute criterion claim that such-and-such a view is mistaken or "naïve"? If there is no absolute criterion, is not any criterion (including the extremely subjective one just mentioned) as good as any other?

My reply is that it is quite possible to provide a basis for rational choice without introducing a *summum bonum.* At any given time, our background structure contains instructions of varying degrees of generality and in which we repose varying degrees of confidence. Since all of our experience has action meaning as well as cognitive meaning, the redness of red berries not only means (cognitively) "eatable" but also "Eat!" We carry about with us thousands of such instructions, which we act on with varying degrees of confidence. If any of them has unfortunate consequences, we either modify it or abandon it. Thus "Eat red berries!" may become "Eat only light red berries!" or "Don't eat berries under any circumstances whatever!"

Now, in the same way that we develop instructions regarding specific behaviors, we also develop instructions regarding instructions, for example, "Attend to the consequences of your acts!" Such second-order instructions, as I shall call them, are what some people want to call moral laws; or rather, since nobody would call all second-order instructions moral laws, some people single out a special sub-set of instructions (such as "Honor thy father and mother," "Do not kill," and "Always tell the truth") and dignify these as moral laws. But I do not think such instructions differ in kind, but only in degree, from "Attend to consequences," or even from "Watch your weight." The scope of every instruction is limited by its relation to context and to circumstances; the difference is simply that an instruction such as "Tell the truth" is applicable in many more contexts and many more circumstances than one such as "Watch your weight." The former is much more general and usually more consequential than the latter, but that is all. Calling the more serious instructions "moral laws" certainly does have the advantage of expressing our sense of their greater social importance, but it does so at the cost of seeming to assign them some sort of special ontological status. I prefer to call them all alike "instructions" because this term calls attention to the fact that they are, all of them, empirical and provisional.

However, whatever we call them, the important point is that these rules serve to guide our criticism and correction of first-order instructions. If someone says, "Look, you ate red berries last night and now you're ill," we are likely not only to modify the old instruction, "Eat red berries!" but also to develop a new second-order instruction, "Hearken to the advice of friends!" Of course, all of these second-order instructions regarding the modification or rejection of first-order instructions in the light of further experience are themselves subject to modification or rejection in the light of further experience. If, for instance, hearkening to the advice of friends turns out to have unfortunate consequences, this second-order instruction may undergo radical qualification.

At any given time we will have available a set of second-order instructions by means of which we can appraise our current first-order instructions. To make a rational choice it is not necessary that these second-order instructions be eternal and immutable. We make a rational choice among various possible first-order instructions whenever we use, instead of ignoring, the best available second-order instructions; and "best available" does not mean "immune to criticism"; it means "has met the test of experience so far."

What I am maintaining, then, amounts to this: all criteria of conduct, like all criteria of explanation, arise in experience and undergo refinement in the light of experience. The best we can do at any given time is to decide what to do on the basis of the information and the criteria that are available to us at that time. The best we can do is to do the best that we can at that time, though we can hope to do a *better* best at some future time, in part as a result of what we learn from the consequences of current decision-making. For we not only acquire new and better information as we proceed; as a result of what we do, we also acquire new, or at least sharpen old, criteria.

People who adopt the language I recommend will have to deny themselves the small pleasure of saying roundly that the man who adopts a self-beneath-the-skin-only criterion is "absolutely" mistaken. Instead, they will point out that he is mistaken by, and in terms of, a set of criteria that have very substantial survival value. To want to say more than this, to want to say that he is "absolutely" mistaken, reflects a dislike, and perhaps a fear, of the view in question (compare: "He's nothing but a dirty red!"), rather than an objective appraisal of it. It is a sign that the speaker is abandoning rational analysis and taking refuge in exclamation.

Of course, many philosophers, including some adherents of absolute criteria, agree that in practice norms do change in the way I have described—that we always make our decisions in a context of assumed, not certain, goods. It is necessary, therefore, to distinguish between naïve absolutists, who claim that some particular criterion is absolutely certain, and sophisticated absolutists, who admit, and even insist, that no actual criterion is ever absolutely certain. The naïve absolutist, curiously enough, is not distinguishable from the radical relativist; both are uncritical dogmatists. they merely happen to affirm their undying allegiance to different criteria. But how does my position differ from the sophisticated absolutist's? The sophisticated absolutist feels sure that there is an ultimate, final context, even though we can never in point of fact actually reach it, while I am willing to settle for contexts, within contexts, within contexts. . . . Here again, obviously, the notion of a limit emerges (see p. 75) and with it, these now familiar questions: Is a limit that is admittedly not attainable anything more than an unknowable thing-in-itself? What are people really asserting when they say that they are sure that such-and-such exists, though admitting that they cannot know anything about it?

The sophisticated absolutist agrees that every actual context is capable of being evaluated by means of some other context. Does the dispute then amount to this, that the absolutist claims that there is, "after all," some context that is absolute and final, though not actual?

Put this way, the dispute may still seem factual: Is there, or isn't there, an absolute criterion, a *summum bonum*? But I believe that it is once more a dispute about language, that is, about the sort of language that is appropriate for describing the context-within-context process of evaluation that everybody, except the naïve absolutist, agrees occurs. The sophisticated absolutist and the sophisticated relativist agree that every context is in principle open to criticism, that we should not dogmatically assume that some context is ultimate and then rest there. Can we not find a diplomatic formula (p. 116) on which both parties might agree?

I believe that here again the notion of language that is functioning primarily on the humanistic side of the linguistic spectrum, while looking as if it were functioning primarily on the designative side, is helpful. Both "There is a *summum bonum*" and "There is no *summum bonum*" are examples of such language. These sentences look like designative sentences; they seem to be making assertions of the sort made in "There will be a summit conference this year" and "There will be no summit conference this year." However, both of these sentences about the *summum bonum* are primarily expressive. Note that I do not say "merely" expressive, for these sentences, like all expressive sentences, also function cognitively. Thus my analysis differs markedly from the type of linguistic analysis that holds "There is a *summum bonum*" to be wholly non-cognitive and "There is no *summum bonum*" to be wholly cognitive and, what is more, true. In contrast, I hold that both sentences are in the same region of the linguistic spectrum and hence that neither of them is either simply true or simply false. Specifically, I hold that, so far as these two sentences assert, they are asserting the same thing, not different things; so far as they differ, they differ only expressively, that is, regarding their attitude toward, their weighing of, the facts being asserted.

Now, first, for "There is a *summum bonum*": this expresses, not the *hope* of actual convergence (for the sophisticated absolutist has ruled out the possibility of any actual, complete convergence), but, rather, an attitude toward the visible fact of diversity, plurality, and incommensurability of criteria. This attitude can be summed up (designatively) by saying that it is a determination to *pursue* convergence, a determination to act now as if convergence were (condition contrary to fact) a possibility in some actual future time.

And similarly regarding "There is no *summum bonum*": it too expresses a present attitude, rather than asserting, as it seems to, the non-existence of some fact. The attitude it expresses can be summed up (designatively) by saying that it is a determination to resist the temptation to accept any particular, actual criterion as final, the determination to be critical, to emphasize the open-endedness of the actual.

If this analysis is correct, "There is a *summum bonum*" and "There is no *summum bonum*" are not in contradiction. For what is asserted in "There is a *summum bonum*" turns out on analysis, and appearances to the contrary, to be identical with what is asserted in "There is no *summum bonum*," namely, that all decisions are made within, and relative to, contexts. Where the sentences differ is in their assessment of the features of this contextual situation which it is important to bring to the decision-maker's attention. Both the sophisticated absolutist and the sophisticated relativist want to keep issues open. Both believe that there is danger of a collapse into dogmatism. Those who say "There is a *summum bonum*" believe that this collapse is more likely to result from despair and hopelessness: "There is a *summum bonum*" is a way of saying, "Don't despair! keep up the pursuit!" Those who say, "There is no *summum bonum*" fear that belief in a *summum bonum* is likely to result in our identifying some particular set of criteria with it. "There is a *summum bonum*" is designed to move us to pursue convergence; "There is no *summum bonum*" is designed to steel us to continue the pursuit. Each sentence calls attention to something of importance in the field. Each in its own way may unfortunately mislead the unwary.

Even if this particular "diplomatic" formula that I have proposed fails to "save the conference," nevertheless it would be a major achievement if the dispute could be shifted from a futile debate over the ontological status of The Good, to a discussion of what language is most appropriate to express the complex affects growing out of our human recognition of our difficulties and responsibilities as decision-makers.

Mention of responsibility brings me to free will—the last problem of metaphysical ethics which I will examine. This problem, like all of the questions of metaphysical ethics, is a second-order problem. It arises in the following way out of reflection on our policy decisions: we do, as a matter of fact, apportion praise and blame to people on the basis of their various policy determinations. "I have done those things that I ought not to have done, and left undone those things that I ought to have done" is something we often say—or at least believe that we should often say. But we also believe that people are not responsible, and so ought not to be blamed, for what they cannot control. Unless I was free to choose between doing *A* and doing *B*, I should not be blamed for having done *B*, instead of *A*. But how can I be free to have chosen *A*, if it would have been possible, before I did *B*, for a psychologist to predict that I would do it, not *A*? Of course, it is not yet possible to make predictions that have a very high degree of probability, but almost everybody believes that such predictions are in principle possible—that our behavior is determined by our heredity and environment. It is here, in the problem of free will, that the humanistic view of life, which insists on the importance of rational choice and on the moral responsibility of the human decider, has seemed to come into direct and violent conflict with the scientific view of life, which holds that human behavior is but a part of a morally neutral and deterministic universe. It is not surprising, therefore, that in the minds of contemporary artists and writers, the conflict between these two world views is largely focused on the apparent loss of freedom in the universe that science discloses (pp. 19-24).

This puzzle results from supposing that assertions of freedom are making some sort of factual claim, which denials of freedom are rejecting, whereas I hold that both the assertions and denials are primarily expressive sentences. That is, though "I am free" and "I am not free" look, for instance, like "I am a soldier of the Queen" and "I am not a soldier of the Queen" (which certainly do contradict each other), they are exactly like "There is a *summum bonum*" and "There is not a *summum bonum*": they differ not in what is being asserted, but in the speakers' differing attitudes toward what is being asserted.

First, then, as regards "I am free." What is being asserted? Not that my acts have a special kind of non-predictable, noumenal cause, still less that they have no cause at all. For adherents of freedom want to hold that they are morally responsible for their acts, and they would not be responsible for anything that "just happens," without any cause at all, nor for something that occurs as a result of noumenal activity that is outside, or beyond, their own personality. In the former case, what happened would not be an act; in the latter, it would not be *their* act. Nor does "I am free" assert that I am free to do anything at all or to abstain from doing anything at all that may occur to me, for nobody believes, or would want to claim, that he is free to jump through the ceiling or transport himself instantly to another planet. Instead, the sentence calls attention to a characteristic that distinguishes human behavior from animal behavior. This characteristic results from our more extensive memory, from our greater capacity to anticipate the future, and, more generally, from the fact that human backgrounds are more highly and more systematically structured (including those structures I have called reserve routines) than are animal backgrounds. Doubtless these differences between men and animals are differences only in degree; and, of course, men differ markedly among themselves in the degree of organization, hierarchy, and structure in their backgrounds. Still, differences in degree *are* differences, and there is, as a result, a characteristically human pattern of behavior. Except in marginal cases, human behavior is not simply an automatic reaction to a cue. There is, or may be, more or less prolonged deliberation and consideration of alternatives; and even where deliberation does not occur (where interpretation is smooth), response is patterned to the specific character of the situation as a whole, rather than being a standardized, all-or-none reaction to some segmental and isolated aspect of the situation.

These are the facts about human behavior to which "I am free" calls attention. But at the same time "I am free" is also an expressive sentence. It focuses our human appreciation of this fact of human nature, our human pride and satisfaction in this capacity of ours for deliberation and for modulation of response. Socrates' remark at his trial—"The unexamined life is not worth living"—exactly reflects all of the varied components in the assertion of human freedom. It calls attention to our human capacity to reflect; it is an injunction to do so; it expresses our human pride in living as only men can live. Other creatures may not take us as seriously as we take ourselves. But we *are* human, and we do take ourselves seriously; and what we take most seriously about ourselves is our capacity to take ourselves and our decisions seriously. Accordingly, to say to oneself, "I am free," or to say to another, "You are free," is in effect to say, "You are not an animal; don't act like one." We say this as a warning against ill-considered, impulsive behavior. We say it to remind ourselves that, because we men have the capacity to make decisions, we should *decide* what to do, rather than merely respond to cues.

Thus, though "I am free" looks like a simple designative sentence asserting that the will is spontaneous or uncaused, it is actually more equivalent to the injunction, "Form as good a policy as you can!" This injunction can be appropriately addressed to anyone. Heredity and early environment doubtless set parameters within which the adult is capable of deliberation. Some men, because of favorable circumstances, have a greater capacity for deliberation (for what, earlier, I called wisdom) than others.

But all men have this capacity to some degree, and, as compared with animals, even the most short-sighted, muddled, and confused of men is a rational decider. In a word, though men differ enormously in their capacity to formulate effective policies, they all have, to some extent, the capacity to form plans and act on them. Talk about freedom calls people's attention to their capacity to deliberate and does so in a way calculated to recommend deliberation to them.

Now what about "I am not free"? This does not assert that human behavior is in all respects exactly like animal or inanimate behavior. No psychologist would deny those facts about human behavior to which, on my analysis, "I am free" calls attention, though some psychologists—behaviorists, for instance—would want to describe these facts in different language. All psychologists would agree that though these facts, however described, make the prediction of human behavior much more difficult than the prediction of relatively simple animal behavior, they do not make prediction impossible: human behavior still conforms to rules. For the most part the rules are not so simple as the rule to which the knee-jerk (or the salivation of dogs) conforms. The rules are usually complex, and there is something in human behavior which may be described as not only acting in accordance with rules but also taking account of rules. Despite all this, however, we can make predictions about what sorts of people are likely to take account of what sorts of rules. That is, there are meta-rules which are reflected in taking-account-of behavior. And, as we have seen, none of this is denied by "I am free."

Thus "I am free" and "I am not free" point to essentially the same characteristic features of human behavior. It may be that "I am not free" concentrates rather more on the similarities between human and inanimate behavior (that both sorts of behavior conform to rules), while "I am free" concentrates on the differences (that the rules are more complex in the case of human behavior). But there is no fundamental difference, let alone a contradiction, here.

The two sentences, however, do differ as regards the expressive component they both contain. "I am free" emphasizes that, within parameters, we always have options. "I am not free" emphasizes that there always are parameters, and that sometimes these are so restrictive that my policy aims are inevitably defeated. No matter, then, that several options happen to be open to me (I may allow that "I am free" in this, to me, unimportant respect); none of these available options will accomplish for me what I really want (hence "I am not free" in what is, to me, the all-important respect).

In a word, "I am free" and "I am not free" do not differ in regard to what they assert, for "I am free" does not maintain that the options open to me are infinitely various; and "I am not free" does not claim that I have no options at all. They differ about whether the options are broad enough. And this depends not only on what we want now, but, even more, on how much, in general, we think it reasonable to expect of life.

"I am free" is suffused with optimism; "I am not free," with pessimism. "I am free" is not unaware of the parameters that limit our options, but it believes that, within these limitations, and given courage, resourcefulness, and skill, we men can accomplish much, which, to the faint-hearted or the foolish, seems quite impossible. On the other hand, "I am not free" sets high expectations for men and is distressed to find that we fail to achieve them. It is therefore very conscious of just those parameters that "I am free" recognizes but minimizes. "I am not free" is oppressed by its sense of how far we men are from knowing all that we would need to know, how far we are from being able to do all that we would have to be able to do, if we were to accomplish all that it demands of us.

But suppose someone breaks in at this point and says: "Of course temperamental differences exist: I don't need you to tell me about them, thank you. But this is irrelevant. On your view, A, who says he is free, and B, who says he is not, agree on what the parameters are within which they can choose. It just happens that these parameters are wide enough for A's modest expectations and too narrow for B's greater ambitions. But if human behavior is completely determined by antecedent events in time, as the sciences claim, A and B had to do whatever it was that they did. They had no options at all, and the question that you say they are disputing—whether the parameters are broad enough—does not even arise."

For my part, I shall not accept this criticism until I am told exactly what "complete determinism" means. And I don't believe this will prove to be an easy, or simple, phrase to explicate. First, as regards "determinism": this word contains a hidden metaphor which is likely to mislead. This is why I prefer to talk about "prediction," which is operationally prospective, rather than about "determinism," which is murkily retrospective, suggesting chains, compulsion, and an outside force somehow dragging us along. The question is not whether A and B "had to do whatever it was that they did," but whether some scientist's ability to predict what they did conflicted with their belief in options and parameters. Put this way the situation looks a little less grim for *A* and *B*.

This brings me to "complete"—whether one talks about "complete determinism" or, for that matter, "complete predictability." No one claims that human behavior is now completely predictable. Does anyone claim that it will ever in fact be possible to predict behavior down to the last detail? Hardly. What, then, is meant? Perhaps that human behavior is "in principle" predictable, or "theoretically" predictable. At this point we find ourselves back at the confusion between a limit that, it is supposed, we can indefinitely approach, and this limit somehow hypostatized as an actually existing state of affairs lurking around in some future time. I suggest that sentences containing the expression "completely predictable" are not sentences in any scientific language, even when spoken by people who are scientists by profession. Instead, they are rather like those sentences in which we declare that so-and-so is "absolutely" mistaken (p. 249). They express the scientist's attitude toward his subject, in this instance his desire to control and master it.

So, leaving aside "completely," the question is, does the possibility of a high degree of predictability conflict with those facts about deliberation which, if I am correct, are being asserted in "I am free"?

Given adequately advanced sciences of psychology and sociology, given sufficient information about some individual's genetic line and about his early upbringing, it would presumably be possible to predict with a high degree of probability whether this individual would grow up to be the sort of man who deliberates carefully or the sort who does not. For instance, we can say, even in the present state of the behavioral sciences, that children of emigrant Puerto Ricans or of Negroes who grow up in a New York slum, join a gang, and become juvenile delinquents at an early age are unlikely either to develop this capacity for examining life or to prize it in others. There is no reason why it should not become increasingly possible to predict how many alternatives a man might consider, which ones would occur to him, and even which would finally weigh most with him. As a matter of fact, we do make such predictions constantly, whenever we try to anticipate what a friend or an opponent will do. While, at present, our predictions are very rough-and-ready and often mistaken, there is no reason to think that men's capacity to make predictions of this kind will not improve as the social sciences progress.

Nor is there any reason to regret this prospective improvement in predictive power. On the contrary, we should welcome it as making possible a great advance in our capacity to plan intelligently, to develop rational policies, and so to improve the human lot.

Advances in the sciences are more likely to open up the parameters of choice for men than to close them down. Suppose that A and B are trying to formulate a policy in circumstances where the time parameters are very narrow. They decide that they have to rule out going to such-and-such a remote place in person, and fall back on sending a message, which will probably be much less effective than a personal confrontation. At some later date, when jet planes have been invented, it may prove possible, within similar time limits, to reach the rendezvous in person. I should say that this advance in technology has increased A's and B's freedom, since it has opened up a possibility previously closed to them. A and B are now free to choose something (travel by jet) that they had not been free to choose on the earlier occasion. And it does not destroy this freedom of theirs—neither the more limited freedom of their earlier circumstances nor the greater freedom of their later circumstances—if we are able to predict, on the basis of our knowledge of them and of their circumstances, that in the earlier circumstances they will send a message and in the later, go in person.

Of course, anyone who thinks "I am free" is a simple designative sentence asserting some sort of spontaneous noumenal causality will rightly detect an incompatibility between freedom and predictability. But since freedom in this sense is also incompatible with moral responsibility, I doubt if many people want to assert it. In any event, since it is not what I am asserting, it is beside the point here. I am simply replying to the criticism that freedom, as I have analyzed it, is incompatible with predictability. Now, on my analysis, "I am free" is functioning in a complex way. In the first place it calls attention to the fact that, on occasion, deliberation occurs. How can our ability to predict that so-and-so will deliberate under such-and-such circumstances conflict with the fact that in these circumstances he does indeed deliberate? After all, that is just what we predicted he would do! In the second place, "I am free" expresses our sense of the value of deliberating. Here again the possibility of prediction is irrelevant. The knowledge that a dish has been prepared in the kitchen instead of in a heaven of cooks does not affect its taste as we eat it. Similarly, the capacity to predict which individuals will examine their lives and which ones will prize this self-examination does not decrease the value of this examination for those who make it.

Thus the account I have given of freedom is entirely compatible with the presuppositions of science regarding the predictability of human behavior. Is it also reconcilable with our beliefs about responsibility? I think so. When we say that "ought implies can," or that "there is no responsibility without freedom," we do not mean that to be responsible we have to be able to do anything we choose—regardless of our psychological limitations or the circumstances in which we are placed. Rather, we mean that we do not, as a matter of fact, hold ourselves responsible unless we believe that we would (not "could") have chosen differently had we considered certain aspects of the situation which we now know and which we believe were within the scope of our consideration at the time we acted. In a word, we hold ourselves responsible for not having done some act Y if (1) Y was among the options (within the parameters) at the time we did X, instead of Y, and (2) if we believe that, had we deliberated more on that occasion, we would have seen reasons for preferring Y over X.

We cannot deliberate at all choice points; still less is unlimited deliberation possible. For this would mean lingering over some relatively trivial problem just because it happens to turn up first, while urgent ones are held back to wait a turn that never comes or, if it comes, comes too late. This being the case, two equally conscientious people may differ sharply about how much deliberation was practical, or good policy, in a given situation. Suppose A and B have done something that offends C.

A. Oh dear! We ought to have known that would offend C.
B. Granted. Had we had time to think the thing through, we could have seen C would be wounded. But we couldn't take the time; we had to act when we did.

In these circumstances, A will feel responsible for offending C; B will not.

On this analysis, there is little difference between the assertion of freedom and the assertion of responsibility. What there is amounts to a difference in tonality: "I am free" looks mainly toward the future, saying in effect, "Deliberate!" On the other hand, "I am responsible" looks chiefly toward the past, saying regretfully, "I ought to have deliberated," while "I am not responsible" says with relief, "More deliberation would not have helped."

So far I have been talking about conscientious people, who may differ in specific cases over whether they are responsible, but who take their responsibility as deciders seriously: who prize their human capacity to formulate policies and who, though they certainly on occasion slip from grace, by and large try to do the best they can. But there are also many people who do not feel responsible to do the best they can. Either they do not deliberate or they do not prize deliberation. In a word and leaving aside cases of psychosis, much behavior is just careless, persistently ill- or un-considered, impulsive.

Such people are not morally responsible; they are *ir*responsible. Many of those who come before the courts for breaking laws of one sort or another are of this type. Yet, though they are not morally responsible, it may nonetheless be necessary, precisely because they are irresponsible, to lock them up. This conception of punishment, it should be clear, is quite different from the view that wrongdoers ought to suffer for their misdeeds. Rightly understood, punishment is preventative, and hopefully remedial, action on the part of society, designed to prevent such persons from damaging society and to help them develop a sense of responsibility. Viewed from this angle, punishment is not a question of metaphysical ethics at all; it is a policy question, which, like so many policy questions, requires far more information than we now possess if we are to deal with it effectively.

There is still another kind of punishment. This is something people inflict only on themselves; it is the feeling of regret or shame that a responsible man feels as he contemplates an act that he would not have performed had he deliberated long enough or weighed alternatives more sensitively. Self-punishment thus has an important social function. The maintenance of even a minimal social order depends on a substantial part of the population acquiring and acting from a sense of responsibility; that is, it depends on their taking decision seriously, acquiring a capacity to blame themselves, and making an effort to do better next time. This is so because the threat of external constraints (force, in the broadest sense) will not alone deter impulsive, irresponsible behavior. Even in the most totalitarian societies, with a maximum of external constraints available and with a readiness to employ them, a sense of responsibility is essential; but this is especially true in democratic societies which try to operate with a minimum of force.

If there is deficient self-punishment, however, there is also a possibility of excessive self-punishment. Excessive self-punishment, a too-delicate sense of responsibility, not only causes the individual himself, and his family and friends, much distress. Like the too-tender conscience which it resembles (pp. 231, 237), it is socially dysfunctional since it inhibits flexibility, resourcefulness, and, generally, the application of intelligence in decision-making.

It is possible, then, to act too impulsively and to be too indifferent toward one's responsibilities as a decider; but it is also possible to deliberate too long. It is possible for decision to become sicklied o'er with the pale cast of thought and to let one's sense of responsibility, one's fear of self-punishment, weigh so heavily as to interfere seriously with action. Obviously what is wanted is some sort of mean between these extremes. But where does the mean lie? Aristotle would say that the norm of responsibility in any particular set of circumstances is the amount that a reasonable, or prudent, man would deliberate in those circumstances.

But who decides who the prudent man is? Other prudent men? Who decides who *they* are? Obviously, prudence is not an absolute norm. Are we then thrown back into radical relativism? No; the circumstances define not only what it is prudent, in those circumstances, to do, but also what, at any given time, we conceive prudence itself to consist in. Like other norms, the norm by which we define prudence changes through time, reflecting our experience with various provisional definitions of prudence.

At this point the problem of freedom, as a question of metaphysical ethics, evaporates and is replaced by a policy problem—specifically, a problem of education: in the first place, we have to find out how to teach people to be conscientious, but not too conscientious; in the second place, we have to discover how much conscientiousness is the right degree of conscientiousness. We have to formulate a policy by which we can make men into reasonable deciders, but this ideal that we set ourselves to aim at in education is not a fixed or static ideal; it moves ahead of us as we advance toward it.

Thus—this is the general conclusion we have reached—all specific moral problems are policy problems. Our problem in any particular set of circumstances is to do the best we can in those circumstances, taking account both of all that we know and can find out about those circumstances and also of all the values we can perceive. Metaphysical ethics does not help us solve policy problems, as some suppose, by providing us with a complete list of values, neatly arranged in a hierarchy of valuableness; still less does it provide us with a set of simple, absolutely valid instructions appropriate for all occasions. Those who conceive metaphysical ethics in this way are more likely to act immorally than morally—that is, they are likely not to be doing the best they can. For the result of taking metaphysical ethics in this sense is to make action at the policy level rigid and inflexible, and hence ill-considered.

But metaphysical ethics, rightly understood, can have a beneficent effect on policy formation. By holding before us ideals—prudence, wisdom, convergence, deliberation, for instance—metaphysical ethics gives day-to-day policy-formation a perspective it otherwise lacks. From this point of view, the very vagueness and elusiveness of these ideals (which is fatal so far as ethical theory is regarded as a sort of exalted policy-planning) is exactly their value: they warn us against taking as final and definitive those particular policies we have currently worked out, those particular values we currently hold dear; they dispose us not only to try to do better but to try better to do better.

VII THE RELIGIOUS LIFE

IN THE LAST chapter I showed that the presuppositions of science and the presuppositions of the ethical life do not conflict. The moral life consists in forming, at every particular choice point, the best policy that we can formulate at that choice point. For this enterprise we need both a knowledge of the relevant facts, which we can hope that the sciences will furnish us, and also an open, alert, and sensitive appreciation of the relevant values. This is where the language of ethics comes in: though it seems at first sight to require us to be some peculiar sort of causal agent, the function of this language is to bring to our attention values we might otherwise overlook, and to do this in a way calculated to cause us to take account of them in our policy planning. Thus the sciences and the humanities actually come together in promoting a more ethical life for men.

In the same way, here in this chapter, I shall argue that though the presuppositions of religion seem to involve metaphysical claims about an "other world," these are simply ways of talking about highly important aspects of *this* world. What is fundamental in religion is not theological descriptions of the religious experience, but that experience itself, and what it does here and now for men.

i. *The Religious Experience*

St. Paul had an experience on the road to Damascus, which he described as seeing the Risen Lord. Unfortunately, "I have seen the Risen Lord" sounds like "I have seen General de Gaulle" or "I have seen a flying saucer," both of which make truth claims. For instance, "I have seen a flying saucer" implies "There is at least one flying saucer," and is therefore contradicted by "There are no flying saucers" or by "That was no flying saucer; that was just your imagination." Similarly, if "I have seen the Risen Lord" is taken as a primarily designative sentence, it is contradicted by "That was no Risen Lord; that was merely an epileptic attack." Hence that seemingly insoluble conflict between science and religion, some of whose repercussions were examined in chapter i.

It is as if we were to suppose that in *Macbeth* Shakespeare meant to say that life is literally a candle. If we were to think this, we would be immediately face to face with a nasty dilemma: we would be obliged to conclude either (1) that Shakespeare was the victim of a monstrous delusion, in which case there is no reason to pay attention to anything he says, or (2) that a miracle occurred, in which case there is something radically wrong with science and common sense. However, "Life is a brief candle" does not make a factual claim which is falsified by "Life is an amino acid." Instead, it calls our attention to some important characteristics of life (short, precarious) which we might otherwise overlook. So, I maintain, with religious descriptions. The sentence "I am married to the Lord" (to take another example of a religious description) does not make a factual claim that would be falsified if the speaker were an unmarried virgin; it calls attention to the way in which the speaker found happiness in union with, and devotion to, something beyond herself.

In a word, if religious descriptions are primarily expressive, the whole difficulty disappears. In saying that they are expressive I am not saying that they are non-cognitive and merely emotive. On my analysis, of course, all expressive sentences (all the humanistic languages) are cognitive because they call our attention to something in the field. But they do not call our attention to what, at first sight, they seem to be calling our attention to. Thus

> Black, black is the color of my true love's hair

does not call our attention to the color of some particular person's hair;

it calls our attention to the precariousness of love, and does so in a way calculated to make us feel its precariousness.

Similarly, "I have seen the Risen Lord" does not call our attention to a literally Risen Lord who has somehow mysteriously (and in contradiction of every known scientific fact) become a part of the field; it calls our attention to an experience that changed St. Paul's life and, indirectly, the whole course of history. It does so not in neutral language but in vivid and dramatic language—but then the experience itself was vivid and dramatic: it involved a radical alteration in St. Paul's whole system of values. This language proved successful not only in focusing and clarifying the experience for St. Paul himself but also in opening up the possibility of novel and important ranges of experience for other people. This is precisely why it changed the course of history.

At this point someone may say: "Very well; I agree that St. Paul's experience on the road to Damascus had the consequences you describe. But consequences are one thing, and the experience itself is another. If it did not consist in seeing the Risen Lord, what exactly did it consist in?" Alas! though this request sounds reasonable, it makes an impossible demand. I cannot say—nobody, not even St. Paul, can say—what this experience, or any experience, was in itself. We can only displace to still another description, which I shall now do. And since I want there to be no doubt that this is just *a* description, I shall make it as neutral as possible. Accordingly, I shall say that the religious experience, however various the contexts in which it occurs, has a central core which seems pretty well identified. Though by no means rare, this experience is not universal (as are, for instance, the feelings of hunger or pain). It varies greatly from person to person and from place to place; it comes and goes. But it is supremely valuable to those who have encountered it. Characteristically they want nothing else and nothing more. There is certainty; there is confidence; there is joy. Yet, though there are ecstatic saints, especially in the oriental religions, the religious experience does not necessarily issue in passive contemplation or withdrawal from the world. Quite as characteristically, the feelings of joy and confidence are accompanied by a massive discharge of creative energy and by vigorous and outgoing activity—by a kind of realistic optimism.

Thus the religious experience is of great importance, not only because of its high intrinsic value to the individuals directly concerned, but also because of its social, pragmatic consequences. Too often, optimism and realism seem mutually exclusive. Too often, optimism is the product of rashness, immaturity, and an insensitivity to the complexities and difficulties of the situation we confront; while a realistic appraisal of difficulties and uncertainties is often accompanied by an inability to make up one's mind. It is difficult to conceive of a more valuable human character than one in which a keen and realistic awareness of the complexities of life is combined with a refusal to despair and a readiness to act vigorously, cheerfully, and decisively.

Unfortunately, despite the fact that the central core of the religious experience is thus readily identified and agreed-on, every society insists on the superiority of its own description and denounces all others as heretical or superstitious. All these conflicts, rivalries, and antagonisms are quite unnecessary. They are the consequences of that central confusion over the nature of language which we have so often discussed. Any description of any experience whatever—the experience of being in love, or of being cold, or hungry, or in pain (p. 121)—involves displacement to symbolism. The choice, among all the available symbols, of the particular symbolism to which we displace is a function not only of the experience we are trying to describe, but also of the configuration of interests that has led us to want to displace to symbolism.

Or to put this differently (I now displace to some alternative symbolism): any description of any experience whatever involves interpretation by means of some particular background structure and is therefore limited by the scope (the contents) of that background structure. To expect to be told "exactly" what some experience is, is either mistakenly to assume it is possible to get at that experience without using any background structure at all or it is unwarrantedly to assign some particular background an exalted metaphysical status (p. 71). In a word, we must distinguish, as much here in the field of religion as elsewhere in experience, between a foreground and the culturally, socially, and historically conditioned backgrounds in terms of which different people structure this foreground. Above all, we must distinguish between (1) the kind of background in which we express the religious experience, that is, focus its affective side, and (2) the kind in which we talk about it, that is, designate its properties and relations.

I have already shown what is asserted and what is expressed in descriptions of the religious experience which (like "I have seen the Risen Lord") are cast in humanistic language. As for descriptions in scientific language: these are simply interpretations by means of a type of background structure that isolates the religious experience (identifies it as a variable) and then relates it to other similarly isolated elements in experience (p. 12). This is what a psychogenetic or causal account of the religious experience amounts to. A number of psychological hypotheses exist which could be used to predict that St. Paul would have the experience that he had. But once we distinguish between foreground (the experience) and background (the particular mode of interpretation we use), we can see that none of these explanations "imperils" the validity of the experience—any more than a dish loses its savor when we learn the recipe by which it has been prepared (p. 257).

There is nothing peculiar, or threatening, about undertaking to explain the religious experience in scientific terms. Scientific explanations seem to undermine its validity and significance, only if we mistakenly suppose that these interpretations and those provided in the humanistic languages are *rival* explanations. But they are not. Suppose that a biographer of Shakespeare, developing some hypothesis about the relation between early weaning and orality, undertakes to explain how Shakespeare came to write *Macbeth*. And suppose we believe the hypothesis to be true, that is, it helps us make sense of the writing of *Macbeth* by relating it to other, more familiar events. This would not affect the *truth* of what is communicated in the play, that is, the capacity of Macbeth's lines about his wife to illumine for us our response to the fact of death, and hence the significance of death for man. In the same way, a psychogenetic account of the religious experience would not alter the power of this experience to move us or to transform our lives.

So far I have discussed descriptions in humanistic language which are primarily expressive, though they look literally designative, and descriptions in scientific language which neither look nor are expressive. And it might be thought that all religious descriptions fall into one or the other of these two categories. But there is a linguistic continuum here as well as elsewhere. It is, for instance, possible for a religious description to be, not merely to look, designative, and yet also to be highly expressive. An example is C. S. Lewis' "surprised by joy." Such descriptions have the great advantage of clarifying and reliving the experience for us (which descriptions in scientific language do not do), but without misleading us into a false and confusing literalism.

So much for what I have loosely called religious descriptions. At some point we pass from description to the more formal and systematically structured type of discourse called theology or philosophy of religion. Obviously some of this more formal writing also functions in a primarily expressive way; and much that functions expressively also looks expressive—for instance, the writings of Meister Eckhart, St. John of the Cross, and St. Bernard of Clairvaux. But much theological discourse neither looks nor is particularly expressive—for instance, St. Thomas' *Summa contra Gentiles* and Professor Tillich's *Systematic Theology;* and such theologians certainly claim to be highly cognitive, to present and weigh evidence, to offer proofs.

On my analysis, theological discourse of this kind functions in a complex way. These theologians believe (mistakenly, as I hold) that at least some religious descriptions are designative, not expressive. They plainly see that there is a prima-facie contradiction between the descriptions (so understood) and the assertions of science. They do not want to abandon the descriptions; yet, because they feel a very strong rationality need (p. 125), they are unwilling to take their stand baldly and flatly on some sort of extra-rational ground—for instance, on faith or authority. Like the child who whistled in the dark, like the ladies who asked where they could buy that adorable sugar, like the Viennese doctors who rejected Freud, they want to have what they can feel are respectable reasons for believing what they want to believe, that the descrpitions are "true." In a predominately scientific age, respectable reasons for holding any belief must be—or at least look—scientific, evidential, rational. Hence the strong cognitive form of much theological discourse.

From this point of view, writers such as Spengler, Toynbee, and Marx are best understood as crypto-theologians. They feel the old longings for certainty, for finality, for ultimates; they reduce these drives—both for themselves and for their disciples—by roundly declaring that they have found The Answers. To give this kind of assurance is the basic function of their writings. Yet it is necessary for them, if their writings are indeed to satisfy this basic function, to dress up their answers in the panoply of "scientific"—historical, economic, or sociological—proof. But what passes for proof is proof only because of the urgency of the underlying drives.

To the extent that the Marxes and the Toynbees and the Tillichs do satisfy people's rational need and their need for religious affirmation, their writings are clearly functional. But the trouble is that not everybody's standards for a rational explanation are sufficiently low to be satisfied by these explanations. Not everybody by any means accepts as evidence what theologians put forward as evidence, nor as proved what they believe themselves to have proved. Thus these writings are not functional for many people; still worse, to the extent that the arguments of the theologians are exposed and deflated, the whole religious outlook on life may be questioned and written off as merely subjective. There is thus some warrant for the deep distrust many Christians—for instance, St. Bernard—have felt for formal theological writing.

If this analysis is correct—if what is important in religion is not theological assertion and counter-assertion, but the religious experience itself with its forever new, forever old, sense of purpose, power, fulfillment and confidence—then religion surely has an immensely important function, not only in the lives of those who have this experience but in the life of society as well. If this experience were to disappear, life would become brutalized and barren, for all of its technological achievements.

But there is a constant tendency for religion to collapse into cliché. The downgrading of poetic insight from expressive metaphor into literal adjective is exactly paralleled by a bowdlerization of religious language, as a result of which some vivid and concrete embodiment of feeling is emptied of expressive content and comes to be believed as literal fact.[1] Thus religious discourse, properly understood, is a humanistic language which does not differ in any absolute way from the languages of poetry and the other arts. And the religious experience itself does not differ in kind, but only in importance (e.g., the supreme value attached to it, the remarkable pragmatic effects issuing from it), from other feelings. But other feelings (e.g., a man's love for his wife, a man's devotion to his country) are highly valuable in themselves and also have practical consequences; that is, they too issue in action. The function of all the humanistic languages is continuously to renew our access to the whole range of feeling, including the religious feeling, to refine and articulate these feelings so that we can undertand them better and enjoy them more fully, and to enable us to communicate our understandings and enjoyments to others, in a mutual interchange from which all of us may profit.

---

[1] Joseph Campbell distinguishes between what he calls the "true poetry of the poet" and the "poetry done to death of the priest" (see "The Historical Development of Mythology," *in* H. A. Murray, ed., *Myth and Mythmaking* [New York: Braziller, 1960], p. 31). This corresponds to the distinction I am drawing here: to do poetry to death is to literalize it.

There will certainly be objections to this account of religion. In the first place, critics may pounce on the term "enjoyment." I say "enjoyment" because I think the religious experience is enjoyed—it is always reported, by those who attain to it, as supremely satisfactory. But "enjoyment" unfortunately has other connotations: it may suggest a delicate savoring, a kind of art-for-art's sake attitude. This is not what I intend. As a matter of fact, some saints, especially the more ecstatic ones, probably have fallen into this attitude. But I agree with those other saints who characterize this passive ecstasy as "spiritual gluttony." To me, the enjoyment that results from finding a suitable language in which to express one's experience, whether religious or otherwise, is not a mere savoring; it is a clarifying and focusing of that experience. Until we are able to do that—to give it a local habitation and a name in some symbolic form—I should say we had neither really experienced it, nor enjoyed it. Further, in my view enjoyment is not an end in itself; enjoyment issues in action.

In the second place, it may be claimed that I have "reduced" religion to mere poetry. But, of course, my analysis of humanistic language shows that poetry itself is not "mere." Poetry, I hold, is genuinely and significantly cognitive. Religious language, too, is cognitive. True, it is not cognitive to the degree that the sciences are cognitive, nor in the way in which some literal-minded people have believed it to be cognitive; but my whole thesis is that the usual sharp dichotomy between cognitive and non-cognitive is unnecessary and destructive. Hence I deny that my view of religion is reductionist.

Third, it may be said that, even if on my view religion is cognitive, I allow it to be only a cognition (clarification) of feeling, not a knowledge of God. But this depends, of course, on what is meant by "God." Philosophers of religion talk for instance about an "encounter with a transcendent and ultimate reality." The danger in using a trans-experiential vocabulary to describe the content of experience is that it is likely to be taken literally, as designating something beyond all experience. For instance, a person who has experienced conversion will sometimes say that "the world has now become meaningful." He cannot intend to say that he now understands the world in detail. Rather he believes that it is in principle understandable. This belief, not the detailed understanding, characterizes his present experience; and this belief is suffused with strong positive affect. In a word, though the phrase "the world is meaningful" seems to refer to the meaning of the world as a whole, a meaning that would be outside of experience, it does not. It refers to the speaker's present attitude toward his present experience. The phrase functions expressively (as clarifying the affect being experienced), not designatively (as claiming literally to transcend experience).

This brings us back to that sense of cosmic meaninglessness which, as I pointed out in chapter i, characterizes so much of modern art. It results, I believe, from first taking religious language literally and then concluding that, since it can't be literally true, it must be literally false. It is easy to see why a man who once believed (literally) in a transcendent Reality beyond experience and who then came to disbelieve in it, would feel despair. But the *experience* of meaningfulness (the suffusion of experience with value and significance) does not depend on assertions about transcendent Reality being literally true. Indeed, the experience of meaningfulness depends less on beliefs of any kind than on commitment to something we think it is worth running a risk for, something we feel to be worth exerting ourselves for. Obviously many people do experience the kind of commitment (or "concern," to use a term Tillich has made fashionable) that makes life meaningful. Accordingly, many people are religious without knowing that they are; they are driven into thinking of themselves as irreligious only because of the language that theologians and philosophers of religion insist on using to describe the religious experience.

Initially, then, it may have looked as if you and I were disputing over whether or not you are having an encounter with a transcendent and ultimate Reality. However, I believe we are only disputing about whether "encounter with a transcendent and ultimate Reality" is the best phrase for describing the experience you are having. You are having an experience of a certain kind. You want to describe it as an encounter with a transcendent and ultimate Reality. But you will hardly maintain that this is the only possible description; you will agree that it is very hard, especially in this area, to say just what one means. Very well; for my part, I don't dispute the fact of the experience or the nature of its content. I don't even dispute the propriety of describing it in the terms you use; I can see why you feel these terms are appropriate. I only point out that in other respects this description is misleading, and ask whether there may not be another description which does not run into these difficulties.

Leaving "Reality" for the moment, consider "transcendent": Now obviously there is transcendence within experience: we are constantly transcending the present by reference to the remembered past, to what is contemporary but elsewhere, and to the future. Knowledge consists in just such transcendence; this is the difference between a "bare" sensum on the one hand, and perception (or cognition) on the other. Talk about "transcendence within experience," if anyone wants to use this sort of talk, is thus reasonably designative and only minimally expressive. But what are we to make of talk about a transcendent being beyond our experience? At this point the function of transcendence-talk has shifted. So far from being designative, it has become strongly expressive, and what it expresses (here I am proposing a description in alternative terms which I regard as more appropriate) is the speaker's experience of a particularly powerful affect, one so powerful that it irradiates not merely this or that segment of his experience but the whole of it. This does not differ in kind but only in degree (enormously, of course) from the way in which a friendly letter read at breakfast can color everything we do all morning, even though the news in the letter "has nothing to do" with our morning's activities.

It is quite correct to say that something more is involved than feeling, and to emphasize that this something more is not just this or that additional item of experience. What is involved is a radical and massive reorganization of the *whole* field of experience, so that everything looks different, everything indeed *is* different. But what is different is still experience. It is easy to understand why anyone who has experienced such a transformation will be unwilling to talk about it in terms appropriate for talking about minor transformations. It is easy, too, to understand why he wants not merely to tell us that something momentous has happened to him, but to make us feel what it felt like when that "something momentous" happened to him. This is why he is not content with a relatively neutral designative language; this is why he must use a highly expressive language: no other language will satisfy the particular configuration of interests that is driving him. Now I happen to think that there are hazards in using "encounter with Reality" as a description of his momentous experience, since this phrase has dualistic implications that are likely to cause trouble; and it ought to be possible to find descriptions (e.g., "surprised by joy") that are expressive without having misleading implications. But call it "Reality," call it by any name you like—as Faust replied to Gretchen when she was pressing him rather closely about his religious beliefs—so long as we can agree about the nature of our disagreement: first, that it doesn't concern the "facts," but the propriety of alternative descriptions of the facts, and, second, that these various descriptions are various precisely because they reflect different configurations of interests.

The interests satisfied by descriptions in scientific language are primarily cognitive—at such times we are curious about the religious experience and want to understand it. But the interest is not exclusively cognitive: there may be esthetic interests in generality, simplicity, and elegance; there may be a practical interest in controlling the experience and regulating its occurrence for the sake of some other end.

The interests satisfied by descriptions in humanistic language are also partly cognitive: at such times we want to understand our experience in the sense of experiencing once again what it felt like. But whereas in the former case understanding consisted in showing the experience to be systematically related to other, more familiar, elements in the field, here understanding means replicating the vividness, force, and power—the "feel"—of the experience in symbolic form. Moreover, in humanistic versions of the religious experience strong practical interests are likely to be reflected: for instance, a desire to get other people to behave differently from the way they are now behaving. Just as "You are free" is an injunction to deliberate, so "I have seen the Risen Lord" is a warning to the Jews to change their ways.

Finally, the interests satisfied by theological language doubtless include both curiosity and practical considerations of the kind just mentioned; but here these and other interests are overlaid by a rational need, which is reflected in the tone of the language and its emphasis on evidence and argumentation.

This, of course, is simply an application of my basic thesis that different background structures (B), which are functionally related to different interests, bring different aspects of the field (F) into focus, and so yield different realities (R). These different R's, and the languages in which they are articulated, cannot possibly conflict.

ii. *Meta-Metaphysics*

Consideration of the language of theology and of philosophy of religion brings us once more to metaphysics. Indeed, "once more" is not quite right: from the very beginning I have been concerned with metaphysics —with questions about the nature of reality and the ways in which men come to know that reality. I have criticized a number of metaphysical theories—for instance, the view that reality consists in facts and that the best way, the only way, to find out the facts is to apply the methods of scientific inquiry rigorously and diligently. And I have put forward an alternative view in which one talks about reality as the end-product of a process in which foregrounds are interpreted by background structures. But this alternative view is not just another (maybe better, maybe worse; at any rate different) metaphysics. What I have proposed is not metaphysics; it is meta-metaphysics.

I have not, that is to say, maintained that earlier metaphysical theories are false and that mine is true. From a *meta*-metaphysical point of view, a metaphysical theory is "functional" or "dysfunctional" (alternatively, "adequate" or "inadequate"), rather than "true" or "false." Obviously, every metaphysical theory is functional in some respects. Otherwise it would not survive long enough to be formulated and transmitted, to become accepted by a society. But metaphysical theories are also dysfunctional in some respects, and they may become seriously dysfunctional if a society's circumstances change sufficiently. At such times, a society's metaphysics may become a heavy burden, requiring elaborate defensive devices to enable men to escape from noticing an "obvious" failure to fit. Then tensions, anxieties, and neuroses may develop.

My criticism of metaphysical dualism in any and all of its many versions was made in these terms. At the beginning of the modern period, when the sciences were just beginning to develop, it was functional to emphasize the factuality of facts and to give facts a primary and independent ontological status. This had the effect of providing a field of operation for the young sciences, in which they would be relatively free from interference by the then predominant humanistic and religious institutions and norms. It was therefore plausible, at that time, to adopt a view that, as it were, hacked out an independent realm of scientific truth. At a time when independent sovereign nation-states were emerging in

Europe, it is not surprising that men's minds should have turned to a similar model of metaphysical independence. Unfortunately for metaphysics, times change. The achievements of the sciences soon made the scientific world-view secure; the humanistic and religious world-view went increasingly on the defensive. By the middle, certainly by the end, of the nineteenth century it was no longer necessary to protect the sciences from the humanistic and religious outlook; rather, it was desirable to rehabilitate this outlook in the face of an increasingly predominant fact-thatism. My first thesis is simply that this counter-revolution has not been successful. As a result, the old metaphysics that was functional at the beginning of the modern period has now become seriously dysfunctional. The evidence for this is, first, the persistent, but inconclusive, struggle of philosophers to revise and reform this metaphysical theory and, second, the revelation in literature and in the arts of a profound cultural malaise, a malaise that shows both a deep desire, and a total inability, to view life steadily and view it whole.

But my second thesis is even more fundamental. It is not just that a particular theory (which I have called fact-thatism) is dysfunctional; in the conditions of modern life *any* metaphysical theory is going to be, or become, dysfunctional if it works on what I shall call the assumption of metaphysical realism—that the task of metaphysics is to discover and characterize an independent Reality out there. This is why all attempts to reform fact-thatism have failed; they have made the basic assumption of metaphysical realism.

There have been periods in the history of culture—static periods or periods of slow change—when metaphysical realism was both natural and appropriate. But in a time like the present, a time of rapid social change and of close-coupled societies, metaphysical realism is very seriously dysfunctional. In the first place, it promotes a rigid and inflexible attitude toward decision-making. When a metaphysical realist finds the environment changing rapidly, when he finally faces up to the fact that the old metaphysical routines no longer work, instead of trying to develop new ones, he is likely to start jumping high and to the right. Moreover, and in the second place, metaphysical realism makes for a narrow and bigoted ethnocentrism. Whatever culture has happened to be politically, militarily, and economically dominant has tended to identify its reality with "Reality" and has sought to impose its value system on others. This is done in subtle and unconscious ways, as well as crudely and openly; and it is usually done in the supposed interests of those lesser breeds. Since Western culture has for centuries happened to have preponderate power, metaphysical realism has been a comfortable view for us Westerners to hold. But suppose predominance shifts to the emergent Afro-Asian nations. We may not find life so pleasant if they become the sort of metaphysical realists we have been.

But what of the alternative view proposed in this book? I recommended, it will be recalled, starting from experience: from experience as it comes, experience as it flows, experience with its color, with its sound and fury, with its eddies and its flats, with its patterns, halts, and resistances. I suggested that within experience so conceived many realities can be, and are, constructed. Each such reality is formulated and transmitted in some language or other. The language that a given society uses enables it to move about in the reality that this language formulates—enables it to deal, more or less effectively, with its experience. These are the "good" features of language, but language also has "bad" features in that, at every level, there is a tendency to literalize language, to identify Reality with the reality constructed in this particular, most familiar language, to allow language to freeze and canalize experience in standard forms and exclusive patterns.

Is this not another metaphysical theory? When I say, as I have just said, that there are many realities instead of one Reality, when I say that these realities are relative to different cultures, am I not doing just what I criticized the metaphysical realists for doing—am I not trying to characterize ultimate reality? And what is worse: in doing covertly what they do openly, in doing what I deny them the right to do, am I not contradicting myself?

Certainly, I would be in contradiction if I were to claim that the view described here is "true." This is precisely the sort of contradiction into which relativists like Hegel and Marx have fallen—Marx, for instance, claimed that all philosophical theories are relative to economics, to modes of production and exchange; but he also claimed that the theory that makes this assertion is "true"—that it is somehow not relative to the economic conditions of the time in which it was formulated. But unlike Marx and Hegel, I do not claim that the theory I am putting forward is "true." I only say that it is more functional today than is metaphysical realism. I do not argue that it will always be functional, or even that it is now functional for everybody.

This is why I call it *meta*-metaphysical. It is a second-order view, inasmuch as instead of merely offering another metaphysical formula, it proposes a way of looking at all metaphysical formulas—including, of course, the formula in which this "way of looking" is itself formulated. In a word, the view put forward here is not immune, and does not claim to be immune, from the general criticisms I have leveled against metaphysics. So far, indeed, from claiming immunity, its main value consists in its recognition that it shares in the common infection. How, then, does it differ from other metaphysical views? Precisely in its knowledge of its infection. Though this may sound like a small difference, it is a difference that makes *all* the difference.

Metaphysics, conceived traditionally as a knowledge of ultimate Reality, frees men from anxiety only at the heavy cost of illusion. Unfortunately, today men are seldom completely convinced; there is usually a lurking doubt, a fear that, if they are not careful, they will discover that it *is* an illusion. Hence anxiety is heaped on anxiety. Meta-metaphysics functions rather as Freudian analysis is said to function: it relieves our anxiety by exposing its roots. By exposing the nature of metaphysical illusions it does not free us from all illusion, but it frees us at least from the greatest illusion of all—the illusion that we can be free of illusion.

I can put this point in terms of the thesis of chapter iv. I argued there that it is impossible to get at reality except through some language or other—that is, except as reality is mediated through some particular set of beliefs and attitudes that have become imbedded in and formulated in a language. I made this observation, of course, in a language of my own —a language involving the use of such terms as "foreground," "background," and "interpretative process." This particular language is certainly not necessary; but it would be quite impossible, of course, to make the observation (either for self-communication or for other-communication) without using *some* language. Thus what I said about language in general applies to the language in which I said it. I am not claiming to know anything except what some people hide from themselves—that we are all ignorant of ultimate reality.

But now, even as I make this assertion, the meta-metaphysical position requires me to add: "Well, that's not quite right. It isn't that I'm claiming reality is unknowable, as against those who claim it is knowable. Rather, I want to say that there are many, many ways of talking about and expressing our human recognition of our human finitude. One of these ways is to talk about an unknowable reality; another happens to be the way I am now talking. But neither of these ways of talking about the human condition (nor any of the innumerable other ways of talking about it) is intrinsically better or truer than the rest."

In one sense, of course, I am simply reaffirming a very old, very respectable philosophical thesis—that knowledge is conditioned and that the path to freedom and maturity is through the hard recognition of its inevitably conditioned character. Most traditional metaphysical theories have recognized and emphasized the conditioned character of knowledge; most have seen the mediating function of language. Indeed, beginning with Plato, there is a long tradition of attempting to help men become more sophisticated about the language they use. But almost all metaphysicians have held that it is possible, in one way or another, to "strip away the veil of language" and so reach in the end something different, something ultimate—Plato's form of the good, St. Thomas' God, Hegel's Absolute, Schopenhauer's Will. The mere mention of these names shows how much disagreement there is about what this unconditioned truth is and about how it can be known. But most philosophers have been sure that it exists and that somehow, because it exists, everything is all right. Don't worry, they say, about the limitations and the finitude of the actual; since everything—all change, all flux, all relativity—is fixed by its dependence upon and relation to the unconditioned, it "really" isn't limited and finite after all.

On the other hand, those who accept the inevitability of mediation for the most part deeply, profoundly regret it. Here the contrast between Hegel and the Existentialists is instructive. No philosopher has been more conscious of mediation than was Hegel: *negativität,* alienation, and mediation are fundamental insights in his theory. But he managed to persuade himself that negativity is a "mere" phase, a "moment" in an absolute process; it is the antithesis in a dialectic movement, and is surpassed and made good in a final synthesis. The Existentialists are Hegelian in their recognition of the mediating character of consciousness, but they have felt obliged to reject the Hegelian synthesis in which mediation is overcome. We are, they are convinced, inevitably, incorrigibly estranged and alienated from reality. I agree with them so far. I too hold that mediation is inevitable and that Hegel's final synthesis is a kind of self-induced illusion—the illusion of taking an expressive sentence to be designative. But I would not myself use their language of alienation and estrangement. The stance of despair which they adopt—or, alternatively, the stance of the heroic Sisyphus—seem to me melodramatic and unnecessary. The stance I would recommend is less heroic, less tragic, more modest. It is, quite simply, a stance of openness to experience. Temperamentally, I focus on the climb up the slope, not on the painful trek back to the bottom to start again.

Of course, there are those who do not have to ask themselves what stance it is appropriate to adopt toward the inevitable fact of mediation, since they still find it possible to affirm absolutes and ultimates. But increasingly, as Bradley remarked more than half a century ago, men are coming to look upon metaphysics as "finding bad reasons for what we believe on instinct." For those who share this suspicion of metaphysics, but who are nevertheless unwilling to take the easy course of shouting "Nonsense!" at the traditionalists, meta-metaphysics may be useful. If metaphysics is finding bad reasons for what we believe on instinct, "to do so," as Bradley added, "is itself an instinct." Or, as I would put it: we men have a strong drive to seek unity and structure in our experience. The old metaphysics purported actually to provide us with the unity we desire; it offered men categorical schemes which claimed to unify experience finally and completely. As we look back on these schemes, we can see that they have all been modeled on, derived from, some predominant feature of the culture of the times. The medieval philosophers, for instance, used a model drawn from the handicraft industries: the universe, as they conceived of it, had been fashioned by a Master Craftsman—as careful, as responsible, as concerned for his work as the ideal guildsman of that era. Descartes, in contrast, used a model derived from geometry, the dominant science of his day; Whitehead, one derived from quantum physics.

Meta-metaphysics does not offer us "just another" model. Its model is derived not from any particular science but from the process of model-construction itself. If we think about the ways in which models structure our experience and guide our scientific and metaphysical theorizing, we see that all sorts of unities (not Unity) are constantly being achieved. These unities are also constantly being transcended. Every set of categories that unifies present experience is productive of further experience which sooner or later outdates this categorical scheme. Thus in meta-metaphysics the emphasis is on the continuing possibility of pursuit, rather than on the certain attainment of unity.

The contrast between the old metaphysics and meta-metaphysics can be represented diagrammatically. The old realistic metaphysics looks like this:

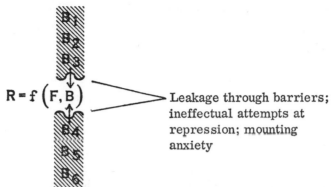

$$R = f\left(F, B\right)$$

Leakage through barriers; ineffectual attempts at repression; mounting anxiety

Not, of course, that this is the way it looks to itself. It interprets the world, not in terms of foregrounds, backgrounds, and interpretative processes, but in terms of independent minds and independent objects. But from *our* point of view the particular version of reality that a given metaphysician claims to be true is simply a function of some one, preferred background structure. Unfortunately, though the metaphysician always tries to erect watertight compartments between this preferred type of background structure and other available structures, there is always more or less seepage: the poor self learns, despite its best efforts, about other cultures, other norms, other perspectives on reality. It is therefore haunted by other realities than its own; it is divided, defensive, anxious.

Meta-metaphysics replaces this series of ineffective watertight compartments with the conception of a linguistic continuum. The self is no

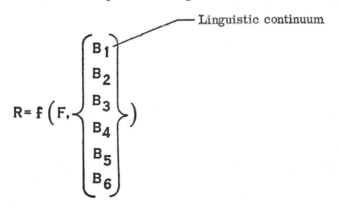

Linguistic continuum

$$R = f\left(F, \left\{\begin{matrix} B_1 \\ B_2 \\ B_3 \\ B_4 \\ B_5 \\ B_6 \end{matrix}\right\}\right)$$

longer divided. It has unity—not a substantial unity, but the unity of its attitude toward experience. It is no longer confronted with alternatives which it takes to be ultimate and among which it therefore feels forced to choose. For instance, the scientific world view and the humanistic world view are no longer perceived as competitive ontologies but as complementary perspectives. The facts disclosed in the sciences are now seen not to be so purely factual as they were once thought to be, nor are values as subjective as they have been thought to be. Instead of a world of "brute" fact, with no place for values (except as the subjective imaginings of disordered minds), or a world of value that turns its back on modern science, we have one world—the world of experience, in which values color all factual statements and in which factual relations structure all formulations of values. The scientific and the humanistic languages do not differ in kind; they differ in their weighings of the various components that are involved in *all* cognitive acts. Some of us, it is true, will prefer one sort of language (one sort of weighing); others will prefer another—because differing needs are primary. But this does not mean that the other languages are less significant or that the worlds they reveal are less real.

The one great sin against the human spirit is closure against the diversity and variety of experience—a narrow dogmatism that insists on the absolute and exclusive validity of some particular language and the particular version of reality that this language articulates. And the central virtue, therefore, is openness to experience, *caritas* for the differences and diversities to be found within experience. I use this term, with its religious associations, deliberately to remind us of the central—and ambivalent—role that religious experience plays in our attitude toward all other segments of experience. Although St. Paul's conversion reveals an astonishing flexibility and resiliency, a *caritas* toward novelty and change, he later relapsed into the rigidity of "those who are not for us are against us." Misguided by an excessive literalism, religion too often degenerates into this kind of orthodoxy; but religion at its best is perhaps the supreme example of openness to experience. This is the implication of the love that is *caritas:* it goes out to meet experience, instead of waiting cautiously to receive it. Openness, or *caritas,* carries us far beyond an attitude of tolerance. Yet tolerance is surely no mean virtue. If we cannot come to appreciate (feel *caritas* for) other languages and other visions of reality than our own, we can at least recognize their right to exist. Indeed, bearing in mind that countless millions of men have found, or may yet find, satisfaction in them, it might just occur to us that we are missing something, even as we are sure *they* are missing something, so far as they exclude themselves from *our* vision. Further, we may, by practice, come to "see something" in them after all, and so extend the range of our experience and our enjoyment. And, at the very least, as soon as we so much as see the possibility of another variety of reality, we at once take a different and more sophisticated attitude toward ourselves and our own experience. Those who know that the Indies exist, even if they never travel there, are no longer hopeless provincials.

These last sentences have emphasized the personal, or private, aspect of openness—the increasing and deepening satisfactions of a life that is open to experience. But openness is not just a matter of private morals. It is also a social and political necessity in the kind of world we live in today.

Complex modern societies depend on specialization of function. As more and more about the world is discovered, there is more and more to learn; everyone tends, perforce, to concentrate on a narrower and narrower segment of the total field. But complex societies also depend on a coordination of these specialized functions. A democratically organized state is possible only if different people with widely different outlooks, skills, and goals understand, tolerate, and openly accept each other's differences. Otherwise coordination is achieved only in the ant heap of the monolithic state, at the cost of individuality, variety, and plurality. All of this applies even more when we pass, as we must hope eventually to do, beyond the democratically organized state to a democratically organized world society, a universal city.

In the days when societies were small, when these small societies were largely autonomous, when the environment was relatively stable, tolerance and understanding within a single society were relatively easy to achieve. Men brought up in much the same traditions unconsciously imbibed a "common core of knowledge"; their speculation and their conduct started out from the same "first principles." Today, however, we can hardly aim at a common core of knowledge; we must rather aim at a common attitude toward knowledge and toward life. Openness to experience—not a mere passive receptivity to every novelty, but the attempt to understand, the readiness to criticize, incorporate, and include —is a political requirement and a moral virtue; it is also a "natural" necessity, for growth is almost the essence of life. This attitude of openness, and not any particular body of doctrine or of belief, is what I take philosophy to be and to offer us.